Statistics for Ad
Mathematics

I. Gwyn Evans

Formerly Head of Department of Statistics,
University College of Wales, Aberystwyth

HODDER AND STOUGHTON
LONDON SYDNEY AUCKLAND TORONTO

In the same series

Pure Mathematics for Advanced Level, J. A. H. Shepperd and C. J. Shepperd. (This book is available either as a complete volume or in two parts.)
Further Pure Mathematics for Advanced Level, J. A. H. Shepperd and C. J. Shepperd.
Applied Mathematics for Advanced Level, W. E. Williams and A. Waltham.

ISBN 0 340 32764 2

First printed 1984
Second impression (with additional chapter and corrections) 1985
Third impression 1986

Typeset in Times New Roman (Monophoto) by Macmillan India Ltd., Bangalore

Printed in Great Britain
Hodder and Stoughton Educational,
a division of Hodder and Stoughton Ltd.,
Mill Road, Dunton Green, Sevenoaks, Kent TN13 2YD,
by Page Bros (Norwich) Ltd.

Contents

Preface

The prime aim of this textbook is to provide a sound introduction to probabilistic and statistical concepts. Although the topics covered are typically those included in current Statistics syllabuses for G.C.E. Advanced Level Mathematics, the book should also prove to be relevant for introductory courses at technical colleges, colleges of education, polytechnics and universities.

The treatment of many of the topics has been determined largely by the experience of the author as an examiner and a moderator of statistics questions set in Advanced Level Mathematics, and as a contributor in service courses for teachers.

Some of the chapter sections appearing fairly early in the text require mathematical knowledge and expertise which may not have been covered when statistics and pure mathematics are taught in parallel and these are best deferred until later in the course, when they may be used as new material for revising some of the basic ideas involved. In particular, this applies to the four sections §2.7, §2.8, §3.7 and §3.10 which have been asterisked (*) in the text, but there may be other sections that could be treated similarly.

The concepts of statistical inference must be introduced gradually since students take a while before they grasp them. To this end the notion of a sampling distribution is crucial and it is advisable to cover the contents of Chapter 5 very thoroughly as a prelude to the subsequent chapters on inference.

The text contains 135 fully worked examples and over 500 exercises of varying degrees of difficulty. With very few exceptions, each section includes a set of exercises on the material covered in that section; each chapter is concluded with a set of revision problems most of which have been drawn from past Advanced Level examination papers. Answers to all the exercises are given at the end of the book. I am indebted to the following four examining boards for permitting me to include questions from their examination papers: Joint Matriculation Board (referenced as JMB); University of Cambridge Local Examinations Syndicate (C); University of London School Examinations Council (L); Welsh Joint Education Committee (WJEC).

Great care has been taken to try to avoid errors in the text. If any have escaped my attention then I would appreciate being notified of them, and indeed, would welcome any suggestions on how the text may be improved.

I. Gwyn Evans

Notation

$=$	is equal to
$\simeq$	is approximately equal to
$\neq$	is not equal to
$<$	is less than
$\leqslant$	is less than or equal to
$>$	is greater than
$\geqslant$	is greater than or equal to
$\sqrt{}$	the positive square root
∞	infinity
$\vert\ \vert$	the numerical value of
Σ	the sum of
Π	the product of
$n!$	n factorial
$\binom{n}{r}$	the number of combinations when selecting r objects from n objects
$\ln x$	the natural logarithm of x
e^x	the exponential function of x
$\{x : a < x < b\}$	the set of x such that x is greater than a and less than b
$[a, b]$	the interval of values from a to b, including both a and b
$(a, b]$	the interval of values from a to b, including b but excluding a
$[a, b)$	the interval of values from a to b, including a but excluding b
(a, b)	the interval of values from a to b, excluding both a and b
S	the set of all possible outcomes of a random experiment
$A, B, C, \ldots$	subsets of S, events
$n(A)$	the number of elements in A
ϕ	the empty set
$\in$	is an element of
A'	the complement of A
$\cup$	the union of
$\cap$	the intersection of
$P(A)$	the probability of the event A
$P(A \vert B)$	the conditional probability of the event A given that the event B has occurred
$X, Y, Z, \ldots$	random variables

x	an arbitrary value of X
$\mathrm{p}(x)$	the probability function $\mathrm{P}(X = x)$ of the discrete random variable X
$\mathrm{f}(x)$	the value of the probability density function f of a continuous random variable X
$\mathrm{F}(x)$	the value of the cumulative distribution function $\mathrm{P}(X \leqslant x)$ of a continuous random variable X having probability density function f
$\mathrm{E}[X]$	the expected value or expectation of the random variable X
$\mathrm{E}[\mathrm{g}(X)]$	the expected value or expectation of $\mathrm{g}(X)$
$\mathrm{V}[X]$	the variance of the random variable X
$\mathrm{SD}[X]$	the standard deviation of the random variable X
μ	a population (distribution) mean
σ^2	a population (distribution) variance
σ	a population (distribution) standard deviation
ξ_p	the p-quantile of a continuous distribution
$\mathrm{B}(n, p)$	the binomial distribution having index n and probability parameter p
$\mathrm{Po}(\lambda)$	the Poisson distribution having mean λ
$\mathrm{Geo}(p)$	the geometric distribution having probability parameter p
$\mathrm{U}(a, b)$	the continuous uniform distribution over the interval (a, b)
$\mathrm{N}(\mu, \sigma^2)$	the normal distribution having mean μ and variance σ^2
φ	the probability density function of the standard normal distribution $\mathrm{N}(0, 1)$
Φ	the cumulative distribution function of $\mathrm{N}(0, 1)$
$\mathrm{Exp}(\alpha)$	the exponential distribution having parameter α
$\sim$	is distributed as
$\bar{x}$	the sample mean
s^2	sample unbiased estimate of a population variance

1 Probability

1.1 Introduction

Probability and statistics are branches of mathematics which have been developed to deal with situations in which there is an element of uncertainty. One broad class of such situations that we shall be concerned with is that associated with *random experiments.*

By an *experiment* we mean any course of action having an observable consequence or outcome. An experiment is said to be *deterministic* if its outcome is completely predictable. A scientific experiment conducted to demonstrate the validity of some law or model is a deterministic experiment since its outcome is known beforehand from the underlying law or model. For example:

(i) when an object is released from a height we know that the object will fall towards the ground;
(ii) when the temperature of water is reduced to below 0°C we know that the water will turn into ice.

A unique feature of a deterministic experiment is that repetitions under identical conditions will always yield the same outcome.

A *random experiment*, on the other hand, is one whose outcome is not precisely predictable and is such that repeating it may lead to different outcomes. Games of chance involving cards, coins or dice are familiar examples of random experiments. Other examples will appear throughout this book.

It often happens that a scientific experiment which is seemingly deterministic actually turns out to be random because of the experimenter's inability to control the experimental conditions or because of the limitations in the accuracy of measuring instruments used to determine the outcomes.

1.2 Sample space

The collection or set of all the possible outcomes of a random experiment is called the *sample space* and will be denoted by S. Each possible outcome is called an *element* (or member) of S. (Note that S corresponds to the universal set in set algebra.)

EXAMPLE 1

When tossing a coin and observing which face is uppermost we have $S = \{h, t\}$, where h denotes 'head' and t denotes 'tail'. Curly brackets will be used to indicate that the order of the elements within the brackets is irrelevant; thus, in this example, we could alternatively write $S = \{t, h\}$.

EXAMPLE 2

When tossing an ordinary cubical die and observing the score obtained we have $S = \{1, 2, 3, 4, 5, 6\}$.

EXAMPLE 3

If 4 seeds are planted and the number that germinate is observed, the sample space is $S = \{0, 1, 2, 3, 4\}$.

EXAMPLE 4

When a card is dealt from an ordinary pack of playing cards its identification requires two specifications, namely its suit (hearts, clubs, diamonds or spades) and its denomination (ace, king, queen, jack, 10, 9, . . . , 3, 2). In this case S will consist of 52 elements, corresponding to the 52 cards in the pack (assuming no jokers), each element being a specification of the denomination and the suit; e.g. the Jack of Hearts.

EXAMPLE 5

When a red die and a black die are tossed simultaneously, an arbitrary outcome may be represented by the ordered pair (x, y) where x denotes the score on the red die and y the score on the black die. Round brackets will be used to indicate that the order of the contents is important. Thus, for example, (3, 5) and (5, 3) are two distinct possible outcomes. Here we have

$$S = \{(x, y): x = 1, 2, 3, 4, 5, 6;\ y = 1, 2, 3, 4, 5, 6\},$$

where it is understood that x is the score on the red die and y is that on the black die. Observe that S has 36 elements.

In each of the above examples the sample space consisted of a finite number of elements. Examples of non-finite sample spaces will be considered in later chapters.

EXERCISE 1.2

Write down the appropriate sample space for each of the following random experiments.

1 A hand of five cards is dealt from an ordinary pack of playing cards and the number of aces in the hand is counted.

2 A litter of five mice is to be examined to determine how many of the mice in the litter are male.

3 Four electric light bulbs, including one which is defective, are to be tested one after the other until the defective bulb is identified, and a record is to be made of the number of bulbs that are tested.

4 Two ordinary cubical dice are tossed simultaneously and the numerical difference between the two scores is to be recorded.

5 Two balls are drawn, one after the other, from a box containing five balls of which two are white and three are red, and a record is to be made of the colours of the two balls in the order in which they are drawn.

6 Each of Peter and Paul chooses one of the integers 1, 2, 3.

1.3 Events

It is often the case that one is not interested in the precise outcome of a random experiment but merely whether or not it is of a particular type or has some specified property. This is certainly the case when assessing a 'hand' in most card games.

A property associated with the outcome of a random experiment is called an *event*. If the observed outcome has this property we say that the event has occurred. For example, when an ordinary die is tossed a possible event of interest may be that 'the score obtained is an odd number', which occurs if the score is 1, 3 or 5.

In addition to its verbal description, an event can be represented by that subset of S consisting of all those elements of S that have the property defined by the event. Thus, in the example given above, the event 'the score obtained is an odd number' may be represented by the subset of S given by $A = \{1, 3, 5\}$.

We shall use the capitals of the leading letters ($A, B, C, D, E, \ldots$) of the alphabet to symbolically denote events and their corresponding subset representations.

EXAMPLE 1

When a card is dealt from an ordinary pack of playing cards and its suit observed, the sample space is given by

$$S = \{\text{hearts, clubs, diamonds, spades}\}.$$

Examples of events in this case are:

A = dealt card is red = {heart, diamond}

B = dealt card is not a spade = {heart, club, diamond}.

EXAMPLE 2

When two dice are tossed together and the sum of the two scores is observed we have $S = \{2, 3, \ldots, 11, 12\}$. Examples of events associated with this random experiment are

event A = sum of the scores is 6 = {6}

event B = sum of the scores is 9 or more = {9, 10, 11, 12}

EXAMPLE 3

When a coin is tossed three times in succession and the faces showing are observed, the sample space is

$$S = \{(h,h,h), (h,h,t), (h,t,h), (t,h,h), (h,t,t), (t,h,t), (t,t,h), (t,t,t)\},$$

where, for example, (h, h, t) represents the outcome that the first toss is a head, the second toss is a head, and the third toss is a tail. Some examples of events associated with this experiment are:

A = exactly two heads = $\{(h,h,t), (h,t,h), (t,h,h)\}$
B = the second toss is a head = $\{(h,h,h), (h,h,t), (t,h,h), (t,h,t)\}$
C = there are more heads than tails = $\{(h,h,h), (h,h,t), (h,t,h), (t,h,h)\}$
D = the same face shows in all three tosses = $\{(h,h,h), (t,t,t)\}$

Having shown that events may be represented as subsets of the sample space S it is convenient to adopt set notation and to make use of various results from set algebra. We now define some particular events that will be of interest in the sequel.

A *sure event* is one that must occur whatever be the outcome. From the definition of the sample space S, every possible outcome is an element of S and consequently S represents a sure event. For example, when a cubical die is tossed, the score obtained must be one of the elements of $S = \{1, 2, 3, 4, 5, 6\}$, so that S must occur.

An *impossible event* is one that cannot occur. Defining the empty set ϕ to be one having no elements we see that ϕ represents an impossible event.

Corresponding to any event A we define the event 'not A', called the *complement of* A and denoted by A', to be the event which occurs if A does not occur. The set representation of A' will be that consisting of all the elements of S that are not elements of A. This is illustrated in the Venn diagram in Fig. 1.1, where the rectangle represents the sample space S, the circular region inside the rectangle represents the subset A of S, and the shaded remaining part of S represents the complement A' of A.

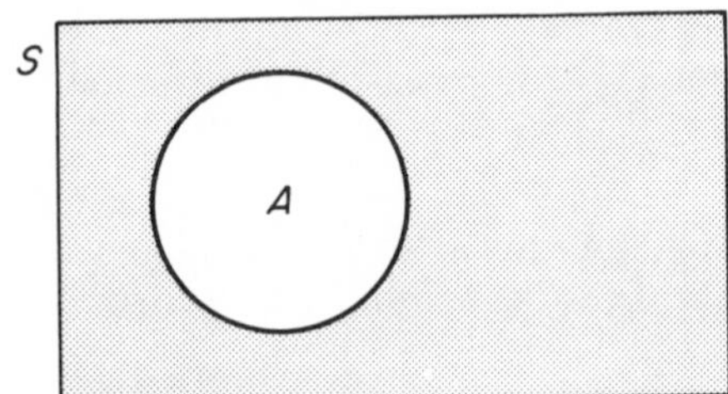

Fig. 1.1 Venn diagram to illustrate A' (shaded region)

For the events A, B defined in Example 2 we have

$$A' = \text{sum of the scores is not } 6 = \{2, 3, 4, 5, 7, 8, 9, 10, 11, 12\},$$
$$B' = \text{sum of the scores is 8 or less} = \{2, 3, 4, 5, 6, 7, 8\}.$$

Observe that $\phi' = S$ and $S' = \phi$.

Corresponding to any two given events A, B we define the events 'A or B or both', called the *union* of A and B and denoted by $A \cup B$, to be the event which occurs if at least one of A and B occurs. The set representation of $A \cup B$ will be that set obtained from pooling together the elements of A and the elements of B, as illustrated in Fig. 1.2.

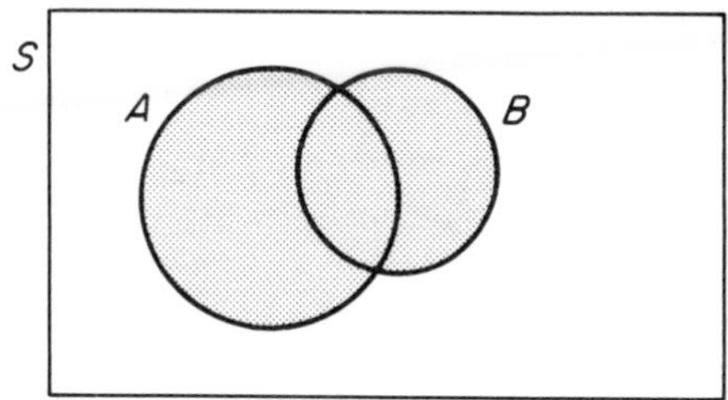

Fig. 1.2 Venn diagram to illustrate $A \cup B$ (shaded region)

For the events A, B defined in Example 2,

$$\begin{aligned} A \cup B &= \text{the sum of the scores is 6 or is 9 or more} \\ &= \{6\} \cup \{9, 10, 11, 12\} = \{6, 9, 10, 11, 12\}. \end{aligned}$$

Observe that $S \cup \phi = S$ and that for any A we have $A \cup A = A$.

We also define the event 'A and B', called the intersection of A and B and denoted by $A \cap B$, to be the event that occurs if both A and B occur. The set representation of $A \cap B$ will be that set consisting of those elements (if any) which appear in both A and B, as illustrated in Fig. 1.3.

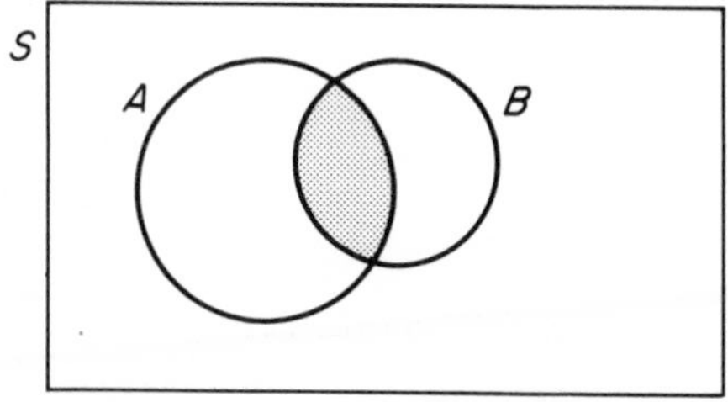

Fig. 1.3 Venn diagram to illustrate $A \cap B$ (shaded region)

For the events A, B defined in Example 2,

$$A \cap B = \text{the sum of the scores is 6 } \textit{and} \text{ is 9 or more}$$

and is clearly an impossible event. Since $A = \{6\}$ and $B = \{9, 10, 11, 12\}$, they have no elements in common; so that $A \cap B = \phi$. Observe that $S \cap \phi = \phi$ and that for any event A we have $A \cap A = A$.

Any two events A, B which cannot occur simultaneously (so that $A \cap B = \phi$), are said to be *mutually exclusive*. This is illustrated in Fig. 1.4. Observe that for any event A, the events A and A' are mutually exclusive.

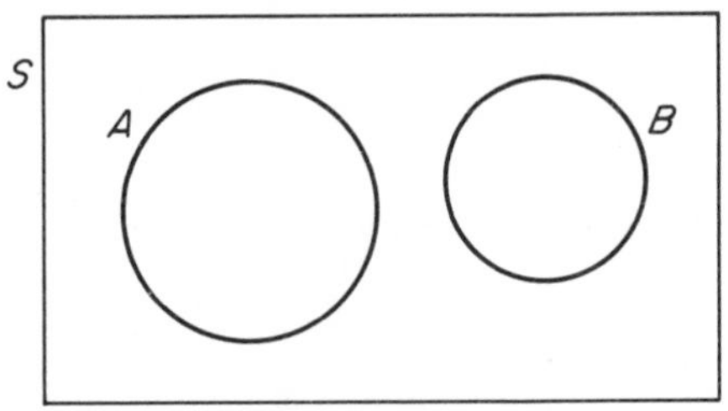

Fig. 1.4 Venn diagram to illustrate mutually exclusive events

EXAMPLE 4 *For the events defined in Example* 3 *give a verbal description and the set representation of each of the events*

(*i*) $A \cup B$,

(*ii*) $A \cap B'$.

(*iii*) *Show that* $A \cap (B \cup D)$ *and* $(A \cap B) \cup D$ *are different events.*

(i) $A \cup B$ = exactly 2 heads or the second toss is a head

$= \{(\text{h,h,t}), (\text{h,t,h}), (\text{t,h,h})\} \cup \{(\text{h,h,h}), (\text{h,h,t}), (\text{t,h,h}), (\text{t,h,t})\}$

$= \{(\text{h,h,t}), (\text{h,t,h}), (\text{t,h,h}), (\text{h,h,h}), (\text{t,h,t})\}$.

(ii) B' = the second toss is not a head $= \{(\text{h,t,h}), (\text{h,t,t}), (\text{t,t,h}), (\text{t,t,t})\}$.

$A \cap B'$ = exactly two heads and the second toss is not a head

= the first and third tosses are heads and the second toss is a tail

$= \{(\text{h,h,t}), \underline{(\text{h,t,h})}, (\text{t,h,h})\} \cap \{\underline{(\text{h,t,h})}, (\text{h,t,t}), (\text{t,t,h}), (\text{t,t,t})\}$,

the underlined elements being those that are common to A and B'. Thus, $A \cap B' = \{(\text{h, t, h})\}$.

(iii) Pooling the elements of B and D we have

$$B \cup D = \{(\text{h,h,h}), \underline{(\text{h,h,t})}, \underline{(\text{t,h,h})}, (\text{t,h,t}), (\text{t, t, t})\}.$$

Also, $A = \{\underline{(\text{h,h,t})}, (\text{h,t,h}), \underline{(\text{t,h,h})}\}$.

Picking out the elements common to these two we have

$$A \cap (B \cup D) = \{(\text{h,h,t}), (\text{t,h,h})\}.$$

Picking out the elements common to A and B we have

$$A \cap B = \{(\text{h,h,t}), (\text{t,h,h})\},$$

which on pooling with D gives

$$(A \cap B) \cup D = \{(\text{h, h, t}), (\text{t, h, h}), (\text{h, h, h}), (\text{t, t, t})\}.$$

This differs from $A \cap (B \cup D)$ in that it contains the two additional elements (h, h, h) and (t, t, t). Interpreted verbally, the event $A \cap (B \cup D)$ is the occurrence of exactly two heads consecutively, whereas the event $(A \cap B) \cup D$ is the occurrence of no head or the occurrence of at least two heads consecutively.

The union and intersection notation may be extended to more than two events. Thus, for three or more events $A, B, C, \ldots$, their union $A \cup B \cup C \cup \ldots$ is the event that at least one of $A, B, C, \ldots$ occurs, and its set representation is obtained by pooling together the elements of A, B, $C, \ldots$. This is illustrated for three events A, B, C in Fig. 1.5.

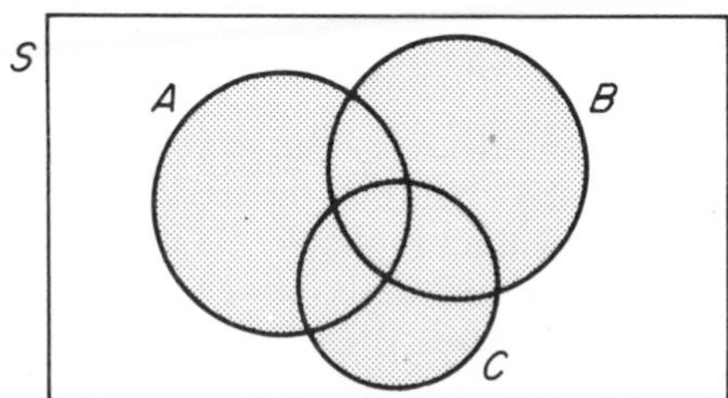

Fig. 1.5 Venn diagram to illustrate $A \cup B \cup C$ (shaded region)

For the events A, B, C, D defined in Example 3,

$$\begin{aligned} A \cup B \cup C \cup D &= \text{at least one of } A, B, C, D \text{ occurs} \\ &= \{(\text{h, h, h}), (\text{h, h, t}), (\text{h, t, h}), (\text{t, h, h}), (\text{t, h, t}), (\text{t, t, t})\} \end{aligned}$$

and is seen to be the event that the outcome is not one of (h, t, t) or (t, t, h).

The intersection of three or more events $A, B, C, \ldots$, written as $A \cap B \cap C \cap \ldots$, is the event that each of $A, B, C, \ldots$ occurs, and its set representation consists of those elements (if any) which are common to the set representations of each of $A, B, C, \ldots$. This is illustrated for three events in Fig. 1.6.

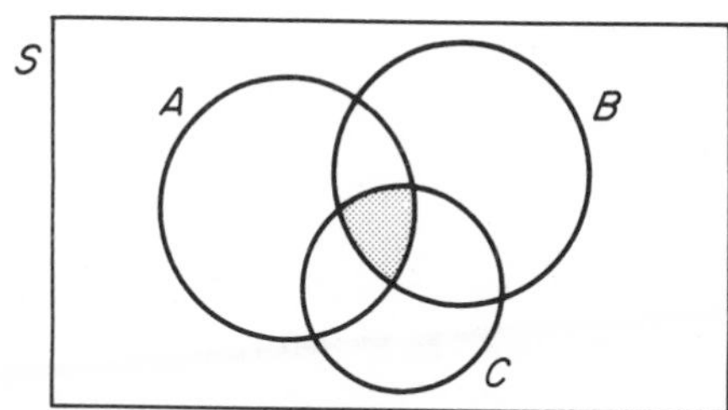

Fig. 1.6 Venn diagram to illustrate $A \cap B \cap C$ (shaded region)

In Example 3 we find that

$$A \cap B \cap C = \{(\text{h}, \text{h}, \text{t}), (\text{t}, \text{h}, \text{h})\}$$

and is the event that exactly two consecutive heads occur, and since there is no element appearing in each of A, B, C, D,

$$A \cap B \cap C \cap D = \phi,$$

the impossible event.

Events A, B, C, . . . are said to be *mutually exclusive* if no two of them can occur simultaneously, that is if $A \cap B = \phi$, $B \cap C = \phi$, etc. For the events A, B, C, D defined in Example 3, it is left as an exercise to show that only A and D are mutually exclusive.

EXERCISE 1.3

1 An ordinary cubical die is thrown. Let A denote the event that the score obtained will be even, B the event that the score will be less than 3, and C the event that the score will be a multiple of 3. Write down the sample space for the possible scores. Give verbal descriptions and set representations of the events: (i) A', (ii) $A \cap B$, (iii) $A \cup C'$, (iv) $A \cup B \cup C$, (v) $A \cap B \cap C$, (vi) $(A \cap C) \cup (B \cap C)$, (vii) $(A \cup B) \cap C$. (viii) Verify that $A \cap B \cap C = \phi$, but that the events A, B, C are not mutually exclusive.

2 A red die and a black die are thrown simultaneously. Write down the sample space for this experiment, expressing each element as an ordered pair. Determine the set representation of each of the events:
(i) $A =$ the sum of the scores is divisible by 4,
(ii) $B =$ the scores are equal,
(iii) $C =$ both scores are even,
(iv) $D =$ the scores differ by at least 4,
(v) $A \cap C$, (vi) $B \cup D$, (vii) $B \cap A'$, (viii) $(A \cup B)'$.
(ix) Determine which pairs of the events A, B, C, D are mutually exclusive and whether any 3 or more of the events are mutually exclusive.

3 Let A denote the event that a sixth-form science student is studying mathematics, B the event that he is studying physics, and C the event that he is studying chemistry. Express symbolically, in terms of A, B and C, the events that the student is studying
(i) mathematics and physics,
(ii) chemistry but not physics,
(iii) neither physics nor chemistry,
(iv) physics or mathematics but not both,
(v) at least one of the three subjects,
(vi) none of the three subjects.

4 Show by means of verbal descriptions of the events concerned (or by means of Venn diagrams) that (i) $(A \cap B)' = A' \cup B'$, (ii) $(A \cup B)' = A' \cap B'$ (in set algebra these are known as De Morgan's laws; the results extend in an obvious manner to more than two events), (iii) $A = (A \cap B) \cup (A \cap B')$, (iv) $A \cup (B \cap C) = (A \cup B) \cap (A \cup C)$.

5 A, B and C are three events. Write down symbolic expressions for the events

(i) A, B and C all occur, (ii) only A occurs, (ii) no more than two of A, B and C occur, (iv) none of A, B, C occur.

1.4 Probabilities of events

By the *probability of an event* we mean a measure of how likely it is that the event will occur. The adopted scale of measurement is from 0 to 1, an impossible event ϕ having probability 0, and a sure event S having probability 1. Symbolically,

$$\mathrm{P}(\phi) = 0, \qquad \mathrm{P}(S) = 1. \tag{1}$$

An event A which is neither ϕ nor S will have probability $\mathrm{P}(A)$, lying strictly within the range from 0 to 1. In some instances, the nature of the random experiment enables one to obtain the value of $\mathrm{P}(A)$ for a given A; for example, if a fair coin is tossed then an appeal to symmetry suggests that the probability of tossing a head is equal to $\frac{1}{2}$. Further examples of this type will be described in §1.5. In other instances, the probability of an event may have to be assessed subjectively; for example, if a company intends to launch a new product it has to use its judgement and experience to assess the probability that the venture will be successful. Finally, there are instances where past data may be used to assess the probability of a particular event; the prime example of such a situation is that where records are used as a basis for compiling mortality tables giving the death rates of persons at various ages.

Now consider a random experiment which can be repeated under identical conditions an indefinitely large number of times, as, for example, the tossing of a coin or a die. Each performance of such a random experiment is called a *trial*. Let A denote an event associated with such a random experiment and suppose that in n trials the event A was observed to occur in exactly r of the trials. Then, the proportion of the trials in which A occurred is

$$R_n(A) = \frac{r}{n},$$

which is referred to as the *relative frequency* of A in the n trials. For large enough n it is intuitively plausible to take $R_n(A)$ as a measure of how likely it is that A will occur in a future trial of the random experiment. In particular, if for two events A and B it was observed that $R_n(A) > R_n(B)$, then we would surely rate A as being more likely than B to occur in a future trial.

Since $R_n(A)$ depends on n, the number of trials, its value will inevitably vary with n, and as such does not provide a unique value for the probability that A will occur in a future trial. However, empirical evidence indicates that as n increases, the corresponding values of $R_n(A)$ for any given A tend to become fairly stable. This is readily verifiable by performing successive trials of a random experiment (such as tossing a die) and for some defined event A (such as 'an even score' when tossing a die), plotting the graph of $R_n(A)$ against n.

Thus, *for an event* A *associated with a random experiment which, at least hypothetically, can be repeated indefinitely, the probability of* A *may be interpreted as the limiting value of its relative frequency when the number of trials is allowed to increase indefinitely.*

It is clear that this interpretation leads to $\mathrm{P}(\phi) = 0$ and $\mathrm{P}(S) = 1$, as stated in (1) above. Let us now use this interpretation of the probability of an event to deduce some other important results.

If in n trials of a random experiment, the event A occurred r times, then its complement A' will have occurred $(n-r)$ times, so that

$$R_n(A') = \frac{n-r}{n} = 1 - R_n(A).$$

Thus, in the limit as n increases indefinitely, we have

$$\mathrm{P}(A') = 1 - \mathrm{P}(A). \qquad (2)$$

This result is also evident from the Venn diagram of Fig. 1.1 on regarding the probability of an event as being the area of the event's representation in a Venn diagram and bearing in mind that $\mathrm{P}(S) = 1$.

Now consider two mutually exclusive events A and B, and suppose that in n trials the event A occurred r_A times and the event B occurred r_B times. Since A and B are mutually exclusive they will not have occurred simultaneously in any trial, and, consequently, the event $A \cup B$ (i.e. either A or B) will have occurred in $(r_A + r_B)$ of the trials. Hence,

$$R_n(A \cup B) = \frac{r_A + r_B}{n} = R_n(A) + R_n(B),$$

so that in the limit as n increases indefinitely,

$$\mathrm{P}(A \cup B) = \mathrm{P}(A) + \mathrm{P}(B).$$

This result also is evident from the Venn diagram of Fig. 1.4. For 3 or more events A, B, C, . . . which are mutually exclusive, we similarly have

$$\mathrm{P}(A \cup B \cup C \cup \ldots) = \mathrm{P}(A) + \mathrm{P}(B) + \mathrm{P}(C) + \ldots. \qquad (3)$$

What about events that are not mutually exclusive? In n trials of a random experiment, suppose that the event A occurred r_A times, the event B occurred r_B times, and the event $A \cap B$ (i.e. both A and B) occurred r_{AB} times. Since each of r_A and r_B includes the r_{AB} times that both A and B occurred, the number of times that $A \cup B$ (i.e. A or B or both) occurred is equal to $(r_A + r_B - r_{AB})$, so that

$$R_n(A \cup B) = \frac{r_A + r_B - r_{AB}}{n} = R_n(A) + R_n(B) - R_n(A \cap B).$$

Taking the limiting values, we have

$$P(A \cup B) = P(A) + P(B) - P(A \cap B), \qquad (4)$$

a result which is also evident from consideration of areas in Fig. 1.3. Observe that if A and B are mutually exclusive then $A \cap B = \phi$ and (4) reduces to (3).

The results (1) to (4) form a basic set of probability rules from which many other rules can be deduced. Consider two events A and B. If A occurs it must do so either in conjunction with the occurrence of B or in conjunction with the occurrence of B' (i.e. the non-occurrence of B). Hence,

$$A = (A \cap B) \cup (A \cap B').$$

Since $A \cap B$ and $A \cap B'$ are mutually exclusive, it follows from (3) that

$$P(A) = P(A \cap B) + P(A \cap B'), \qquad (5)$$

which is also evident from the Venn diagram in Fig. 1.7, the area of A being equal to the sum of the areas of $A \cap B'$ and $A \cap B$.

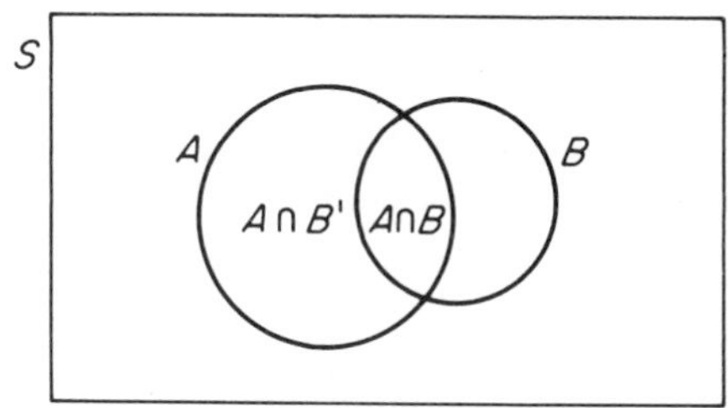

Fig. 1.7 Venn diagram to illustrate $A = (A \cap B) \cup (A \cap B')$

Rearranging (5), the probability that of the two events A, B only A will occur is

$$P(A \cap B') = P(A) - P(A \cap B), \qquad (6)$$

and on interchanging A and B, the probability that only B occurs is

$$P(A' \cap B) = P(B) - P(A \cap B). \qquad (7)$$

EXAMPLE 1 *A and B are two events such that* $P(A \cap B) = 0{\cdot}4$ *and* $P(A \cup B) = 0{\cdot}7$. *Given further that* $P(A) = P(B) = p$, *find the value of* p.

From (4)

$$P(A \cup B) = P(A) + P(B) - P(A \cap B),$$

so that in this example we have

$$0{\cdot}7 = 2p - 0{\cdot}4$$

and therefore, $p = 0{\cdot}55$.

EXAMPLE 2 *Given that* $P(A \cup B) = 7/8$, $P(A \cap B) = 1/4$ *and* $P(A') = 5/8$, *find the values of* (*i*) $P(A)$, (*ii*) $P(B)$, (*iii*) $P(A \cap B')$, (*iv*) $P(A' \cup B')$. (*v*) *Find also the probability that only one of* A, B *will occur.*

(i) Using (2)

$$P(A) = 1 - P(A') = 1 - \frac{5}{8} = \frac{3}{8}.$$

(ii) Using (4), $P(A \cup B) = P(A) + P(B) - P(A \cap B)$, so that here

$$\frac{7}{8} = \frac{3}{8} + P(B) - \frac{1}{4},$$

from which $P(B) = 3/4$.

(iii) Using (6), $P(A \cap B') = P(A) - P(A \cap B)$

$$= \frac{3}{8} - \frac{1}{4} = \frac{1}{8}.$$

(iv) From question 4 Exercise 1.3, or otherwise, $A' \cup B' = (A \cap B)'$, so that on using (2)

$$P(A' \cup B') = 1 - P(A \cap B) = \frac{3}{4}.$$

(v) Only one of A, B occurs $= (A \cap B') \cup (A' \cap B)$. Since the right-hand side is the union of two mutually exclusive events, we have, on using (6) and (7),

$$\begin{aligned} P(\text{only one of } A, B \text{ occurs}) &= P(A \cap B') + P(A' \cap B) \\ &= \{P(A) - P(A \cap B)\} + \{P(B) - P(A \cap B)\} \\ &= \quad 1/8 \quad + \quad 1/2 \quad = 5/8. \end{aligned}$$

(Some readers may find it instructive to draw a Venn diagram for this example.)

EXERCISE 1.4

1 Given that A and B are mutually exclusive events such that $P(A) = 0{\cdot}5$ and $P(B) = 0{\cdot}2$ find $P(A' \cap B')$.

2 Given that $P(A) = 0{\cdot}5$, $P(A \cup B) = 0{\cdot}8$ and $P(A \cap B) = 0{\cdot}2$, find the probabilities of the events: (i) A', (ii) B, (iii) $A \cap B'$, (iv) $A' \cap B$.

3 Events A and B are such that $P(A) = 0{\cdot}4$, $P(B') = 0{\cdot}7$ and $P(A \cup B) = 0{\cdot}58$. Find (i) $P(A \cap B)$, (ii) $P(A' \cap B')$, (iii) $P(A' \cup B)$.

4 Events A and B are such that $P(A) = 0{\cdot}36$, $P(B) = 0{\cdot}25$ and $P(A \cap B') = 0{\cdot}24$. Find the values of (i) $P(A')$, (ii) $P(A \cap B)$, (iii) $P(A' \cap B)$, (iv) $P(A' \cap B')$, (v) $P(A' \cup B')$. (vi) Find the probability that exactly one of A, B occurs.

5 A, B and C are three events with A and B being mutually exclusive. Show that

$$P(A \cup B \cup C) = P(A \cup B) + P(C) - P(A \cap C) - P(B \cap C).$$

Given that $P(A) = 0{\cdot}4$, $P(B) = 0{\cdot}3$, $P(C) = 0{\cdot}2$, $P(B \cap C) = 0{\cdot}1$, $P(A \cap C) = 0{\cdot}08$, find the probabilities of the events (i) $A \cup C$, (ii) $A' \cap B$, (iii) $A \cup B \cup C$, (iv) $(A \cup B) \cap C$, (v) none of A, B, C occurs.

6 A, B and C are mutually exclusive and exhaustive events (i.e. $A \cap B = B \cap C = A \cap C = \phi$, and $A \cup B \cup C = S$) such that $P(A) = h(1-\alpha)$, $P(B) =$

$h(1+2\alpha)$, $P(C) = h(2-\alpha)$. Find the value of h and the set of possible values for α.

1.5 The case of equally likely outcomes

In a game of chance which is played fairly it is reasonable to suppose that all the possible outcomes are equally likely to occur in any one play of the game. For example, when throwing a perfectly balanced cubical die it seems reasonable to suppose that each of the six faces is just as likely as any other to be uppermost. Similarly, when making a 'blind' selection of one object from a finite collection of objects it is reasonable to suppose that each object in the collection has the same chance of being the selected object. Such a 'blind' selection is usually referred to as a *random selection.*

Now consider a random experiment having sample space S consisting of N elements and that a trial of the experiment is conducted in such a way that it is reasonable to suppose that the outcome is equally likely to be any one of the N possible outcomes. Then each possible outcome, or element of S, will have probability $1/N$ of occurring in the trial. If A is an event associated with this experiment such that the set representation of A consists of $n(A)$ elements, then the probability of A occurring will be given by

$$P(A) = \frac{n(A)}{N}.$$

EXAMPLE 1 *A coin is tossed three times. Find the probabilities of the events: (i) A = three heads, (ii) B = at least one head, (iii) C = one head or one tail.*

To answer this question we shall assume that the coin is perfectly balanced and that each toss is done in an arbitrary manner so as to justify the assumption that all the possible outcomes are equally probable to occur.

Here, the sample space for the faces showing in the three tosses is $S = \{(h,h,h), (h,h,t), (h,t,h), (t,h,h), (h,t,t), (t,h,t), (t,t,h), (t,t,t)\}$. In view of the assumption being made, each of the $N = 8$ elements of S has probability $1/8$ of occurring.

(i) A = three heads $= \{(h,h,h)\}$. Since $n(A) = 1$ we have

$$P(A) = \frac{1}{8}.$$

(ii) B = at least one head,

$= \{(h,h,h), (h,h,t), (h,t,h), (t,h,h), (h,t,t), (t,h,t), (t,t,h)\}$,

so that $n(B) = 7$ and $P(B) = 7/8$.
Alternatively, B' = no head $= \{(t,t,t)\}$, so that $P(B) = 1/8$, and therefore

$$P(B) = 1 - P(B') = \frac{7}{8}.$$

(iii) C = one head or one tail

$$= \{(h,h,t), (h,t,h), (t,h,h), (h,t,t), (t,h,t), (t,t,h)\}.$$

Hence, $n(C) = 6$ and $P(C) = 6/8 = 3/4$.
Alternatively, we may write $C = C_1 \cup C_2$, where

$$C_1 = \text{one head} = \{(h,t,t), (t,h,t), (t,t,h)\},$$
$$C_2 = \text{one tail} = \{(h,h,t), (h,t,h), (t,h,h)\}.$$

Since C_1 and C_2 are mutually exclusive

$$P(C) = P(C_1) + P(C_2) = \frac{3}{8} + \frac{3}{8} = \frac{3}{4}.$$

EXAMPLE 2 *In a sixth form of* 60 *pupils,* 16 *are studying mathematics,* 11 *are studying physics and* 7 *are studying both mathematics and physics. Find the probability that a pupil selected at random from this sixth form is studying either mathematics or physics or both.*

Let A denote the event that the chosen pupil is studying mathematics and B the event that the chosen pupil is studying physics. We need to evaluate $P(A \cup B)$. From the given data we have

$$N \equiv n(S) = 60, \quad n(A) = 16, \quad n(B) = 11, \quad n(A \cap B) = 7.$$

Since the pupil is to be selected at random we assume that each of the 60 pupils has probability 1/60 of being selected, so that

$$P(A) = \frac{16}{60}, \quad P(B) = \frac{11}{60}, \quad P(A \cap B) = \frac{7}{60}.$$

Hence $P(A \cup B) = P(A) + P(B) - P(A \cap B)$

$$= \frac{16}{60} + \frac{11}{60} - \frac{7}{60} = \frac{1}{3}.$$

EXERCISE 1.5A

1 One card is chosen at random from a pack of twenty cards which are numbered from 1 to 20, respectively. Find the probabilities that the number on the chosen card is: (i) even, (ii) divisible by 5, (iii) greater than 10, (iv) a perfect square.

2 A cubical die has two faces numbered 1, another two numbered 2, and the remaining two faces are numbered 3. The score obtained after the die has been thrown is the number on the uppermost face. The die is to be thrown twice. Find the probabilities that (i) the score on the first throw will be 3 and that on the second throw will be less than 3, (ii) at least one of the two scores will be an even number, (iii) the sum of the scores will be 4.

3 Assuming that all eight possible sex distributions in order of birth of the children of families having three children are equally probable, find the probabilities that in a randomly chosen family of three children there will be

(i) at least one boy, (ii) at least two boys, (iii) exactly one boy, (iv) at most one boy, (v) more boys than girls.

4 Fifty girls in a beauty contest draw lots for their order of appearance before the judges. Twenty of the girls are blondes and the remainder are brunettes; twenty-five of the girls have blue eyes and the remainder have brown eyes; five of the girls are blue-eyed blondes. Find the probability that the first girl to appear before the judges will be a brown-eyed brunette.

Counting aids

Whenever the above method is applicable it is not necessary to make a listing of the elements of the sample space or of the set representation of an event, since it is sufficient to know only the *number* of elements in each case. The following examples illustrate a general principle known as the *multiplication rule*, that is often useful for determining the number of elements in a sample space or in a set representation of an event.

EXAMPLE 3 *Find the number of elements in the sample space for the score obtained when a cubical die is tossed (i) twice, (ii) three times.*

(i) In this case each outcome will be an ordered pair of scores corresponding to the scores obtained on the first and second tosses, respectively. Since there are 6 possible scores (1, 2, 3, 4, 5, 6) in each toss and each possible score on the first toss may be paired with each possible score on the second toss it follows that the total number of possible ordered pairs of scores is $6 \times 6 = 36$.
(ii) Extending the above argument each of the 6 possible scores on the third toss can be combined with each of the 36 ordered pairs of scores on the first two tosses, thus giving a total of $36 \times 6 = 216$ possible outcomes of triples of scores.

EXAMPLE 4 *Find the number of elements in the sample space of the outcomes when a coin and a die are tossed simultaneously.*

Here, each of the 2 possible outcomes (h or t) for the coin can be paired with each of the 6 possible scores on the die. Hence the total number of paired outcomes is equal to $2 \times 6 = 12$.

Generalising the method used in the above examples we have *the multiplication rule*:

> If k random experiments are performed simultaneously or sequentially and the ith experiment has n_i possible outcomes ($i = 1, 2, \ldots, k$) then the combined experiment has $n_1 \times n_2 \times \ldots \times n_k$ possible outcomes, each being an ordered k-tuple.

The following examples illustrate the usefulness of the above rule when sampling from a collection of objects.

EXAMPLE 5 *Two cards are dealt from a well-shuffled pack of 52 playing cards. Find the probabilities that (i) the first card is an ace, (ii) the second card is an ace, (iii) at least one of the two cards is an ace.*

Each element of the sample space S for this experiment consists of an ordered pair whose two components signify the first and the second cards, respectively. Since the first component may be any one of the 52 cards and the second component may be any one of the 51 cards remaining after the first card has been dealt, the total number of elements in S is $n(S) = 52 \times 51 = 2652$. Since the peak has been well-shuffled it is reasonable to suppose that all 52×51 pairs of cards are equally probable.
(i) Let A denote the event that the first card is an ace and let $n(A)$ denote the number of elements in S having an ace as its first component.

The first component of an element in A may be any one of the four aces and for each of these the second component may be any one of the remaining 51 cards. Thus

$$n(A) = 4 \times 51.$$

Hence

$$\mathrm{P}(A) = \frac{4 \times 51}{52 \times 51} = \frac{1}{13}.$$

(This particular result could have been obtained more easily by setting up the simpler sample space for the first card only, but the above method is more instructive in preparation for answering (ii).)
(ii) Let B denote the event that the second card is an ace and let $n(B)$ denote the number of elements in S having an ace as its second component. The second component of an element in B may be any one of the four aces and for each of these the first component may be any one of the remaining 51 cards. Thus

$$n(B) = 51 \times 4,$$

and

$$\mathrm{P}(B) = \frac{51 \times 4}{52 \times 51} = \frac{1}{13}.$$

(The fact that $\mathrm{P}(B) = \mathrm{P}(A)$ surprises many when they first meet it. An alternative method more in keeping with how people's minds operate in this type of problem is given in §1.7.)
(iii) Here we need to find $\mathrm{P}(A \cup B)$. Note that A and B are not mutually exclusive since both cards could be aces, so we shall use the result

$$\mathrm{P}(A \cup B) = \mathrm{P}(A) + \mathrm{P}(B) - \mathrm{P}(A \cap B).$$

Now, $n(A \cap B) =$ the number of elements in S in which both components are aces

$$= 4 \times 3 = 12.$$

Hence

$$\mathrm{P}(A \cup B) = \frac{1}{13} + \frac{1}{13} - \frac{12}{52 \times 51} = \frac{33}{221} = 0{\cdot}1493 \text{ (to four decimal places).}$$

EXAMPLE 6 *Find the probabilities of the events in Example 5 if, instead, the two cards are drawn at random with replacement (that is, the first card drawn is replaced in the pack which is then shuffled before the next card is drawn).*

Since the first card drawn is replaced in the pack before the second is drawn,

$$n(S) = 52 \times 52, \quad n(A) = 4 \times 52, \quad n(B) = 52 \times 4, \quad n(A \cap B) = 4 \times 4.$$

Hence

(i) $P(A) = \dfrac{4 \times 52}{52 \times 52} = \dfrac{1}{13}$,

(ii) $P(B) = \dfrac{52 \times 4}{52 \times 52} = \dfrac{1}{13}$,

(iii) $P(A \cup B) = \dfrac{1}{13} + \dfrac{1}{13} - \dfrac{4 \times 4}{52 \times 52} = \dfrac{25}{169} = 0{\cdot}1479$ (to four decimal places).

EXAMPLE 7 (The classical birthday problem) *Find the probability that at least two people in a group of n people have their birthdays on the same day.*

Number the days in a year from 1 to 365; we shall ignore the possibility of anyone having been born on February 29th of a leap year. Then the days on which the n persons have their birthdays can be represented by an n-tuple $(s_1, s_2, \ldots, s_n)$ where each s_i is one of the integers from 1 to 365. Using the multiplication rule, the number of such n-tuples in the sample space for the birthdays of the n people will be $n(S) = 365^n$.

We shall assume that all the elements of S are equally probable, as would be reasonable for a randomly selected group of n people. Let A denote the event that at least two of the s_i are the same. Then A' is the event that all the s_i are different. and it is easier to find $n(A')$ than $n(A)$. We see that

$$n(A') = 365 \times 364 \times 363 \times \ldots \times (366 - n)$$

provided $n \leqslant 366$. Hence

$$P(A') = \frac{365 \times 364 \times 363 \times \ldots \times (366 - n)}{365^n},$$

and

$$P(A) = 1 - P(A').$$

The following table gives the values of $P(A)$ for selected values of n.

n	=	4	8	16	22	23	24	32	56	64
$P(A)$	=	0·016	0·074	0·284	0·476	0·507	0·518	0·753	0·988	0·997

It follows from this table that the odds are better than evens of there being common birthdays among a group of at least 23 people. Observe that the event is bound to occur if the group consists of 366 or more people, and from the table, it is virtually certain to occur for a group of just 64 or more people.

EXERCISE 1.5B

1 A fair die is tossed three times. Find the probability that the three scores, in the order thrown, will be three consecutive integers in increasing magnitude.

2 Three fair dice are tossed simultaneously. Find the probabilities that (i) the three scores are different, (ii) at least two of the scores are the same.

3 Stating clearly any assumptions that you make, find an expression for the probability that at least two students in a class of n students have their birthdays in the same month. Deduce the smallest value of n for this probability to exceed $\frac{1}{2}$.

4 Two cards are drawn at random, one after the other from a pack of 20 cards which are numbered from 1 to 20, respectively. For each of the cases when the drawing is (a) with replacement and (b) without replacement, find the probabilities that: (i) the first number drawn will be 10 or less and the second will be 11 or more; (ii) the sum of the two numbers drawn will be an odd number.

5 Two balls are drawn at random from a box containing 10 red, 30 white, 20 green and 15 black balls. For each of the cases when the balls are drawn (a) with replacement and (b) without replacement, calculate the probabilities that (i) both balls are white, (ii) the first ball is red and the second is white, (iii) neither ball is black, (iv) the first ball is black, (v) there is at least one green ball, (vi) there is exactly one red ball.

Unordered samples

Above we considered sampling from a collection of objects and we took into account the order in which the sample was obtained. The order is not always relevant, as for example in many card games in which it is the collection of cards in a hand which determines its value and not the order in which the cards are received. If a sample of k objects is drawn without replacement from a collection of n objects and the order in which they are drawn is irrelevant then we refer to the k objects that are drawn as an *unordered sample of size k*.

When the order is irrelevant the sample space for a sample of a given size will be smaller (i.e. will contain fewer elements) than when order is taken into account.

EXAMPLE 8 *Find the number of different hands that are possible when three cards are dealt from a pack of five cards numbered from* 1 *to* 5 *inclusive.*

A hand in this case will consist of three cards having three different numbers chosen from the numbers from 1 to 5. The possible hands are seen to be

$$\{1, 2, 3\}, \{1, 2, 4\}, \{1, 2, 5\}, \{1, 3, 4\}, \{1, 3, 5\}, \{1, 4, 5\},$$
$$\{2, 3, 4\}, \{2, 3, 5\}, \{2, 4, 5\}, \{3, 4, 5\}$$

and we see that there are 10 of them.

This method of listing all possible unordered samples would be tedious if the number involved were larger than in the above example, as, for instance, if one required the number of different hands that are possible when 13 cards are dealt from an ordinary pack of playing cards. Clearly, there is a need for a more efficient method.

Consider one of the hands in Example 8, say $\{1, 2, 3\}$. Taking account of the order in which these three cards were dealt we see that this particular hand could have arisen in $3 \times 2 = 6$ different ways (since the first card dealt could be any one of the cards 1, 2, 3 and the second card dealt could be either one of the remaining two cards).

Thus, the hand $\{1, 2, 3\}$ could arise from any one of 6 possible ways when order is taken into account. Since the same applies to each of the 10 hands it follows that the number of possible hands is exactly 1/6 of the number of possibilities when the order in which the cards are received is taken into account. But we know that the latter number is $5 \times 4 \times 3 = 60$ and consequently the number of hands is equal to $60/6 = 10$.

Let us now apply this alternative method to an example in which the listing method would be prohibitively tedious.

EXAMPLE 9 *Find the total number of possible hands when* 13 *cards are dealt from an ordinary pack of* 52 *playing cards.*

If we think of a particular hand of 13 cards we first observe that on taking into account the order in which the cards were dealt the number of ways in which this hand might have arisen is equal to $13 \times 12 \times 11 \times 10 \times 9 \times 8 \times 7 \times 6 \times 5 \times 4 \times 3 \times 2 = 13!$ (factorial 13). It follows that each unordered hand of 13 cards can arise from 13! different orderings of the cards as dealt.

We also know that when ordering is taken into account the total number of possibilities is equal to

$$52 \times 51 \times 50 \times \ldots \times 40 = \frac{52!}{39!}.$$

It follows that the total number of hands possible is equal to

$$\frac{52!}{39!} \div 13! = \frac{52!}{39!\,13!},$$

which is written symbolically as ${}_{52}C_{13}$ or $\binom{52}{13}$ and is generally referred to as the number of *combinations* of 13 objects chosen from 52 objects. It may be helpful to interpret this as representing 'choice' rather than 'combinations', so that the above expression is then the number of possible choices when 13 objects are chosen from 52 objects. Unfortunately, there is no short and easy way of evaluating $\binom{52}{13}$, whose exact value is 635 013 559 600.

Generalising the method used above we have the following result:

The total number of unordered samples of k objects chosen without replacement from a collection of n objects is equal to $\binom{n}{k}$, *where*

$$\binom{n}{k} = \frac{n!}{k!\,(n-k)!}.$$

EXAMPLE 10 *A box contains seven red, four white and nine black balls. Three balls are drawn out at random without replacement from the box. Calculate the probabilities that (i) two are red and the other is black, (ii) there is one ball of each colour, (iii) there is at least one white ball, (iv) all three balls have the same colour.*

The box contains a total of 20 balls and the total number of ways of choosing three balls from 20 is $n(S) = \binom{20}{3} = 1140$. Since the balls are drawn at random we may assume that all these possible ways are equally probable.

(i) Let A be the event that two red balls and one black ball are drawn. The number of ways of choosing two red from the seven red balls in the box is $\binom{7}{2} = 21$ and the number of ways of choosing one black from the nine black balls in the box is $\binom{9}{1} = 9$. Since each choice of two red balls may combine with each choice of one black ball it follows that

$$n(A) = 21 \times 9 = 189$$

and

$$\mathrm{P}(A) = \frac{n(A)}{n(S)} = \frac{189}{1140} = \frac{63}{380}.$$

(ii) Let B denote the event that there is one ball of each colour. For B to occur the three drawn balls must consist of one red, one white and one black ball. Thus

$$n(B) = \binom{7}{1}\binom{4}{1}\binom{9}{1} = 7 \times 4 \times 9 = 252,$$

and

$$\mathrm{P}(B) = \frac{252}{1140} = \frac{21}{95}.$$

(iii) Let C be the event that there is at least one white ball. Then C' is the event that there is no white ball. Since there are 16 non-white balls

$$n(C') = \binom{16}{3} = 560,$$

and

$$\mathrm{P}(C') = \frac{560}{1140} = \frac{28}{57}.$$

Hence

$$\mathrm{P}(C) = 1 - \mathrm{P}(C') = \frac{29}{57}.$$

(iv) Let D be the event that all three balls have the same colour. Then

$$D = D_r \cup D_w \cup D_b,$$

where D_r is the event that all three balls are red, D_w the event that all three balls are white, and D_b the event that all three balls are black. Since D_r, D_w, D_b are clearly mutually exclusive

$$\begin{aligned} P(D) &= P(D_r) + P(D_w) + P(D_b) \\ &= \frac{\binom{7}{3} + \binom{4}{3} + \binom{9}{3}}{1140} \\ &= \frac{(35+4+84)}{1140} = \frac{41}{380}. \end{aligned}$$

EXERCISE 1.5C

1 A box contains five red balls, four white balls and three blue balls. Three balls are drawn at random without replacement from the bag. Calculate the probabilities that the chosen balls are (i) all red, (ii) of different colours, (iii) all of the same colour.

2 Four cards are to be drawn at random, without replacement, from a pack of nine cards which are numbered from 1 to 9 respectively. Calculate the probabilities that (i) both 1 and 9 will be drawn, (ii) the largest number drawn will be 8, (iii) at least three even numbers will be drawn.

3 A hand of three cards is dealt from an ordinary pack of 52 playing cards. Find the probabilities that the hand consists of (i) three aces, (ii) two kings and one other card which is not a king, (iii) an ace, a king and a queen.

4 Four numbers are chosen at random without replacement from a collection of ten numbers, six of which are positive and the remaining four are negative. Find the probability that the product of the four chosen numbers will be positive.

5 A subcommittee of three is chosen at random from a committee of ten men, two of whom are brothers. Calculate the probabilities that the subcommittee will include (i) one and only one of the two brothers, (ii) both brothers.

1.6 Conditional probability

It occasionally happens that some partial information is available on the outcome of a random experiment, the effect of which is to rule out some of the elements of the sample space as possible outcomes. Typical of such situations is that in which the outcome is known to possess a certain property not possessed by all the possible outcomes. For example, suppose that the faces numbered 1, 2, 3 on a fair die are coloured red and that the faces numbered 4, 5, 6 are coloured blue. The sample space for the score when the die is thrown is $S = \{1, 2, 3, 4, 5, 6\}$. Given that the uppermost face is red (event A) we know that the score must be one of 1, 2 and 3, so that the *effective sample space* is now $A = \{1, 2, 3\}$. Let B denote the event that the score is an even number. Since, in this example, the elements of A are equally probable, and the only even score in A is 2, it follows that, the probability of B given that A has occurred is 1/3, which we write as $P(B|A) = 1/3$.

To generalise, suppose that it is known that the outcome of a random experiment is such that the event A has occurred (recall that an event is a property associated with the outcomes of a random experiment). It then follows that the actual outcome must be an element of the set representation of the event A, so that the effective sample space is now the set A. We may then be interested in determining the probability that some other event B has occurred; this probability is referred to as the *conditional probability* of B given that A has occurred and is denoted by $P(B|A)$.

It is important to appreciate the distinction between $P(B)$ and $P(B|A)$. $P(B)$ is the probability of B with respect to the sample space S of the experiment since nothing is known about the outcome, whereas $P(B|A)$ is the probability of the event B with respect to the sample space A, it being known that the outcome is an element of A. Strictly, we should have written $P(B)$ as $P(B|S)$, but our approach from the outset has been to set up a sample space before discussing events.

Given that the event A has occurred, the event B will also have occurred only if the outcome is an element of the set $A \cap B$. Now consider the Venn diagram in Figure 1.8. Recall that in such a diagram, a probability is represented by an area, the area of S being assumed to be unity. Taking S to have some arbitrary area, the probability of the event A, say, is equivalent to the area of A expressed as a proportion of the area of S (i.e. area A/area S). But if it is known that A has occurred, then the area of A should be taken as unity when determining probabilities of other events, so that the probability of some other event B can be obtained by expressing the area of $A \cap B$ as a proportion of the area of A. (Observe that any part of B which is outside A will be impossible when it is known that A has occurred.) It follows that

$$P(B|A) = \frac{P(A \cap B)}{P(A)}. \qquad (1)$$

The same result can be obtained using the limiting relative frequency interpretation of a probability. Recalling that interpretation (see §1.4), $P(B|A)$ is the limiting value of the relative frequency of B in those trials in

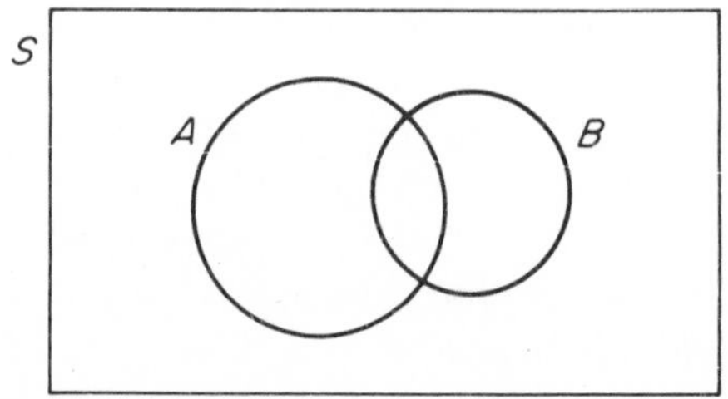

Fig. 1.8 Venn diagram to demonstrate $P(B|A)$

which A has occurred. Suppose that in n trials, A occurred r_A times, B occurred r_B times, and $A \cap B$ (i.e. both A and B) occurred r_{AB} times. Then, for the r_A trials in which A occurred, the relative frequency of B is given by

$$R_n(B|A) = \frac{r_{AB}}{r_A} = \frac{r_{AB}/n}{r_A/n} = \frac{R_n(A \cap B)}{R_n(A)}.$$

In the limit, as n is increased indefinitely, this ratio agrees with (1) above.

Interchanging A and B in (1) we have

$$P(A|B) = \frac{P(A \cap B)}{P(B)}. \tag{2}$$

Combining (1) and (2) it follows that

$$P(A \cap B) = P(B|A)\,P(A) = P(A|B)P(B). \tag{3}$$

EXAMPLE 1 *A subcommittee of four people was selected at random from a committee consisting of eight males and four females. Given that there is at least one female on the subcommittee, calculate the conditional probability that there are exactly two females on the subcommittee.*

If S is the sample space for the four people selected, then

$$n(S) = \binom{12}{4} = 495,$$

and, because the selection is made randomly, all these possibilities are equally probable.

Let A denote the event that at least one female will be chosen, and B the event that exactly two females will be chosen. We require $P(B|A)$. From (1),

$$P(B|A) = \frac{P(A \cap B)}{P(A)}.$$

Since A = at least one female, A' = no female (i.e. four males chosen), and

$$n(A') = \binom{8}{4} = 70.$$

Since the elements of S are equally probable,

$$P(A') = \frac{70}{495} = \frac{14}{99},$$

and therefore

$$P(A) = 1 - \frac{14}{99} = \frac{85}{99}.$$

Here, B = exactly two females (and therefore exactly two males), so that

$$A \cap B = \text{two females and two males},$$

$$n(A \cap B) = \binom{4}{2}\binom{8}{2} = 6 \times 28 = 168,$$

and

$$P(A \cap B) = \frac{168}{495} = \frac{56}{165}.$$

Hence

$$P(B|A) = \frac{56}{165} \times \frac{99}{85} = \frac{168}{425}.$$

EXAMPLE 2 *A and B are the events such that* $P(A) = 0{\cdot}6$, $P(B) = 0{\cdot}2$ *and* $P(A|B) = 0{\cdot}5$. *Calculate (i)* $P(A \cap B)$, *(ii)* $P(B|A)$, *(iii)* $P(A'|B')$, *and (iv) the probability that A has occurred given that at least one of A, B has occurred.*

(i) From (3)

$$P(A \cap B) = P(A|B)P(B) = 0{\cdot}5 \times 0{\cdot}2 = 0{\cdot}1.$$

(ii) From (1)

$$P(B|A) = \frac{P(A \cap B)}{P(A)} = \frac{0{\cdot}1}{0{\cdot}6} = \frac{1}{6}.$$

(iii) From (1)

$$P(A'|B') = \frac{P(A' \cap B')}{P(B')}.$$

Now,

$$P(A' \cap B') = 1 - P(A \cup B) = 1 - [P(A) + P(B) - P(A \cap B)]$$
$$= 1 - 0{\cdot}7 = 0{\cdot}3,$$

and $P(B') = 1 - P(B) = 0{\cdot}8$.
Hence,

$$P(A'|B') = \frac{0{\cdot}3}{0{\cdot}8} = \frac{3}{8}.$$

(iv) Here, we require

$$P(A|A \cup B) = \frac{P[A \cap (A \cup B)]}{P(A \cup B)} = \frac{P(A)}{P(A \cup B)} = \frac{0{\cdot}6}{0{\cdot}7} = \frac{6}{7}.$$

EXERCISE 1.6

1 A fair coin was tossed three times. Given that the first two tosses fell alike calculate the conditional probability that the third toss gave a head.

2 Two balls were drawn at random one after the other without replacement from a box which contained ten balls, of which six were black. Given that the first ball drawn was black, calculate the conditional probability that the second ball drawn was also black.

3 A box contains two red balls numbered 1 and 2, and two white balls numbered 1 and 2. Two balls were drawn at random from the box without replacement. Find the conditional probabilities that both balls drawn were white (i) given that at least one of them was white, (ii) one of them was the white ball numbered 1.

4 A and B are two events such that $P(A) = 1/2$, $P(B) = 1/3$ and $P(A \cap B) = 1/4$. Find the values of (i) $P(A|B)$, (ii) $P(B|A)$, (iii) $P(A'|B)$, (iv) $P(A'|B')$.

5 Four cards were drawn at random without replacement from a pack of nine cards numbered from 1 to 9, respectively. Given that the largest number drawn was 8, calculate the probability that the smallest number drawn was 3 (a continuation of Exercise 1.5C).

6 The four aces and the four kings are removed from a pack of playing cards. Two of these eight cards were chosen at random without replacement.
(i) Given that at least one of the two chosen cards was an ace, calculate the conditional probability that both cards were aces.
(ii) Given that one of the two chosen cards was the ace of hearts, calculate the conditional probability that the other card was also an ace.

7 Three events A, B and C have probabilities 2/5, 1/3 and 1/2, respectively. Given that $P(A \cap C) = 1/5$ and $P(B \cap C) = 1/4$, find the values of $P(C|B)$ and $P(A' \cap C')$.

1.7 Total probability of an event and Bayes' formula

EXAMPLE 1 *Two cards are dealt at random from an ordinary pack of 52 playing cards. Find the probability that the second card is an ace.*

We have already provided one solution to this problem in Example 5 (ii) of §1.5. We shall now use a different method.

Let A_1 denote the event that the first card is an ace and A_2 the event that the second card is an ace. We require $P(A_2)$. Now, A_2 will occur only if either (i) A_1 occurs or (ii) A_1' occurs, so that

$$A_2 = (A_1 \cap A_2) \cup (A_1' \cap A_2).$$

Since the right-hand side is the union of two mutually exclusive events we have

$$P(A_2) = P(A_1 \cap A_2) + P(A_1' \cap A_2).$$

From (3) of §1.6,

$$P(A_1 \cap A_2) = P(A_1)P(A_2|A_1) = \frac{4}{52} \times \frac{3}{51} = \frac{12}{52 \times 51},$$

and

$$P(A_1' \cap A_2) = P(A_1')P(A_2|A_1') = \frac{48}{52} \times \frac{4}{51} = \frac{192}{52 \times 51}.$$

Hence

$$P(A_2) = \frac{204}{52 \times 51} = \frac{1}{13},$$

exactly as obtained in Example 5(ii) of §1.5.

The above example is one in which the random experiment consisted of a sequence of stages, here confined to just two stages corresponding to dealing the first and second cards, respectively. Whenever a random experiment is, or may be regarded as consisting of, a sequence of stages the probability calculations can be conveniently displayed in a *probability tree diagram*, in which the various branches indicate the possibilities at each stage and to which we can attach probabilities. The probability tree diagram for the above example is shown in Fig. 1.9. Note that the sum of the probabilities on branches from any one point always sum to unity.

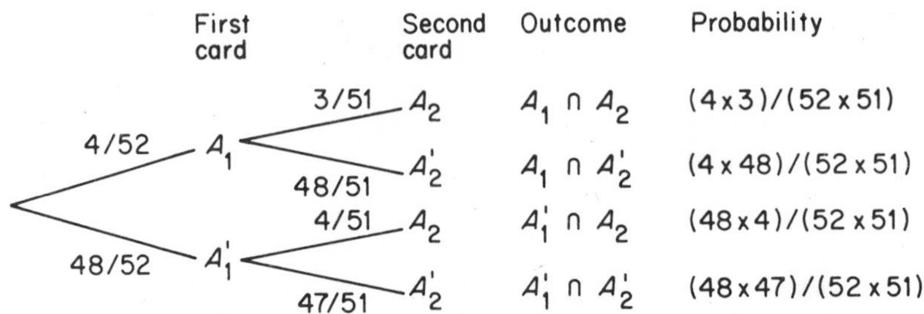

Fig. 1.9 Probability tree diagram for Example 1, §1.7

Directly from the tree we have

$$P(A_2) = P(A_1 \cap A_2) + P(A_1' \cap A_2) = (4 \times 3 + 48 \times 4)/(52 \times 51) = \frac{1}{13}.$$

The extension of a probability tree for a sequence of more than two stages will be considered in §1.8.

To extend a result used in the above solution, consider three events A_1, A_2 and A_3 which are *exhaustive*, i.e. $A_1 \cup A_2 \cup A_3 = S$, and *mutually exclusive* so that $A_1 \cap A_2 = \phi$, $A_2 \cap A_3 = \phi$, $A_1 \cap A_3 = \phi$. (In terms of a Venn diagram the region representing S is subdivided by A_1, A_2 and A_3 into three distinct subregions.) Now consider some other event B. If B occurs it must be in conjunction with the occurrence of one and only one of A_1, A_2, A_3, so that

$$B = (B \cap A_1) \cup (B \cap A_2) \cup (B \cap A_3).$$

The right-hand side is the union of mutually exclusive events and consequently

$$\begin{aligned} P(B) &= P(B \cap A_1) + P(B \cap A_2) + P(B \cap A_3) \\ &= P(A_1)P(B|A_1) + P(A_2)P(B|A_2) + P(A_3)P(B|A_3) \qquad (1) \end{aligned}$$

which is referred to as the *total probability rule*, the probability of the event B being the sum of the probabilities of the various ways in which it may occur. The rule extends in an obvious way to four or more events which are mutually exclusive and exhaustive.

EXAMPLE 2 *Three machines M_1, M_2, and M_3 in a certain factory produce 50%, 25% and 25%, respectively, of the total daily output of a particular type of article. It is known that 2% of the articles produced on M_1 and on M_2 are defective, and that 4% of those produced on M_3 are defective. If one article is chosen at random from a day's production, calculate the probability that it is defective.*

Let D denote the event that the chosen article is defective, and let A_1, A_2 and A_3 denote the events that the article was produced on M_1, M_2 and M_3, respectively. Since A_1, A_2 and A_3 are mutually exclusive and exhaustive

$$P(D) = P(A_1)P(D|A_1) + P(A_2)P(D|A_2) + P(A_3)P(D|A_3).$$

Since the machines produce 50%, 25% and 25% of the articles, respectively,

$$P(A_1) = 0{\cdot}5, \quad P(A_2) = P(A_3) = 0{\cdot}25.$$

Also, since the percentages of defectives produced are 2%, 2% and 4%, respectively,

$$P(D|A_1) = P(D|A_2) = 0{\cdot}02, \quad P(D|A_3) = 0{\cdot}04.$$

Hence $P(D) = 0{\cdot}5 \times 0{\cdot}02 + 0{\cdot}25 \times 0{\cdot}02 + 0{\cdot}25 \times 0{\cdot}04 = 0{\cdot}025$.

Since the random experiment in this example also involves two stages, the first being the machine which produced the chosen article and the second being the choice of article from those produced on the machine, a probability tree diagram could be used as indicated in Fig. 1.10 from which the required answer may be obtained by adding up the three asterisked probabilities.

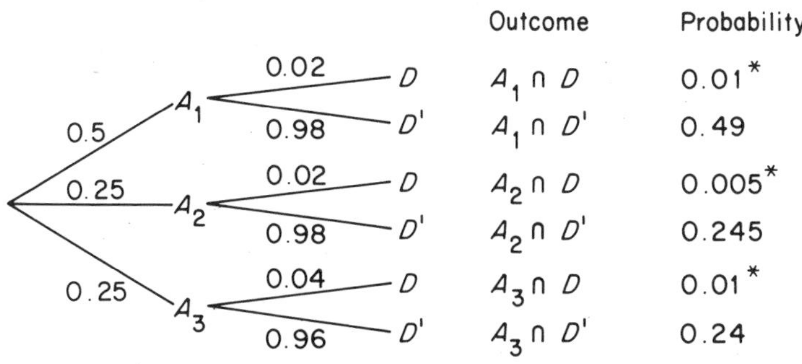

Fig. 1.10 Probability tree diagram for Example 2, §1.7

EXERCISE 1.7A

1 A mouse placed in a laboratory T-maze has the choice of turning left for food or turning right and receiving a mild electric shock. On its first run, a mouse is just as likely to turn left as it is to turn right. On any subsequent run, the probability that the mouse will turn left is (i) 0·6 if it received food on the preceding run, and (ii) 0·8 if it received a shock on the preceding run. Calculate

the probability that the mouse will turn left on its second run (continued in Exercise 1.8, 3).

2 Suppose that the weather on any day is classified as either wet or dry and that the probability is p that the weather on any particular day will be the same classification as that on the previous day. Given that it is wet on a Thursday, find an expression for the probability that the following Saturday will be wet.

3 Two balls are drawn at random without replacement from a box chosen at random from three boxes. One of the boxes contains five red and five white balls, another contains four red and six white balls, and the remaining box contains six red and four white balls. Calculate the probabilities that the two balls drawn will (i) both be red, (ii) both be of the same colour.

4 Of the total daily production of a particular type of article at a factory, 40% are produced on machine A, 10% are produced on machine B, and 50% are produced on machine C. All the articles produced on A are coloured red; of the articles produced on B, 30% are red, 50% are blue and 20% are green; of the articles produced on C, 50% are red, 20% are blue and 30% are green. Calculate the probability that an article chosen at random from a day's output will not be coloured red.

Bayes' formula

EXAMPLE 3 *In Example 2, given that a randomly chosen article is defective, calculate the conditional probability that it was produced on M_1.*
In the notation of Example 2 we are required to find $\mathrm{P}(A_1|D)$. Now

$$\mathrm{P}(A_1|D) = \frac{\mathrm{P}(A_1 \cap D)}{\mathrm{P}(D)} = \frac{\mathrm{P}(A_1)\mathrm{P}(D|A_1)}{\mathrm{P}(D)}$$

$$= \frac{0{\cdot}5 \times 0{\cdot}02}{0{\cdot}025} = \frac{2}{5},$$

on using results obtained in Example 2.

In the solution given above we have used a special case of the following general result due to the Reverend Thomas Bayes.

Let $A_1, A_2, \ldots$ be mutually exclusive and exhaustive events. Then, for any event B, and for any $r = 1, 2, \ldots$

$$\mathrm{P}(A_r|B) = \frac{\mathrm{P}(A_r)\mathrm{P}(B|A_r)}{\mathrm{P}(B)},$$

where

$$\mathrm{P}(B) = \mathrm{P}(A_1)\mathrm{P}(B|A_1) + \mathrm{P}(A_2)\mathrm{P}(B|A_2) + \ldots$$

which is known as *Bayes' formula.*

The derivation of this result is immediate on noting that

$$\mathrm{P}(A_r|B) = \frac{\mathrm{P}(A_r \cap B)}{\mathrm{P}(B)} = \frac{\mathrm{P}(A_r)\mathrm{P}(B|A_r)}{\mathrm{P}(B)}$$

and using the result for $\mathrm{P}(B)$ given in (1) above.

The most frequent application of Bayes' formula is in a situation such as that in Example 3 where an event (D) has been observed to occur and it is required to determine the respective probabilities that each of the various possibilities (A_1, A_2, . . .) also occurred.

EXAMPLE 4 *A motorist travels regularly from one town to another. On each occasion he chooses a route at random from four possible routes. From his experience the probabilities of completing the journey in under three hours via these routes are* 0·5, 0·8, 0·9 *and* 0·9, *respectively. Given that on a certain occasion he completed the journey in under three hours calculate the probability that he travelled by the first of the four routes.*

Let A_1, A_2, A_3, and A_4 denote the events that he travelled by the first, second, third and fourth routes, respectively, and let E denote the event that he completed the journey in under three hours. We are required to find $\text{P}(A_1|E)$.

Now

$$\text{P}(A_1|E) = \frac{\text{P}(A_1 \cap E)}{\text{P}(E)},$$

but $\text{P}(A_1 \cap E) = \text{P}(E|A_1)\text{P}(A_1) = 0{\cdot}5 \times 0{\cdot}25 = 0{\cdot}125$, and

$$\begin{aligned}\text{P}(E) &= \text{P}(A_1 \cap E) + \text{P}(A_2 \cap E) + \text{P}(A_3 \cap E) + \text{P}(A_4 \cap E)\\ &= \text{P}(E|A_1)\text{P}(A_1) + \text{P}(E|A_2)\text{P}(A_2) + \text{P}(E|A_3)\text{P}(A_3) + \text{P}(E|A_4)\text{P}(A_4)\\ &= 0{\cdot}5 \times 0{\cdot}25 + 0{\cdot}8 \times 0{\cdot}25 + 0{\cdot}9 \times 0{\cdot}25 + 0{\cdot}9 \times 0{\cdot}25\\ &= 0{\cdot}775.\end{aligned}$$

Hence

$$\text{P}(A_1|E) = \frac{0{\cdot}125}{0{\cdot}775} = \frac{5}{31}.$$

(The probability tree diagram for this example is left as an exercise.)

EXERCISE 1.7B

1 A local football team plays equal numbers of home and away matches in a season. Its probability of winning a home match is 3/4 and its probability of winning an away match is 2/5. Given that a randomly chosen one of the matches played by this team last season was won by the team find the conditional probability that it was an away match.

2 A hot-drinks vending machine supplies coffee, tea and cocoa, the demands for which are in the ratios 4 : 3 : 3. The probability that the machine is unable to supply coffee on demand is 0·02, and the corresponding probabilities for tea and cocoa are 0·03 and 0·02, respectively. Given that the machine is unable to supply a particular customer's choice, calculate the probabilities that the customer required (i) coffee, (ii) tea, (iii) cocoa.

3 Of the voters in a certain electoral district, 50 % voted Labour, 40 % voted Conservative and the remaining 10 % voted otherwise. One of the major issues in the election was the fluoridation of the domestic water supply in the district. This was favoured by 80 % of those who voted Labour, by 20 % of those who voted Conservative, and by 45 % of those who voted otherwise. A voter chosen at random is known to favour fluoridation. Find the probability that this particular voter voted Conservative in the election.

4 A judicial court in a certain country may return any one of three verdicts, namely 'guilty', 'not guilty', or 'not proven'. Of all the cases that have been tried by this court, 70% of the verdicts were 'guilty', 20% were 'not guilty', and 10% were 'not proven'. Suppose that when the court's verdict is 'guilty', 'not guilty' or 'not proven', the respective probabilities of the accused person being innocent are 0·05, 0·95 and 0·25. Find the conditional probability that an innocent person tried by this court will be found 'guilty'.

5 Three firms, F_1, F_2 and F_3 have tendered for a contract, and their probabilities of being awarded the contract are 0·5, 0·3 and 0·2, respectively. If F_1 gets the contract the probability is 0·75 that the work will be completed on schedule; the corresponding probabilities if F_2 or F_3 is awarded the contract are 0·6 and 0·45, respectively. Given that the work was not completed on schedule, calculate the probability that the contract was awarded to F_1.

1.8 The product rule

Consider a random experiment which may be regarded as consisting of $n\ (\geqslant 2)$ stages. Let $A_1, A_2, \ldots, A_n$ be events associated with the respective outcomes of the n stages. We met such an experiment with $n = 2$ in Example 1 of §1.7, in which two cards were dealt from an ordinary pack of playing cards. For $n = 2$, the probability that A_1 occurs at the first stage and A_2 occurs at the second stage is

$$\mathrm{P}(A_1 \cap A_2) = \mathrm{P}(A_1)\mathrm{P}(A_2|A_1).$$

For $n = 3$, the probability that A_1 occurs at the first stage, A_2 at the second stage, and A_3 at the third stage is

$$\begin{aligned}\mathrm{P}(A_1 \cap A_2 \cap A_3) &= \mathrm{P}(A_1)\mathrm{P}(A_2 \cap A_3|A_1)\\ &= \mathrm{P}(A_1)\mathrm{P}(A_2|A_1)\mathrm{P}(A_3|A_1 \cap A_2),\end{aligned}$$

and, in general, we have

$$\begin{aligned}\mathrm{P}(A_1 \cap A_2 \cap \ldots \cap A_n) = {} & \mathrm{P}(A_1)\mathrm{P}(A_2|A_1)\mathrm{P}(A_3|A_1 \cap A_2)\ldots\\ & \times \mathrm{P}(A_n|A_1 \cap A_2 \cap \ldots \cap A_{n-1})\end{aligned}$$

which is known as the *product rule for probabilities*.

EXAMPLE 1 *Three balls are drawn at random, one after the other without replacement, from a box containing* 8 *white and* 12 *red balls. Find the probability that the balls, in the order drawn, will alternate in colour.*

Let A_1, A_2, A_3, respectively, denote the events that the first ball drawn is white, the second ball drawn is white, and the third ball drawn is white, and let B denote the event that the balls alternate in colour. Then,

$$B = (A_1 \cap A_2' \cap A_3) \cup (A_1' \cap A_2 \cap A_3').$$

Since the right-hand side is the union of two exclusive events,

$$\mathrm{P}(B) = \mathrm{P}(A_1 \cap A_2' \cap A_3) + \mathrm{P}(A_1' \cap A_2 \cap A_3').$$

Using the product rule

$$\mathrm{P}(A_1 \cap A_2' \cap A_3) = \mathrm{P}(A_1)\mathrm{P}(A_2'|A_1)\mathrm{P}(A_3|A_1 \cap A_2').$$

Since the box initially contains 8 white and 12 red balls,

$$\mathrm{P}(A_1) = \frac{8}{20} = \frac{2}{5}.$$

Given that A_1 has occurred the box now contains 7 white and 12 red balls, and therefore

$$\mathrm{P}(A_2'|A_1) = \frac{12}{19}.$$

Given that both A_1 and A_2' have occurred, for the third draw the box will contain 7 white and 11 red balls, so that

$$\mathrm{P}(A_3|A_1 \cap A_2') = \frac{7}{18}.$$

Hence,

$$\mathrm{P}(A_1 \cap A_2' \cap A_3) = \frac{2}{5} \times \frac{12}{19} \times \frac{7}{18} = \frac{28}{285}.$$

Similarly,

$$\mathrm{P}(A_1' \cap A_2 \cap A_3') = \frac{12}{20} \times \frac{8}{19} \times \frac{11}{18} = \frac{44}{285}.$$

Hence

$$\mathrm{P}(B) = \frac{28}{285} + \frac{44}{285} = \frac{72}{285} = \frac{24}{95}.$$

The probability tree diagram is shown in Fig. 1.11, in which W represents a white

1st ball	2nd ball	3rd ball	Outcome	Probability
8/20 W	7/19 W	6/18 W	(W, W, W)	
		12/18 R	(W, W, R)	
	12/19 R	7/18 W	(W, R, W)	$\frac{(8 \times 12 \times 7)}{(20 \times 19 \times 18)}$
		11/18 R	(W, R, R)	
12/20 R	8/19 W	7/18 W	(R, W, W)	
		11/18 R	(R, W, R)	$\frac{(12 \times 8 \times 11)}{(20 \times 19 \times 18)}$
	11/19 R	8/18 W	(R, R, W)	
		10/18 R	(R, R, R)	

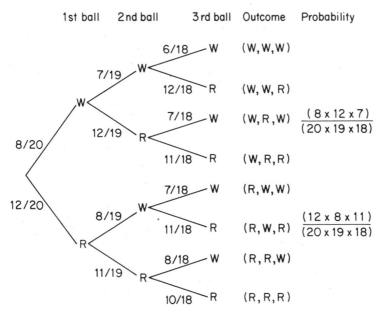

Fig. 1.11 Probability tree diagram for Example 1, §1.8

ball and R a red ball. The probabilities have been given only for the two outcomes of interest, namely (W, R, W) and (R, W, R). The sum of these two probabilities gives the required answer. (Alternatively, we could have obtained the answer to this problem from first principles based on the method described in §1.5.)

EXAMPLE 2 *A transmitted message consists of a sequence of α's and β's. The probability that the first letter transmitted is an α is equal to* 1/5. *In any transmission after the first the probability that an α is transmitted is equal to* 1/4 *if the preceding transmission was an α, and is equal to* 1/3 *if the preceding transmission was a β. Find the probabilities that (i) the first α to appear in a sequence will be the third transmitted letter, (ii) there will be exactly two α's transmitted among the first three letters transmitted.*

Let A_1, A_2 and A_3 denote the events that the first, second and, third letter transmitted is an α. From the given information we have $P(A_1) = 1/5$, $P(A_2|A_1) = P(A_3|A_2) = 1/4$, $P(A_2|A_1') = P(A_3|A_2') = 1/3$.
(i) Here we require

$$P(A_1' \cap A_2' \cap A_3) = P(A_1')P(A_2'|A_1')P(A_3|A_2')$$
$$= \frac{4}{5} \times \frac{2}{3} \times \frac{1}{3} = \frac{8}{45}.$$

(ii) Let B denote the event that there are exactly two α's among the first three letters transmitted. Then

$$B = (A_1 \cap A_2 \cap A_3') \cup (A_1 \cap A_2' \cap A_3) \cup (A_1' \cap A_2 \cap A_3),$$

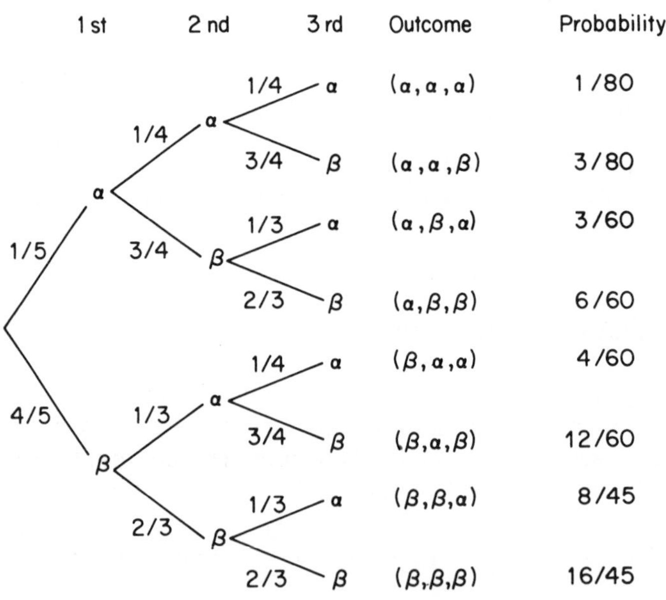

Fig. 1.12 Probability tree diagram for Example 2, §1.8

and

$$\begin{aligned}\mathrm{P}(B) &= \mathrm{P}(A_1 \cap A_2 \cap A_3') + \mathrm{P}(A_1 \cap A_2' \cap A_3) + \mathrm{P}(A_1' \cap A_2 \cap A_3) \\ &= \mathrm{P}(A_1)\mathrm{P}(A_2|A_1)\mathrm{P}(A_3'|A_2) + \mathrm{P}(A_1)\mathrm{P}(A_2'|A_1)\mathrm{P}(A_3|A_2') \\ &\quad + \mathrm{P}(A_1')\mathrm{P}(A_2|A_1')\mathrm{P}(A_3|A_2) \\ &= \frac{1}{5}\times\frac{1}{4}\times\frac{3}{4} + \frac{1}{5}\times\frac{3}{4}\times\frac{1}{3} + \frac{4}{5}\times\frac{1}{3}\times\frac{1}{4} = \frac{37}{240}.\end{aligned}$$

The probability tree diagram is shown in Fig. 1.12.

(i) The probability that the first α to appear is the third letter transmitted is the probability of the sequence being (β, β, α) and from the diagram this is equal to 8/45.

(ii) From the diagram, the probability that there are exactly two α's among the first three transmissions is equal to $\dfrac{3}{80} + \dfrac{3}{60} + \dfrac{4}{60} = \dfrac{37}{240}$.

EXERCISE 1.8

1 Find the probability that the first three cards dealt from an ordinary pack of 52 playing cards will all be hearts.

2 Three valves are drawn at random, one after the other without replacement, from a box containing three faulty and seven good valves.
(i) Find the probability that at least one good valve will be drawn.
(ii) Given that the first valve drawn is a good one, find the conditional probability that all three drawn are good ones.

3 In Exercise 1.7A, question 1, find the probability that the mouse will turn left on its third run.

4 A fair cubical die is tossed. If the score obtained is a multiple of 3, a ball is drawn at random from a box containing five red, three white and eight blue balls, whereas if the score obtained is not a multiple of 3, a ball is drawn at random from a box containing three red and five white balls. (i) Find the probability that a red ball is drawn. (ii) Given that a white ball is drawn find the probability that the score thrown was (a) a multiple of 3, (b) 5.

5 In Example 2 calculate the probabilities that the first and the third letters transmitted are the same. Given that the third letter transmitted was β find the probability that the first two letters transmitted consisted of one α and one β.

1.9 Independent events

Consider again the situation in Example 1 in §1.7 in which two cards are dealt from an ordinary pack of 52 playing cards. Let A_1 denote the event that the first card is an ace and let A_2 denote the event that the second card is an ace. In the solution to Example 1 we showed that

$$\mathrm{P}(A_2|A_1) = \frac{3}{51}, \quad \mathrm{P}(A_2|A_1') = \frac{4}{51}, \quad \text{and} \quad \mathrm{P}(A_2) = \frac{1}{13}.$$

It follows that the probability of the second card dealt being an ace depends on whether we know that the first card is an ace, or that the first card is not an ace, or that we are completely ignorant of the first card. Thus given that A_1 (or A'_1) has occurred changes the value of the probability that A_2 has occurred. We then say that A_2 is independent of A_1.

Now suppose that the two cards are dealt with replacement, the first card being replaced in the pack which is then shuffled before the second card is dealt. In this case it is clear that

$$P(A_2|A_1) = P(A_2|A'_1) = P(A_2) = \frac{1}{13},$$

so that the probability of the second card being an ace is now unaltered by being informed whether or not the first card was an ace. In this case we say that A_2 and A_1 are *independent events.*

Definition: An event A is said to be independent of an event B if and only if

$$P(A|B) = P(A), \tag{1}$$

that is, if the probability of A occurring is unaffected by the knowledge that B has occurred.

EXAMPLE 1 *Three fair coins are tossed simultaneously. Let A denote the event that three heads or three tails are obtained, B the event that at least two heads are obtained, and C the event that at most two heads are obtained. Determine whether or not A is independent of* (i) *B, and* (ii) *C.*

From Example 1 §1.5 the sample space for this experiment is

$$S = \{(h, h, h), (h, h, t), (h, t, h), (t, h, h), (h, t, t), (t, h, t), (t, t, h), (t, t, t)\},$$

where each element represents the faces showing on the three coins assumed to be distinguishable. Since the coins are fair we shall assume that the eight elements of S are equally probable.

A = three heads or three tails = $\{(h, h, h), (t, t, t)\}$,
B = at least two heads = $\{(h, h, h), (h, h, t), (h, t, h), (t, h, h)\}$,
C = at most two heads = $\{(h, h, t), (h, t, h), (t, h, h), (h, t, t), (t, h, t), (t, t, h), (t, t, t)\}$.

Hence

$$P(A) = \frac{2}{8}, \quad P(B) = \frac{4}{8}, \quad P(C) = \frac{7}{8}.$$

(i)

$$P(A|B) = \frac{P(A \cap B)}{P(B)}.$$

But $A \cap B = \{(h, h, h)\}$ so that $P(A \cap B) = 1/8$. Hence

$$P(A|B) = \frac{1/8}{4/8} = \frac{1}{4} = P(A),$$

from which it follows that A is independent of B.

(ii) Similarly,

$$P(A|C) = \frac{P(A \cap C)}{P(C)} = \frac{1/8}{7/8} = \frac{1}{7}.$$

Since $P(A|C) \neq P(A)$ it follows that A is not independent of C.

The above definition is appropriate for determining whether or not the event A is independent of the event B. Interchanging A and B will give the appropriate definition for determining whether or not the event B is independent of the event A. We now show that these two are equivalent.

Since

$$P(B|A) = \frac{P(B \cap A)}{P(A)} = \frac{P(A|B)P(B)}{P(A)},$$

it follows that $P(B|A) = P(B)$ if and only if $P(A|B) = P(A)$. That is, the event B is independent of the event A if and only if the event A is independent of the event B. In view of this equivalence, we can refer to two events as being independent or being not independent, rather than the one event being independent or not independent of the other event.

Furthermore, since

$$P(A|B) = \frac{P(A \cap B)}{P(B)},$$

it follows that $P(A|B) = P(A)$ if and only if

$$P(A \cap B) = P(A)P(B), \qquad (2)$$

which is a much more convenient formula for determining whether or not two events are independent since it does not involve conditional probabilities. We shall adopt this form of result as a formal definition for independence even though it does not have the same intuitive appeal of the definition given earlier.

EXAMPLE 2

In Example 1 we have

$$P(A) = \frac{1}{4}, \quad P(B) = \frac{1}{2}, \quad \textit{and} \quad P(A \cap B) = \frac{1}{8} = P(A)\,P(B),$$

so that the events A and B are independent. Also we have

$$P(C) = \frac{7}{8} \quad \text{and} \quad P(A \cap C) = \frac{1}{8} \neq P(A)P(C),$$

so that the events A and C are not independent. It is left as an exercise to show, using either (1) *or* (2), *that the events B and C in Example* 1 *are not independent.*

EXAMPLE 3 *Given that A and B are independent, show that A′ and B are also independent.*

We are given that $P(A \cap B) = P(A)P(B)$ and we need to show that $P(A' \cap B) = P(A')P(B)$. From (7) of §1.4, we have

$$\begin{aligned} P(A' \cap B) &= P(B) - P(A \cap B) \\ &= P(B) - P(A)\,P(B), \text{ (since } A \text{ and } B \text{ are independent)} \\ &= P(B)\,\{1 - P(A)\} \\ &= P(A')\,P(B), \end{aligned}$$

which establishes the result required for A' and B to be independent.

The distinction between mutual exclusiveness and independence is not always fully understood. A fundamental difference between the two is that, whereas the mutual exclusiveness of two events A and B can be ascertained from the events themselves (by showing that $A \cap B = \phi$), the independence of A and B can be ascertained only from probabilistic considerations. The following illustration demonstrates the distinction. Consider two football teams, say Arsenal and Birmingham, that play in the same division of the football league. On a particular Saturday in the football season, let A and B be the events that Arsenal and Birmingham, respectively, win their matches. If on that Saturday Arsenal happen to be playing Birmingham, then clearly A and B are mutually exclusive but are not independent, whereas if they are not playing each other, A and B are independent but not mutually exclusive.

EXERCISE 1.9A

1 One card is drawn at random from an ordinary pack of 52 playing cards. If A is the event that the chosen card is a heart and B is the event that the chosen card is an honour (ace, king, queen, jack or ten), show that A and B are independent.

2 Show that two events, each having non-zero probability, cannot be mutually exclusive and independent.

3 A red die and a black die are thrown simultaneously. Let A denote the event that the score on the red die is 1 and B the event that the sum of the two scores is 7. Find $P(A)$, $P(B)$, $P(A \cap B)$, $P(A|B)$ and $P(B|A)$.
Are A and B independent?

4 Two independent events are such that the probability of both occurring is $1/6$ and the probability of neither occurring is $1/3$. Find the probability of each of the two events occurring.

5 Let A denote the event that a family has children of both sexes, and B the event that a family has at most one girl. Assuming that all possible sex distributions of the children ordered according to age are equally probable show that (i) for a randomly chosen family of three children, the events A and B are independent, (ii) for a randomly chosen family of two children, the events A and B are not independent.

6 The two events A and B are such that $P(A) = 1/4$ and $P(A \cup B) = 1/3$. Find $P(B)$ in each of the cases when (i) A and B are mutually exclusive, (ii) A and B are independent.

7 Given that A and B are independent, show that A' and B' are also independent.

8 Two cards are dealt from an ordinary pack of 52 playing cards. Let A denote the event that the first card is a spade, B the event that the second card is a king, and C the event that the first card is either an ace or a king. Determine which pairs of the events A, B and C are independent.

Independence of three or more events

Definition: Three events A, B and C are said to be *pairwise independent* if and only if each pair of events chosen from A, B, C are independent (i.e. A and B are independent, B and C are independent, and A and C are independent), and are said to be *totally independent* or simply *independent* if, in addition to being pairwise independent,

$$P(A \cap B \cap C) = P(A)P(B)P(C).$$

EXAMPLE 4 *A fair coin is tossed twice. Let A denote the event that a head is obtained on the first toss, B the event that a head is obtained on the second toss, and C the event that exactly one head is obtained. Discuss the independence of A, B and C.*

The sample space for this random experiment is

$$S = \{(h, h), (h, t), (t, h)\ (t, t)\},$$

whose elements may be assumed to be equally probable.

A = head on first toss = $\{(h, h), (h, t)\}$; $P(A) = \frac{1}{2}$.

B = head on second toss = $\{(h, h), (t, h)\}$; $P(B) = \frac{1}{2}$.

C = exactly one head = $\{(h, t), (t, h)\}$; $P(C) = \frac{1}{2}$.

Since $A \cap B = \{(h, h)\}$,

$$P(A \cap B) = \tfrac{1}{4} = P(A)P(B),$$

from which it follows that A and B are independent. Similarly, $P(A \cap C) = P(A)P(C)$ and $P(B \cap C) = P(B)P(C)$, so that A and C are independent, and B and C are independent. Hence the events A, B, C are pairwise independent.

Now, $A \cap B \cap C = \phi$, so that $P(A \cap B \cap C) = 0 \neq P(A)\ P(B)\ P(C)$. Hence A, B, C are not totally independent.

It is instructive to interpret this result intuitively. That A and B are independent is intuitively obvious because they relate to two different tosses of the coin, the outcome of the first toss clearly having no influence at all on the probabilities of the possible outcomes of the second toss. The independence of A and C is not so obvious, but it may be shown that $P(C|A) = P(C) = 1/2$, indicating that knowledge of A having occurred does not affect the probability of C having occurred. Similarly, the independence of B and C is not immediately obvious, but again we find $P(C|B) = P(C) = 1/2$. Now consider $P(C|A \cap B)$, the conditional probability that C has occurred given that both A and B have occurred. From the definitions of A, B and C it is clear that $P(C|A \cap B) = 0$, since the occurrence of both A and B means that both tosses gave heads, whereas C is the event that there was one head and one tail. Thus $P(C|A \cap B) \neq P(C)$; that is, the probability of C occurring is influenced by the knowledge that both A and B have occurred, even though it is not influenced by the knowledge that a specified one of them had occurred. The moral of this example is not to jump to the conclusion that three events are totally independent when, in fact, they are only pairwise independent.

The total independence of four or more events is even more complicated. The details will not be given here, but, basically, for the total independence of any number of events it is necessary that the probability of the simultaneous occurrence of every possible subcollection of the events should equal the product of the individual probabilities of the events in that subcollection. Thus, for example, four events A, B, C, D are totally independent if and only if

$$P(A \cap B) = P(A)P(B),\ P(A \cap C) = P(A)\,P(C),\ P(A \cap D) = P(A)P(D),$$

$$P(B \cap C) = P(B)P(C),\ P(B \cap D) = P(B)P(D),\ P(C \cap D) = P(C)P(D),$$

i.e. the events are pairwise independent,

$$P(A \cap B \cap C) = P(A)P(B)P(C),\quad P(A \cap B \cap D) = P(A)P(B)P(D),$$

$$P(A \cap C \cap D) = P(A)P(C)P(D),\quad P(B \cap C \cap D) = P(B)P(C)P(D),$$

and $P(A \cap B \cap C \cap D) = P(A)P(B)P(C)P(D)$.

EXERCISE 1.9B

1 Two balls are drawn at random without replacement from a box containing four white and two black balls. Discuss the independence of the three events A, B and C, where A = exactly one of the two balls drawn is white, B = the second ball drawn is white, and C = both balls drawn are white.

2 A box contains 16 cards, two of which are labelled 111, three are labelled 112, three are labelled 121, three are labelled 211, and the remaining five are labelled 222. One card is drawn at random from the box. Let A_1, A_2, A_3, respectively, denote the events that the drawn card has the digit 1 in the first, second and third positions. Show that $P(A_1 \cap A_2 \cap A_3) = P(A_1)P(A_2)P(A_3)$, but that A_1, A_2 and A_3 are not totally independent.

3 A red die and a green die are thrown simultaneously. Let A denote the event that an even score is obtained on the red die, B the event that an odd score is obtained on the green die, and C the event that the sum of the two scores is odd. Show that A, B and C are pairwise independent but not totally independent.

4 A bag contains nine marbles, all of which have coloured spots on them. Three of the marbles have red spots only, one has white spots only, one has blue spots only, and one has green spots only. Of the three remaining marbles, one has red, white and green spots; one has red, white and blue spots; and the third has red, blue and green spots. One marble is drawn at random from the bag. Let R denote the event that the chosen marble has red spots on it, W the event that it has white spots, B the event that it has blue spots, and G the event that it has green spots. Determine (i) which pairs (if any), (ii) which triples (if any), of the events R, W, B, G are independent.

1.10 Independent random experiments

Definition: Two or more random experiments or two or more trials of one random experiment are said to be *independent* if and only if they are performed in such a way that the probabilities of the various possible outcomes of any one of them are the same whatever be the outcomes of the others.

We are frequently concerned with a situation in which random experiments are performed simultaneously or sequentially and which are intuitively independent in the sense defined above. For example:

(i) when a die and a coin are tossed simultaneously, it is clear that neither (tossing a die or tossing a coin) will influence the probabilities of the possible outcomes of the other;
(ii) when a die is tossed several times in succession, it is clear that the probabilities of the various scores in any toss will not be influenced by the scores obtained in the other tosses;
(iii) when a sample of k objects is drawn *with replacement* from a collection of n objects, it is clear that since the collection remains the same at each draw the probabilities at each draw are not influenced by the outcomes of the other draws.

Let A_1, A_2 and A_3 be events associated exclusively with the outcome of the first, second and third experiment, respectively, of three independent random experiments. Then, clearly A_1, A_2 and A_3 are independent and we have $P(A_1 \cap A_2) = P(A_1)P(A_2)$, $P(A_1 \cap A_3) = P(A_1)P(A_3)$, $P(A_2 \cap A_3) = P(A_2)P(A_3)$ and $P(A_1 \cap A_2 \cap A_3) = P(A_1)P(A_2)P(A_3)$. These results extend in an obvious way to four or more independent random experiments.

EXAMPLE 1 *If four fair dice are tossed simultaneously, calculate the probabilities that (i) each die shows an even score, (ii) at least one* 6 *is tossed.*

The tossing of four fair dice is equivalent to four independent trials of the random experiment in which one fair die is tossed.
(i) Let A_1, A_2, A_3, and A_4 denote the events that the first, second, third and fourth tosses, respectively, gives an even score.

We require $P(A_1 \cap A_2 \cap A_3 \cap A_4) = P(A_1)P(A_2)P(A_3)P(A_4)$.

But

$$P(A_1) = P(A_2) = P(A_3) = P(A_4) = \frac{1}{2}$$

Hence

$$P(A_1 \cap A_2 \cap A_3 \cap A_4) = \left(\frac{1}{2}\right)^4 = \frac{1}{16}.$$

(ii) Let B_1, B_2, B_3 and B_4 denote the events that the first, second, third and fourth tosses, respectively, do not result in a score of 6. Then $C = B_1 \cap B_2 \cap B_3 \cap B_4$ is the event that no 6 is tossed and C' is the event that at least one 6 is tossed. Now,

$$P(C') = 1 - P(C) = 1 - P(B_1)P(B_2)P(B_3)P(B_4),$$

where

$$P(B_1) = P(B_2) = P(B_3) = P(B_4) = \frac{5}{6}.$$

Hence

$$P(C') = 1 - \left(\frac{5}{6}\right)^4 = \frac{671}{1296}.$$

EXAMPLE 2 *Independently for each shot fired at a target by* A *there is a probability of* 1/3 *that the shot will hit the target, and independently for each shot fired at a target by* B *the corresponding probability is* 1/4.

(i) *If each of* A *and* B *has two shots at the target, find the probability that at least one of the four shots will hit the target.*

(ii) *If* B *is allowed just two shots at the target, find the smallest number of shots that* A *should be allowed for there to be a probability of at least* 0·9 *of the target being hit.*

(i) Let E be the event that the target is hit at least once in the four shots. Then E' is the event that all four shots miss the target.

Now let A_1 and A_2 denote the events that the first and second shots fired by A miss the target, and similarly define B_1 and B_2. Then

$$E' = (A'_1 \cap A'_2 \cap B'_1 \cap B'_2).$$

We are given that the outcomes of A's shots are independent and that the outcomes of B's shots are independent. It would seem reasonable to assume also that the outcomes of shots by A and of shots by B are also independent, in which case

$$P(E') = P(A'_1)P(A'_2)P(B'_1)P(B'_2)$$

$$= \frac{2}{3} \times \frac{2}{3} \times \frac{3}{4} \times \frac{3}{4} = \frac{1}{4}.$$

Hence $P(E) = 1 - P(E') = \frac{3}{4}$.

(ii) Here, suppose that A is allowed n shots at the target.

Let E denote the event that the target is hit at least once in the $(n+2)$ shots, so that E' is the event that the target is missed by all $(n+2)$ shots. Then, extending the notation used in (i) we have

$$P(E') = P(B'_1 \cap B'_2 \cap A'_1 \cap A'_2 \cap \ldots \cap A'_n) = \left(\frac{3}{4}\right)^2 \times \left(\frac{2}{3}\right)^n,$$

and

$$P(E) = 1 - \frac{9}{16}\left(\frac{2}{3}\right)^n.$$

We need to find the smallest n for which $P(E) \geqslant 0{\cdot}9$; that is

$$1 - \frac{9}{16}\left(\frac{2}{3}\right)^n \geqslant 0{\cdot}9$$

or

$$\left(\frac{2}{3}\right)^n \leqslant \frac{1\cdot6}{9} = \frac{8}{45}.$$

Taking logarithms,

$$n \log\left(\frac{2}{3}\right) \leqslant \log\frac{8}{45}.$$

Since $\log\left(\frac{2}{3}\right)$ is negative we then have

$$n \geqslant \frac{\log(8/45)}{\log(2/3)} = 4\cdot26,$$

so that A must be allowed at least 5 shots for there to be a probability of 0·9 or more for the target to be hit.

EXERCISE 1.10

1 A fair die is tossed and a card is drawn randomly from an ordinary pack of 52 playing cards. Find the probabilities that (i) the score thrown is even and the card drawn is red, (ii) the score thrown is even or the card drawn is red.

2 A certain mechanism consists of three components and will operate properly only if all three components are functioning. Assuming that the three components function independently of one another and have probabilities 0·02, 0·05 and 0·1, respectively, of developing a fault, find the probability that the mechanism will not operate properly. Given that the mechanism is not operating properly find the probability that it is because exactly one of the components has developed a fault.

3 A computer produces an answer to a certain calculation in the form of an n-digit binary number. Independently for each digit there is a small probability p that it is incorrect. Find an expression for the probability that the answer is correct.

4 Three men at a shooting range have probabilities $\frac{1}{6}$, $\frac{1}{4}$ and $\frac{1}{3}$, respectively, of hitting the bull's eye with one shot. Each man fires one shot.
(i) Find the probability that exactly one hits the bull's eye.
(ii) Given that only one shot hit the bull's eye find the probability that it was fired by the man with the smallest probability of hitting the bull's eye.

5 Independently, three brothers speak the truth with probabilities 0·9, 0·8 and 0·7, respectively. One day each was asked who had been responsible for a certain misdemeanour. Find the probabilities that (i) all three will reply truthfully, (ii) exactly two of them will reply truthfully.

6 Independently for each torpedo fired at a ship there is a probability of $\frac{1}{2}$ that the torpedo will sink the ship, a probability of $\frac{1}{4}$ that it will merely damage the ship without sinking it, and a probability of $\frac{1}{4}$ that it will miss the ship. Assuming that two damaging shots will sink the ship, find the probability that up to 3 torpedoes will need to be fired at a ship to sink it. (Hint: You may find it easier to find the probability of the complementary event.)

7 A man plays a series of three games in each of which his probabilities of winning, losing and drawing are $\frac{1}{2}$, $\frac{1}{4}$ and $\frac{1}{4}$, respectively. Find the probability that he will win more games than he will lose.

8 A man with only £700 requires £800 for a specific purpose. He regards this purpose as sufficiently important to be willing to risk losing his £700 by taking part in a gambling game in which he has probability $\frac{2}{5}$ of winning whatever amount he stakes and probability $\frac{3}{5}$ of losing his stake. He decides to stake £100 in the first play of the game. If he wins this game he will have the necessary £800. If he loses, he will play the game again with a stake of £200, retiring if he wins and playing again with a stake of £400 if he loses. He will continue in this way, each time doubling his stake in any new game until he is broke or he has a total of £800. Find the probability that he will end up with £800.

1.11 The binomial probability law

In this section we restrict consideration to a random experiment in which one's only interest is whether or not a particular event will occur. The occurrence of the event in any trial of the experiment will be called a *success* (s) and its non-occurrence will be called a *failure* (f). We refer to such a trial as being a *Bernoulli trial.* The tossing of a coin is the simplest example of a Bernoulli trial since there are only two possible outcomes, either of which may be regarded as a success, the other being regarded as a failure.

Suppose that in any Bernoulli trial the probability of a success is equal to p. We shall now consider the probability of obtaining exactly r successes in n independent Bernoulli trials for an arbitrary value of r from 0 to n, inclusive. Before deriving the general result let us consider some specific examples.

EXAMPLE 1 *If in each trial of a random experiment the probability of a success is p, find the probabilities of (i) exactly one success in three independent trials, (ii) exactly three successes in five independent trials.*

Since the probability of a success in any trial is p, the probability of a failure in any trial is $1-p = q$, say.

(i) In 3 independent trials the sample space for the outcomes is

$$S = \{(\mathrm{s,s,s}), (\mathrm{s,s,f}), (\mathrm{s,f,s}), (\mathrm{f,s,s}), (\mathrm{s,f,f}), (\mathrm{f,s,f}), (\mathrm{f,f,s}), (\mathrm{f,f,f})\},$$

where s denotes a success and f denotes a failure. Observe that here we have an example where the elements of S are *not* equally probable (unless $p = \frac{1}{2}$). Since the trials are independent, the respective probabilities of the elements of S, in the order in which they appear above, are

$$p^3, p^2q, p^2q, p^2q, pq^2, pq^2, pq^2, q^3.$$

In particular then, the probability of exactly one success is the sum of the probabilities of the elements (s, f, f), (f, s, f) and (f, f, s) and is seen to be $3pq^2$.

Similarly, we find that in the three trials,

the probability of 0 success = q^3
the probability of 1 success = $3pq^2$
the probability of 2 successes = $3p^2q$
the probability of 3 successes = p^3.

Observe that these probabilities are the respective terms in the expansion of $(q+p)^3$.

(ii) In five independent Bernoulli trials, the sample space will involve $2^5 = 32$ elements, since each of the five components of any element may be either s or f. This is too many for us to contemplate making a listing and the task would be even more prohibitive for a larger number of trials. We therefore seek an alternative method which does not require a listing of the individual outcomes.

Here we are interested in the event that there are exactly three successes in the five trials. Three successes occur if the outcomes of the five trials consist of three s's and two f's in some order. Since the trials are independent, each of these possible outcomes will have probability p^3q^2. It remains to find how many such outcomes there are. Each outcome will consist of five components, one corresponding to each trial. The number of ways in which these five will consist of three s's is $\binom{5}{3}$, being equivalent to choosing three of the five trials to be an s. It follows that the probability of exactly three successes in five trials is $\binom{5}{3}p^3q^2 = 10p^3q^2$. Proceeding in a similar fashion we could derive the probabilities of 0, 1, 2, 3, 4 and 5 successes in the five trials. It transpires that these probabilities are the respective terms in the expansion of $(q+p)^5$.

With the above examples to guide us let us now find the probability of exactly r successes occurring in n independent trials, where r may be any one of the integers 0, 1, 2, . . . , n. First observe that any outcome which consists of exactly r successes will have r of its components equal to s, and $(n-r)$ equal to f. The probability of any such outcome is thus $p^r q^{n-r}$. To determine the *number* of such outcomes we observe that this is equivalent to the number of ways of choosing r of the n trials to be s and is therefore equal to $\binom{n}{r}$. Hence, the probability of exactly r successes in n independent trials is given by

$$P(r) = \binom{n}{r} p^r q^{n-r} \tag{1}$$

for any $r = 0, 1, 2, \ldots, n$, which is known as the *binomial probability law*; the individual probabilities P(0), P(1), . . . , P(n) being the respective terms in the binomial expansion of $(q+p)^n$.

Tables are widely available from which the values of P(r) for selected values of n and p may be deduced. (In view of the variation in the tables used by the various examining boards we shall not give detailed consideration to the use of tables, but it will be assumed that such tables are available.)

From (1) we have

$$\frac{P(r+1)}{P(r)} = \frac{\binom{n}{r+1} p^{r+1} q^{n-r-1}}{\binom{n}{r} p^r q^{n-r}} = \frac{(n-r)p}{(r+1)q},$$

so that

$$P(r+1) = \frac{(n-r)p}{(r+1)q} P(r), \tag{2}$$

which is a useful recursive formula for calculating successive individual terms of the binomial probability law, especially if a calculator or computer is used.

EXAMPLE 2 *Find the probability that in* 10 *throws of a fair die a score which is a multiple of* 3 *will be obtained in at least* 8 *of the throws.*

In this case a success is a score which is a multiple of 3, that is a score of 3 or 6. Since the die is fair the probability of this is $p = \frac{1}{3}$.

The probability of exactly r successes in the ten throws is

$$P(r) = \binom{10}{r}\left(\frac{1}{3}\right)^r \left(\frac{2}{3}\right)^{10-r},$$

so that the probability of at least 8 successes is

$$\begin{aligned} &P(8) + P(9) + P(10) \\ &= \binom{10}{8}\left(\frac{1}{3}\right)^8\left(\frac{2}{3}\right)^2 + \binom{10}{9}\left(\frac{1}{3}\right)^9\left(\frac{2}{3}\right) + \left(\frac{1}{3}\right)^{10} \\ &= \frac{1}{3^{10}}(45 \times 4 + 10 \times 2 + 1) = \frac{201}{3^{10}} \simeq 0{\cdot}0034. \end{aligned}$$

The approximation to this answer was obtained using a calculator with a power function facility, which is necessary in the calculation of binomial probabilities if the tables available do not include the appropriate values of n and p.

Using the recursive formula (2) with $n = 10$, $p = \frac{1}{3}$, $p/q = \frac{1}{2}$, we have $P(9) = \frac{1}{9} P(8)$ and $P(10) = \frac{1}{20} P(9)$. Since $P(8) = 180/3^{10}$ we have $P(9) = 20/3^{10}$ and $P(10) = 1/3^{10}$ as given in the above solution.

EXAMPLE 3 *Records have shown that* 5% *of the items manufactured at a certain factory are defective. Find the probability that a random sample of* 20 *such items will include at most two defectives.*

Here we shall regard a defective item as a success, the probability of which is

$p = 0{\cdot}05$. The probability of exactly r defectives in a random sample of 20 items is then $\mathrm{P}(r) = \binom{20}{r}(0{\cdot}05)^r(0{\cdot}95)^{20-r}$; and the probability of at most two defectives in the sample is

$$\mathrm{P}(0)+\mathrm{P}(1)+\mathrm{P}(2)$$

$$= (0{\cdot}95)^{20} + \binom{20}{1}(0{\cdot}05)(0{\cdot}95)^{19} + \binom{20}{2}(0{\cdot}05)^2(0{\cdot}95)^{18}$$

$$= (0{\cdot}95)^{18}(0{\cdot}95^2 + 20 \times 0{\cdot}05 \times 0{\cdot}95 + 190 \times 0{\cdot}05^2)$$

$$\simeq 0{\cdot}9245$$

Here again, the recursive formula (2) could have been used to obtain this approximate answer on a calculator. However, most tables of the binomial include $n = 20$ and $p = 0{\cdot}05$, and, as such, would provide an alternative means for obtaining an approximation to the above answer.

EXERCISE 1.11

1 Assuming that each child is equally likely to be a boy or a girl, use the binomial probability law to find the probabilities that in a family of three children there will be (i) exactly one boy, (ii) at least one boy, (iii) at least two boys. (Compare Exercise 1.5A, question 3).

2 Find the exact value of the probability of tossing exactly three heads in five tosses of a fair coin.

3 Find, correct to four decimal places, the probability of throwing at least two 6s in six throws of a fair die.

4 A multiple-choice test consists of eight questions, each question listing four alternative answers of which only one is correct. For a candidate who guesses the answer to each of the questions, calculate the probabilities that this candidate will (i) answer exactly three questions correctly, (ii) pass the test, having obtained the correct answers to at least six questions.

5 A man keeps two fuses for electrical plugs in reserve. Suppose that in any electrical appliance which is in use there is a probability of $0{\cdot}1$ that the fuse in the plug of the appliance will blow and have to be replaced. On a night when six appliances are in use calculate the probability that the man will not have enough fuses to replace fuses that blow.

6 Suppose that when an aeroplane is in flight there is, independently for each engine, a probability p that an engine will fail. Suppose further that an aeroplane will have a successful flight provided at least half of its engines function throughout the flight. Find the range of values of p for which a two-engined aeroplane has a better chance than a four-engined aeroplane of making a successful flight.

7 A fair coin is tossed n times. Show that for $n \geqslant 3$, the probability that all or all but one of the n tosses fall alike is $(n+1)/2^{n-1}$. Find the corresponding probability when $n = 2$.

8 Each of two persons tosses three fair coins. Find the probability that they will toss equal numbers of heads.

REVIEW PROBLEMS ON CHAPTER 1

1 Four ballpoint refills are to be drawn at random without replacement from a bag containing ten refills, of which 5 are red, 3 are green, and 2 are blue. Find (i) the probability that both blue refills will be drawn, (ii) the probability that at least one refill of each colour will be drawn. (*JMB 1981*)

2 Cards are to be dealt one after the other from a pack of playing cards. Calculate the probability that (i) the first two cards dealt will both be diamonds, (ii) the third card will be the first diamond, (iii) the first card will be red and the second card will be black, (iv) of the first two cards dealt, one will be a diamond and the other black, (v) the last four cards dealt will be red. (*L 1980*)

3 Three numbers are chosen at random without replacement from the set $\{1, 2, 3, \ldots, 10\}$. Calculate the probabilities that for the three numbers drawn (i) none will be greater than 7, (ii) the smallest will be 7, (iii) their sum will be 7. (*JMB 1982*)

4 A box contains 3 red, 4 white, and 6 blue balls. Three players A, B and C draw in turn one ball from the box; drawn balls are not replaced. A draws first and if he draws a red ball wins the round; if he does not win, then B draws and wins if he draws a white ball; if B does not win then C draws and wins if he draws a blue ball. If none of them wins, the round is void and the banker keeps the stakes. Find each player's probability of winning and show that the probability of a void round is 87/286. The players complain that the probability of a void round is too high and the banker suggests that if the balls are replaced after each drawing this probability will be reduced. Determine whether he is right and find the new probability of a win for each of the players. (*C 1981*)

5 Four cards are to be drawn at random without replacement from a pack of ten cards numbered from 1 to 10, respectively. (i) Calculate the probabilities that (a) the largest number drawn will be 6, (b) the product of the four numbers drawn will be even, (c) all four numbers drawn will be consecutive integers. (ii) Given that at least two of the four numbers drawn were even, find the probability that every number drawn was even. (*WJEC 1980*)

6 In an examination with a large entry, 20% of the candidates are 'school-based', the remainder being 'private' (or 'external') candidates. It is observed that on average 60% of the school-based and 10% of the private candidates pass the examination. Find the probability that a candidate selected at random from the complete mark list has passed. Find (i) the probability that a randomly selected school entering eight candidates has (a) no failures, (b) not more than two failures; (ii) the probability that exactly two of the ten private entries at a randomly selected centre pass. (*C 1981*)

7 In a sports quiz, there are five questions to be answered. Two questions are on rugby and three are on swimming. Each question is in a separate sealed plain envelope. The envelopes are numbered from 1 to 5 and each of four competitors A, B, C and D, in that order, selects one envelope at random. (i) Calculate, for each competitor, the probability that (a) he will pick a question on rugby, (b) he will be the first to pick a question on rugby. (ii) It is known that C picked a rugby question and that D picked a swimming question. Show that the probability that A picked a rugby question is equal to the probability that B picked a rugby question. (iii) Find the probability that

A and B pick questions on the same sport and then C and D pick questions on the same sport. (*L 1982*)

8 Each of three identical boxes A, B and C has two drawers. Box A contains a prize in each drawer. Box B contains a prize in one drawer only. Box C does not contain any prizes. A box is chosen at random and a drawer is opened and found to be empty. Find the probability that a prize will be found (i) if the other drawer in the same box is opened, (ii) if one of the other two boxes is chosen at random and a drawer is opened. (*L 1981*)

9 A box contains twelve balls numbered from 1 to 12. The balls numbered 1 to 5 are red, those numbered 6 to 9 are white, and the remaining three balls are blue. Three balls are to be drawn at random without replacement from the box. Let A denote the event that each number drawn will be even, B the event that no blue ball will be drawn, and C the event that one ball of each colour will be drawn. Calculate (i) $P(A)$, (ii) $P(B)$, (iii) $P(C)$, (iv) $P(A \cap C)$, (v) $P(B \cup C)$, (vi) $P(A \cup B)$. (*WJEC 1982*)

10 Four of 10 apples are of variety A and all are good. The remaining six apples are of variety B, and, of these, three are good and three are bad. X denotes the event that a random selection of four apples contains two of variety A and two of variety B, and Y denotes the event that a random selection of four apples contains exactly one bad apple. Find $P(X)$, $P(Y)$, $P(X \cap Y)$, $P(Y|X)$. (*C 1981*)

11 Each of two bags A and B contains five white and four black balls, while a third bag C contains three white and six black balls. (i) Suppose that one of the three bags was chosen at random and that two balls drawn at random without replacement from the chosen bag were both black. Calculate the probability that the chosen bag was C. (ii) Suppose, instead, that two of the three bags were chosen at random and that one ball was drawn at random from each of the chosen bags. Given that both balls drawn were black, calculate the probability that C was one of the chosen bags. (*WJEC 1979*)

12 Three bags each contain ten balls which are identical apart from colour. Bag A contains four red and six white balls, bag B contains five red and five white balls, and bag C contains eight red and two white balls. (i) From bag A, two balls are drawn at random and without replacement. Find the probability that they are both of the same colour. (ii) The original contents of bag A having been restored, the following procedure is carried out. One ball is drawn at random from bag A: if it is red, a ball is then drawn at random from bag B; if it is white, a ball is then drawn at random from bag C. The event that the ball from A is red is denoted by X and the event that the second ball (drawn from bag B or C) is red is denoted by Y. Find the probabilities (a) $P(Y)$, (b) $P(X \cup Y)$, (c) $P(X|Y)$. (*C 1982*)

13 Write down an equation, in terms of probabilities, corresponding to each of the statements (i) the events A and B are independent, (ii) the events A and C are mutually exclusive. The events A, B and C are such that A and B are independent and A and C are mutually exclusive. Given that $P(A) = 0{\cdot}4$, $P(B) = 0{\cdot}2$, $P(C) = 0{\cdot}3$, $P(B \cap C) = 0{\cdot}1$, calculate $P(A \cup B)$, $P(C|B)$, $P(B|A \cup C)$. Also calculate the probability that one and only one of the events B, C will occur (*WJEC 1978*)

14 Two events A and B are such that $P(A) = 0{\cdot}4$ and $P(A \cup B) = 0{\cdot}7$. (i) Find the value of $P(A' \cap B)$. (ii) Find the value of $P(B)$ if A and B are mutually

exclusive. (iii) Find the value of $P(B)$ if A and B are independent. (*JMB 1977*)

15 In a country with a large population the probability that an individual selected at random has fair hair is $\frac{2}{5}$, all others being classified as having dark hair. The conditional probability of having blue eyes is $\frac{1}{2}$ for those with fair hair and $\frac{1}{4}$ for those with dark hair. The conditional probability of having curly hair is $\frac{1}{4}$ for those with fair hair and blue eyes, $\frac{3}{20}$ for those with fair hair and without blue eyes, $\frac{3}{10}$ for those with dark hair and blue eyes, and $\frac{1}{6}$ for those with dark hair and without blue eyes. Find (i) the probability that an individual has curly hair, (ii) the probability that a straight-haired individual has blue eyes, (iii) the probability that an individual has either curly or dark hair (or both). Show that the two hair properties ('fair' and 'curly') are independent of each other. (*C 1981*)

16 The following information is known about events A, B, and C. Events A and B are mutually exclusive. Events A and C are independent. Given that $P(A) = \frac{1}{3}$, $P(B) = \frac{1}{6}$, $P(A \cup C) = \frac{5}{9}$, $P(B \cup C) = \frac{4}{9}$, find (i) $P(A \cap B)$, (ii) $P(A \cup B)$, (iii) $P(A \cap C)$, (iv) $P(B \cap C)$. State, giving a reason, whether B and C are independent, mutually exclusive or neither. (*L 1982*)

17 (i) The three events A, B and C have respective probabilities $\frac{2}{5}$, $\frac{1}{3}$ and $\frac{1}{2}$. Given that A and B are mutually exclusive, $P(A \cap C) = \frac{1}{5}$ and $P(B \cap C) = \frac{1}{4}$, (a) show that only two of the three events are independent, (b) evaluate $P(C|B)$ and $P(A' \cap C')$. (ii) When Alec, Bert and Chris play a particular game their respective probabilities of winning are 0·3, 0·1, and 0·6, independently for each game played. They agree to play a series of up to five games, the winner of the series (if any) to be the first player to win three games. Given that Bert wins the first two games of the series show that (a) Bert is just over 10 times more likely than Alec to win the series, (b) there is a slightly better than even chance that there will be a winner in the series. (*WJEC 1981*)

18 Suppose that for married couples eligible to vote in an election, the probability that a husband will vote is $\frac{3}{5}$, the probability that a wife will vote is $\frac{1}{2}$, and the probability that a wife will vote given that her husband votes is $\frac{2}{3}$. Calculate the probabilities that, for a randomly chosen couple, (i) both will vote, (ii) neither will vote, (iii) only one of them will vote. If two married couples are chosen at random and they act independently, calculate the probability that exactly one man and exactly one woman will vote. (*JMB 1980*)

19 The probability that a student will pass an examination in mathematics is equal to $\frac{2}{3}$, and, independently, the probability that the student will pass an examination in chemistry is equal to $\frac{3}{5}$. Find the probabilities that a student will (i) pass both examinations, (ii) pass in mathematics and fail in chemistry, (iii) fail both examinations. Twenty students take both examinations. Find, to 3 significant figures, the probabilities that (iv) at least 2 students will pass both examinations, (v) less than 2 students will fail both examinations. Show that the ratio of the probability that exactly two will pass both examinations to the probability that exactly five will pass both examinations is approximately 0·041. (*L 1982*)

20 There is a probability of 0·2 that a computer card punched by a trainee operator will contain at least one error. Find the probability that a random sample of 4 cards punched by a trainee operator will include just one card which is free from error. There is a probability of 0·05 that a card punched by an experienced operator will contain at least one error. Find, to three significant figures, the probability that in a random sample of 20 cards punched by an experienced operator no more than three of the cards will contain errors. Of the total number of cards punched in a day by a pool of operators, 4% are punched by trainee operators and 96% by experienced operators. Show that the probability that a card chosen at random from a day's output by this pool will contain at least one error is equal to 0·056. Given that each of two cards chosen at random from a day's output contains at least one error, calculate the conditional probability that one card was punched by a trainee and the other was punched by an experienced operator. (*WJEC 1981*)

21 A coin for which the probability of throwing a head is p, is thrown ten times. Write down the probability that (i) the first six throws are heads and the seventh throw is a tail, (ii) a run of exactly six heads starts at the rth throw for $r = 2$, for $r = 3$ and for $r = 4$, (iii) the fourth throw is a tail and the last six throws are heads. Hence find the probability P, in terms of p, that a run of exactly six heads occurs somewhere in the ten throws. Find the value of p that maximises P. (*C 1981*)

22 A census of married couples showed that 50% of the couples had no car, 40% had one car and the remaining 10% had two cars. Three of the married couples are chosen at random. (i) Find the probability that one couple has no car, one has one car and one has two cars. (ii) Find the probability that the three couples have a combined total of three cars. The census also showed that both the husband and the wife were in full-time employment in 16% of those couples having no car, in 45% of those having one car, and in 60% of those having two cars. (iii) For a randomly chosen married couple find the probability that both the husband and wife are in full-time employment. (iv) Given that a randomly chosen married couple is one where both the husband and wife are in full-time employment, find the conditional probability that the couple has no car. (*JMB 1981*)

2 Discrete Random Variables

2.1 Random variables

A *random variable* is a numerically valued characteristic associated with the outcomes of a random experiment. We shall denote a random variable by the capital of a letter towards the end of the alphabet (usually one from R to Z). As a more formal definition, a random variable is a function (i.e. a rule) which assigns a numerical value to every element of a sample space. Although not defined as such, we have already met several examples of random variables in Chapter 1.

EXAMPLE 1 Consider the random experiment of Example 3, §1.3 where a coin is tossed three times in succession. The sample space for the observed outcomes is given by

$$S = \{(h,h,h), (h,h,t), (h,t,h), (t,h,h), (h,t,t), (t,h,t), (t,t,h), (t,t,t)\},$$

where each ordered triple in S represents the outcome (h = head, t = tail) in the first, second and third tosses, respectively. Examples of random variables which may be of interest in this experiment include the following:
(i) X = the number of heads tossed. Taking the outcomes in the order listed in S above, the values of X corresponding to the eight elements in S are 3, 2, 2, 2, 1, 1, 1, 0, respectively.
(ii) Y = the number of heads tossed minus the number of tails tossed; the values of Y for the listed ordering of the elements of S are 3, 1, 1, 1, -1, -1, -1, -3.

The set of all possible distinct values that a random variable may take is called the *range space* of the random variable. For the random variables X and Y in Example 1 the range spaces are seen to be

$$R_X = \{0, 1, 2, 3\}, \quad \text{and} \quad R_Y = \{-3, -1, 1, 3\},$$

respectively.

In this chapter we shall restrict consideration to random variables which are such that the possible values they may take can be listed individually. Such a random variable is said to be *discrete*. The random variables X and Y above are discrete random variables, each of which can take only a finite number (four in fact) of values. The next example is of a discrete random variable which can take infinitely many values.

EXAMPLE 2 *Consider the random experiment in which a die is tossed until a* 6 *occurs. Define the random variable Z to be the number of tosses that are required.*

It is clear that the number of tosses for a 6 to occur may be any positive integer. Thus, the range space of Z is

$$R_Z = \{1, 2, 3, \ldots\}.$$

To generalise the ideas introduced in the above examples, a capital letter will be used to represent the *verbal description* of a random variable. Thus, for instance, in Example 1, X literally represents the collection of words 'the number of heads tossed'; Y and Z in the above examples are interpreted similarly. Having designated that a random variable be represented by a particular capital letter (e.g. X), an arbitrary value that the random variable may take is denoted by the corresponding small letter (e.g. x). The range space, R_X, of a random variable X, is then the set of values obtained on applying the description X to every element in turn of the sample space S of the corresponding random experiment. Thus, for each element s of S, we obtain a value $x = X(s)$, and R_X will be the set whose elements are the *distinct* values of x that are generated. However, in many cases, as for instance in Examples 1 and 2 above, the range space of a random variable can be obtained directly without actually having to list the elements of S.

EXERCISE 2.1

Write down the range space of each of the random variables defined below.

1 The score obtained when a die is tossed.
2 The number of heads obtained when two coins are tossed simultaneously.
3 The number of boys in a family of five children.
4 The number of honour cards (ace, king, queen, jack, ten) in a hand of 13 cards dealt from an ordinary pack of 52 playing cards.
5 The maximum of the three scores obtained when three dice are tossed together.
6 The number of telephone calls into an exchange during a period of five minutes.
7 The number of cards that have to be dealt from an ordinary pack of 52 playing cards until the first ace is dealt.
8 The number of times a coin has to be tossed if tossing stops as soon as a head is obtained.

2.2 Distribution of a discrete random variable

Having set up the range space (the set of all possible values) of a random variable the next step is to determine the probabilities of the various values that the random variable may take. First observe that the *sum of all these probabilities must be equal to unity*, since their sum is precisely the sum of the probabilities of the various elements of the sample space of the underlying random experiment. A description of how this one unit of probability is shared among the possible values that a random variable may take is called the *probability distribution of the random variable.*

EXAMPLE 1 *Find the probability distribution of the random variable X defined in Example* 1 *of* §2.1.

We shall assume that the coin is a fair one so that each of the eight elements of S listed in Example 1, §2.1, may be assumed to occur with probability 1/8.

For X = the number of heads tossed, we have $R_X = \{0, 1, 2, 3\}$. Since X takes the value 0 only if the outcome is (t, t, t), the probability of which is 1/8, $P(X = 0) = 1/8$. There are three elements of S for which $X = 1$, that is for which only one head occurred, and therefore $P(X = 1) = 3/8$. Similarly, we find $P(X = 2) = 3/8$ and $P(X = 3) = 1/8$.

For convenience, the probability distribution of this random variable X is displayed in Table 2.1:

Table 2.1

x	0	1	2	3
$P(X = x)$	$\frac{1}{8}$	$\frac{3}{8}$	$\frac{3}{8}$	$\frac{1}{8}$

Observe that the sum of the probabilities is equal to unity. Having obtained the probability distribution of a random variable it is always advisable to check that the probabilities do sum to unity.

Alternatively, we might have recognised that the tossing of a coin three times is equivalent to carrying out three independent Bernoulli trials, in each of which the probability of a success (a head) is $\frac{1}{2}$ (assuming the coin to be fair). Then, directly from the binomial probability law (§1.11), the probability of obtaining exactly x heads in 3 tosses is $\binom{3}{x}\left(\frac{1}{2}\right)^3$ for $x = 0, 1, 2, 3$. Hence

$$P(X = x) = \binom{3}{x}\left(\frac{1}{2}\right)^3, \qquad x = 0, 1, 2, 3,$$

which provides an alternative way to Table 2.1 for describing the probability distribution of X. The distribution is depicted diagrammatically in Fig. 2.1. It is seen from this diagram that the distribution is *symmetrical*, the left-hand 'half' being a mirror image of the right-hand 'half' (the dividing line being that through the midpoint $x = 1\frac{1}{2}$).

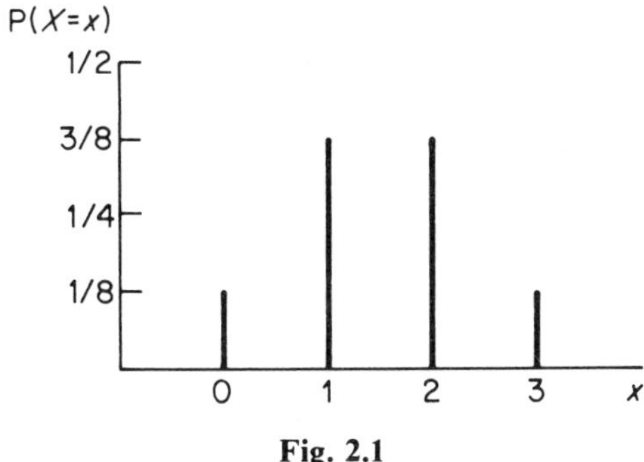

Fig. 2.1

EXAMPLE 2 *Four balls are to be drawn at random without replacement from a box containing 8 red and 4 white balls. Let X denote the number of red balls that will be drawn. Find the probability distribution of X.*

Here the range space of X is $R_X = \{0, 1, 2, 3, 4\}$ and we need to determine the probability of each element of R_X. We have

$$P(X = 0) = P(4\text{ white}) = \binom{4}{4}\Big/\binom{12}{4} = 1/495,$$

$$P(X = 1) = P(1\text{ red and }3\text{ white}) = \binom{8}{1}\binom{4}{3}\Big/\binom{12}{4} = 32/495,$$

$$P(X = 2) = P(2\text{ red and }2\text{ white}) = \binom{8}{2}\binom{4}{2}\Big/\binom{12}{4} = 168/495,$$

$$P(X = 3) = P(3\text{ red and }1\text{ white}) = \binom{8}{3}\binom{4}{1}\Big/\binom{12}{4} = 224/495,$$

$$P(X = 4) = P(4\text{ red}) = \binom{8}{4}\Big/\binom{12}{4} = 70/495.$$

Thus, the probability distribution is as displayed in Table 2.2.

Table 2.2

x	0	1	2	3	4
$P(X = x)$	$\frac{1}{495}$	$\frac{32}{495}$	$\frac{168}{495}$	$\frac{224}{495}$	$\frac{70}{495}$

Observe that the probabilities in the last row of Table 2.2 do sum to unity. We also see from the table that the most probable number of red balls that will be drawn is 3. The distribution is depicted diagrammatically in Fig. 2.2, and is seen not to be symmetrical. A distribution which is not symmetrical is usually referred to as a *skew* distribution.

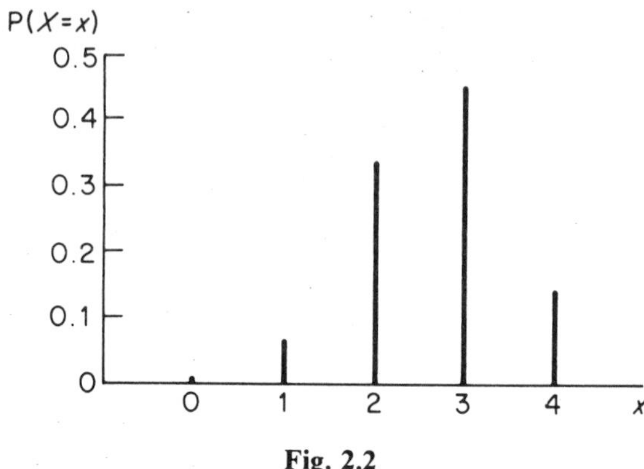

Fig. 2.2

EXAMPLE 3 *Two fair dice, one red and the other blue, are tossed together. Find the probability distribution of the numerical difference between the two scores.*

The sample space for the outcome when the red die and the blue die are tossed will consist of 36 ordered pairs, the first component of each pair being the score on the red die and the second the score on the blue die. Since the dice are fair, each of the 36 possibilities may be assumed to occur with probability $\frac{1}{36}$.

Let X denote the numerical difference between the two scores. Since each score may be any one of the numbers from 1 to 6 the range space of X is $R_X = \{0, 1, 2, 3, 4, 5\}$. For $X = 0$, the scores on the two dice must be the same and the outcome must be one of (1, 1), (2, 2), (3, 3), (4, 4), (5, 5), (6, 6). Since there are six of these, $\text{P}(X = 0) = \frac{6}{36}$. For $X = 1$, the scores must differ by 1 and the possibilities are (1, 2), (2, 1), (2, 3), (3, 2), (3, 4), (4, 3), (4, 5), (5, 4), (5, 6), (6, 5). Since there are 10 of these, $\text{P}(X = 1) = \frac{10}{36}$. Proceeding in the same way for each of the other possible values of X we obtain the probability distribution of X as displayed in Table 2.3.

Table 2.3

x	0	1	2	3	4	5
$\text{P}(X = x)$	$\frac{6}{36}$	$\frac{10}{36}$	$\frac{8}{36}$	$\frac{6}{36}$	$\frac{4}{36}$	$\frac{2}{36}$

Again, observe that the probabilities in the second row of the table do add up to unity. This is another example of a skew distribution.

EXERCISE 2.2

1 Find the probability distribution of the number of heads that will be obtained when a fair coin is tossed four times.

2 Three balls are drawn at random without replacement from a box containing three white and nine black balls. Find the probability distribution of the number of white balls that will be drawn. Deduce the most probable number of white balls that will be drawn.

3 Find the probability distribution of the maximum of the two scores obtained when a fair die is tossed twice.

4 Electric light bulbs are tested individually to ensure that they are in working order. Suppose that there is a probability of 0·1 that such a bulb is defective. Find the probability distribution of the number of defective bulbs among the first four bulbs tested.

5 A batch of 25 items includes four items which are defective. A random sample of three items is drawn form this batch. Let X denote the number of defective items among those sampled. Find the probability distribution of X for each of the cases where (i) sampling is with replacement; (ii) sampling is without replacement.

6 A discrete random variable X has the probability distribution displayed in the following table, where $0 < p < 1$.

x	0·5	1	1·5	2
$P(X = x)$	p	p^2	$2p^2$	p

Find the value of p.
(Retain your answers to these exercises for use in Exercise 2.4A).

2.3 Expected value

Consider a random experiment and an associated discrete random variable X having range space $R_X = \{x_1, x_2, \ldots, x_k\}$. Suppose that in n independent trials of this experiment, X is observed to take the value x_1 in n_1 of the trials, the value x_2 in n_2 of the trials, . . . ,and the value x_k in n_k of the trials, where $n_1 + n_2 + \ldots + n_k = n$. The *average* or *mean value of* X in these n trials is

$$\frac{n_1 x_1 + n_2 x_2 + \ldots + n_k x_k}{n} = x_1 R_n(x_1) + x_2 R_n(x_2) + \ldots + x_k R_n(x_k),$$

where $R_n(x_i)$ is the relative frequency of occurrence of the value x_i in the trials for $i = 1, 2, \ldots, k$. If we now allow n to increase indefinitely then we may replace $R_n(x_i)$ by $p_i \equiv P(X = x_i)$, as explained in § 1.4, so that the *long-run average value* of X in an indefinitely large number of trials may be written as

$$x_1 p_1 + x_2 p_2 + \ldots + x_k p_k \equiv \sum_{i=1}^{k} x_i P(X = x_i) = E[X], \qquad (1)$$

which we define to be the *expected value* (or *expectation*) of the random variable X. Thus $E[X]$ may be interpreted as the average value of X in an indefinitely large number of trials of the experiment with respect to which X is defined.

EXAMPLE 1 *A box contains two red balls, three black balls, and five white balls. A person pays* 10 *pence for the privilege of drawing one ball at random from the box. He will receive* 40 *pence if he draws a red ball,* 20 *pence if he draws a black ball, but nothing if he draws a white ball. Find his expected profit.*

Let X pence denote the person's profit in one draw. The possible values of X are $40-10=30$, $20-10=10$, and -10, according to whether he draws a red, a black, or a white ball, the probabilities of which are $\frac{2}{10}$, $\frac{3}{10}$ and $\frac{5}{10}$, respectively. Thus, the probability distribution of X is as displayed in Table 2.4.

Table 2.4

x	30	10	-10
$P(X=x)$	$\frac{1}{5}$	$\frac{3}{10}$	$\frac{1}{2}$

Using (1) the expected profit is

$$E[X]=30\times\frac{1}{5}+10\times\frac{3}{10}-10\times\frac{1}{2}=4.$$

Thus, if a person were to perform this experiment of drawing one ball from the box, under the conditions specified, several times (the ball drawn being replaced after each draw), his average (expected) profit per draw would be 4 pence.

Observe that the value $E[X]=4$ is not a possible value of X, which demonstrates that our formal definition of expected value may not be consistent with what would be a reasonable linguistic interpretation of 'expected value'. For instance, with reference to our example, if asked what we expect the profit to be we would be most unlikely to state a value, as $E[X]$ above, which cannot possibly arise. We would be more likely to choose the value which is most probable to occur, which from the above table is -10, that is, a loss of 10 pence. It is important to distinguish between the most probable value and the expected value (as defined here) of a discrete random variable.

EXAMPLE 2 *Find the expected value of the numerical difference between the two scores obtained when a fair die is tossed twice.*

Let X denote the numerical difference between the two scores, i.e. $X=|\text{1st score}-\text{2nd score}|$. It is clear that X will have the same probability distribution as the random variable X define in Example 3, §2.2, which is displayed in Table 2.5.

Table 2.5

x	0	1	2	3	4	5
$P(X=x)$	$\frac{6}{36}$	$\frac{10}{36}$	$\frac{8}{36}$	$\frac{6}{36}$	$\frac{4}{36}$	$\frac{2}{36}$

Thus, the expected value of X is

$$\mathrm{E}[X] = 0\times\frac{6}{36}+1\times\frac{10}{36}+2\times\frac{8}{36}+3\times\frac{6}{36}+4\times\frac{4}{36}+5\times\frac{2}{36}=\frac{35}{18},$$

which again is seen to be an impossible value of X.

EXAMPLE 3 *Find the expected number of heads that will be obtained when a fair coin is tossed three times*

Let X denote the number of heads in three tosses. We derived the distribution of X in Example 1 of §2.2, and, for convenience, it is reproduced in Table 2.6.

Table 2.6

x	0	1	2	3
$\mathrm{P}(X = x)$	$\frac{1}{8}$	$\frac{3}{8}$	$\frac{3}{8}$	$\frac{1}{8}$

Here,

$$\mathrm{E}[X] = 0\times\frac{1}{8}+1\times\frac{3}{8}+2\times\frac{3}{8}+3\times\frac{1}{8} = 1\tfrac{1}{2},$$

which is seen to be equal to the average of the four possible values (0, 1, 2, 3) that X may take. This is because the distribution is symmetrical (see Fig. 2.1). For any random variable having a symmetrical distribution, its expected value will always be equal to the average of the values in the range space.

EXERCISE 2.3A

1 In a certain game a player pays a stake of 5p to a banker and he then throws a fair die. If he throws a score of 6 he will receive 15p from the banker; if he throws a score which is an odd number he will receive his stake back; otherwise, he loses his stake. Show that the game is a fair one in the sense that the player's expected gain per play is zero.

2 Let X denote the number of heads that will be obtained in four tosses of a fair coin. Obtain the distribution of X and display it in a table. Hence find the expected number of heads (i) by calculating $\mathrm{E}[X]$, (ii) by some simpler method.

3 A litter of eight mice consists of three females and five males. A random sample of four mice is taken from the litter for a particular experiment. Calculate the expected number of female mice in the sample.

4 A box contains four red and six black balls.
(i) If a random sample of three balls is to be drawn from the box (without replacement) find the expected number of black balls in the sample.
(ii) If balls are to be drawn from the box one after the other without replacement until a black ball is drawn, find
(a) the most probable number of balls that will have to be drawn,
(b) the expected number of balls that will have to be drawn.

5 In a raffle in which 500 tickets were sold at 10p each, there are three prizes of values £10, £5 and £2 respectively. Find the expected loss of a person who purchased (i) one ticket, (ii) two tickets.

2.3.1 Expected value of a function

Let X denote a discrete random variable having range space $\{x_1, x_2, \ldots, x_k\}$ and probability distribution such that

$$P(X = x_i) = p_i, \qquad i = 1, 2, \ldots, k.$$

Consider $h(X)$, some function of X. We define the *expected value* (or *expectation*) of $h(X)$ to be

$$E[h(X)] = \sum_{i=1}^{k} h(x_i)p_i \equiv h(x_1)p_1 + h(x_2)p_2 + \ldots + h(x_k)p_k. \qquad (2)$$

Using a similar argument to that in §2.3, $E[h(X)]$ is the average value of $h(X)$ in an indefinitely large number of trials of the random experiment with respect to which X is defined.

Using (2) above we find, for example, that

$$E[X^2] = \sum_{i=1}^{k} x_i^2 p_i = x_1^2 p_1 + x_2^2 p_2 + \ldots + x_k^2 p_k,$$

$$E[3X-2] = \sum_{i=1}^{k} (3x_i - 2)p_i = (3x_1 - 2)p_1 + (3x_2 - 2)p_2 + \ldots + (3x_k - 2)p_k,$$

$$E[2^X] = \sum_{i=1}^{k} 2^{x_i}p_i = 2^{x_1}p_1 + 2^{x_2}p_2 + \ldots + 2^{x_k}p_k.$$

EXAMPLE 4 *Let X denote the number of heads obtained when a fair coin is tossed three times, and let Y denote the product of the number of heads and the number of tails obtained in the three tosses. Find the expected value of Y.*

Since the number of heads in the three tosses is X, the number of tails is $(3-X)$ and therefore

$$Y = X(3-X).$$

From Table 2.6, the probability distribution of X is as displayed in the first two rows of Table 2.7; the third row of the table shows the values of $y = x(3-x)$.

Using (2) above we find

$$E[Y] \equiv E[X(3-X)] = 0 \times \frac{1}{8} + 2 \times \frac{3}{8} + 2 \times \frac{3}{8} + 0 \times \frac{1}{8} = 1\tfrac{1}{2}.$$

Table 2.7

x	0	1	2	3
$P(X = x)$	$\frac{1}{8}$	$\frac{3}{8}$	$\frac{3}{8}$	$\frac{1}{8}$
$y = x(3-x)$	0	2	2	0

Alternatively, from the last two rows of Table 2.7, the distribution of Y is as shown in Table 2.8.

Table 2.8

y	0	2
$P(Y = y)$	$\frac{1}{4}$	$\frac{3}{4}$

Then, using (1) we find

$$E[Y] = 0 \times \frac{1}{4} + 2 \times \frac{3}{4} = 1\tfrac{1}{2},$$

exactly as obtained previously.

Although the second method used in the above example requires a little extra effort, it has the advantage of being more informative about the random variable $Y = X(3-X)$, and would be particularly appropriate whenever it was required to determine properties of Y other than its expected value.

We shall now establish three useful properties of the expectation operator E[ ], which are fairly obvious on recalling that the expected value is simply the average value in an indefinitely large number of trials of the underlying random experiment.

Let X denote a discrete random variable having range space $R_X = \{x_1, x_2, \ldots, x_k\}$ and such that $P(X = x_i) = p_i$, $i = 1, 2, \ldots, k$. Then, for any constant c,

$$E[c] = c. \tag{3}$$

That is, *the expected value of any constant is that constant.* To prove this we use (2) with $h(X) \equiv c$, so that $h(x_i) = c$ for $i = 1, 2, \ldots, k$. Hence, from (2)

$$E[c] = \sum_{i=1}^{k} cp_i = c \sum_{i=1}^{k} p_i = c,$$

since $\sum_{i=1}^{k} p_i = 1$.

The second property is that for any constant c and any function $h(X)$,

$$E[ch(X)] = cE[h(X)]. \tag{4}$$

From (2) we have

$$\begin{aligned}\mathrm{E}[c\mathrm{h}(X)] &= \sum_{i=1}^{k} c\mathrm{h}(x_i)p_i = c\mathrm{h}(x_1)p_1 + c\mathrm{h}(x_2)p_2 + \ldots + c\mathrm{h}(x_k)p_k \\ &= c\{\mathrm{h}(x_1)p_1 + \mathrm{h}(x_2)p_2 + \ldots + \mathrm{h}(x_k)p_k\} \\ &= c\mathrm{E}[\mathrm{h}(X)].\end{aligned}$$

Finally, for any two functions $\mathrm{h}_1(X)$ and $\mathrm{h}_2(X)$,

$$\mathrm{E}[\mathrm{h}_1(X)+\mathrm{h}_2(X)] = \mathrm{E}[\mathrm{h}_1(X)]+\mathrm{E}[\mathrm{h}_2(X)]. \tag{5}$$

That is, *the expected value of the sum of two functions is equal to the sum of their expected values.*

Again using (2), we have

$$\begin{aligned}\mathrm{E}[\mathrm{h}_1(X)+\mathrm{h}_2(X)] &= \sum_{i=1}^{k} \{\mathrm{h}_1(x_i)+\mathrm{h}_2(x_i)\}p_i \\ &= \sum_{i=1}^{k} \mathrm{h}_1(x_i)p_i + \sum_{i=1}^{k} \mathrm{h}_2(x_i)p_i \\ &= \mathrm{E}[\mathrm{h}_1(X)]+\mathrm{E}[\mathrm{h}_2(X)].\end{aligned}$$

The result in (5) extends to the sum of three or more functions.

Applying the above properties we have, for example

(i) $\mathrm{E}[2X^2+3X] = \mathrm{E}[2X^2]+\mathrm{E}[3X]$
$\qquad = 2\mathrm{E}[X^2]+3\mathrm{E}[X].$

(ii) $\mathrm{E}[3X-2] = \mathrm{E}[3X]-\mathrm{E}[2]$
$\qquad = 3\mathrm{E}[X]-2.$

(iii) $\mathrm{E}[(X-1)^2] = \mathrm{E}[X^2-2X+1]$
$\qquad = \mathrm{E}[X^2]-2\mathrm{E}[X]+1.$

As a cautionary note, observe well that the above properties apply only to a *linear combination of functions* of X. In particular, we have not established any property for the expected value of the product of two or more functions of X. Thus, for example, even though $X^2 = X \cdot X$, it is *not* true that $\mathrm{E}[X^2]$ and $\mathrm{E}[X]\cdot\mathrm{E}[X] \equiv \{\mathrm{E}[X]\}^2$ are equal, a result we shall prove in a subsequent section.

EXAMPLE 5 *Use the above properties to find* $\mathrm{E}[Y]$, *where* Y *is the random variable defined in Example* 4.

From Example 4,

$$Y = X(3-X) = 3X - X^2.$$

Hence,

$$\mathrm{E}[Y] = 3\mathrm{E}[X]-\mathrm{E}[X^2].$$

We now use the probability distribution of X, displayed in Table 2.7, to evaluate $\mathrm{E}[X]$ and $\mathrm{E}[X^2]$. We have

$$\mathrm{E}[X] = 0\times\frac{1}{8}+1\times\frac{3}{8}+2\times\frac{3}{8}+3\times\frac{1}{8} = 1\tfrac{1}{2},$$

and

$$\mathrm{E}[X^2] = 0^2\times\frac{1}{8}+1^2\times\frac{3}{8}+2^2\times\frac{3}{8}+3^2\times\frac{1}{8} = 3.$$

Hence

$$\mathrm{E}[Y] = 3\times 1\tfrac{1}{2}-3 = 1\tfrac{1}{2},$$

exactly as obtained in Example 4.

EXERCISE 2.3B

1 Use the properties of $\mathrm{E}[\ \ ]$ derived in this section to obtain expanded forms for (i) $\mathrm{E}[1-2X]$, (ii) $\mathrm{E}[\frac{1}{2}(3X-5)]$, (iii) $\mathrm{E}[X^3-5]$, (iv) $\mathrm{E}[(2X^2+X)^2]$, (v) $\mathrm{E}[(1-2X)(1+X)]$.

2 For the distribution displayed in Table 2.4, (i) verify that $\mathrm{E}[X^2]$ and $\{\mathrm{E}[X]\}^2$ have unequal values, and (ii) evaluate $\mathrm{E}[|X-10|]$.

3 The random variable X can take only the values 0, 1, 2. Given that $\mathrm{P}(X=0) = \mathrm{P}(X=1) = p$ and that $\mathrm{E}[X^2] = \mathrm{E}[X]$, calculate the value of p.

4 If X has range space $R_X = \{0, 1\}$, show that $\mathrm{E}[X^2-X] = 0$.

5 $Y_1 \equiv \mathrm{h}_1(X)$ and $Y_2 \equiv \mathrm{h}_2(X)$ are two functions of a discrete random variable X. Given that $\mathrm{E}[Y_1] = \mu_1$ and $\mathrm{E}[Y_2] = \mu_2$, show that

$$\mathrm{E}[(Y_1-\mu_1)(Y_2-\mu_2)] = \mathrm{E}[Y_1Y_2]-\mu_1\mu_2.$$

2.4 Summary measures

It is often convenient and necessary to have quantitative assessments of some main features of a probability distribution. This is particularly so when comparing two or more distributions. We shall consider quantitative assessments or *summary measures* for two particular features of a distribution. The first of these consists of quoting a number which is indicative of the order of magnitude of the values that the random variable may take and is referred to as a measure of *location* (since it locates the whereabouts of the distribution on the variable axis). The second summary measure we shall consider is one which gives some indication of the scatter or spread of the distribution and is referred to as a measure of *dispersion.*

2.4.1 Measures of location

The objective is to quote a single number which in some sense is representative of the values that the random variable may take. Here we consider two such measures, the mode and the mean.

The Mode

Since only a single number is required it would seem very reasonable to choose that value (if such exists) of the random variable which is the most probable to occur. This value is called *the mode* of the distribution.

For the random variable in Example 2, §2.2, the range space of X is $\{0, 1, 2, 3, 4\}$ and, from Table 2.2, it is seen that the mode of the distribution of X is 3. In Example 3 of §2.2, the random variable X has range space $\{0, 1, 2, 3, 4, 5\}$ and, from Table 2.3, the mode of its distribution is 1. In each of these examples the distribution has a unique mode, that is, a single value which is more probable to occur than any other possible value. This is not always the case. For instance, from Table 2.1, the distribution of X, the number of heads in three tosses of a fair coin is such that $P(X = 0) = P(X = 3) = \frac{1}{8}$ and $P(X = 1) = P(X = 2) = \frac{3}{8}$; in this example, there are two equally most probable values (namely 1 and 2), and, consequently, the distribution has no unique mode. A more extreme example of a distribution not having a unique mode is that of a random variable whose possible values are all equally probable to occur, as, for example, the distribution of the score obtained in one throw of a fair die. The fact that a discrete distribution may not have a unique mode is a prime reason why the mode is not appropriate as a general measure of location. Nevertheless, when it does exist uniquely, the mode is a good choice as a single number representation of the values a random variable may take.

The Mean

The most widely used measure of location is the *mean*, defined to be the expected value of the random variable under consideration.

The mean of a distribution is conventionally denoted by the small Greek letter μ (mu). Consider a discrete random variable X having range space $\{x_1, x_2, \ldots, x_k\}$ and whose distribution is given by $P(X = x_i) = p_i$ for $i = 1, 2, \ldots, k$. The mean of the distribution of X is defined to be

$$\mu \equiv E[X] = \sum_{i=1}^{k} x_i p_i = x_1 p_1 + x_2 p_2 + \ldots + x_k p_k. \quad (1)$$

As a measure of location, the mean has the advantage over the mode in that it is unique for any discrete random variable whose range space consists of a finite number of elements. Also, being the long-run average value of X (as explained in §2.3) it is an intuitively reasonable choice of a single number to be representative of the distribution.

One disadvantage of the mean is that its value may not be one of the possible values of the random variable. For instance, in Example 1 of §2.3, the random variable X had range space $\{30, 10, -10\}$ but $\mu \equiv E[X] = 4$; and in Example 2 of §2.3, the random variable had range space $\{0, 1, 2, 3, 4, 5\}$ and $\mu \equiv E[X] = \frac{35}{18}$. Despite this limitation, we shall see later that the mean of a distribution plays an important role in statistics.

As noted at the end of §2.3, for a random variable whose distribution is symmetrical, the mean is equal to the average of the values that the random variable may take. Thus, for example, as shown in Example 3 of §2.3, the mean of the distribution of the number of heads in three tosses of a fair coin is $\mu = \frac{1}{4}(0+1+2+3) = 1\frac{1}{2}$.

EXERCISE 2.4A

1–6 Find the mode (if it exists) and the mean of each of the distributions you derived in Exercise 2.2.

2.4.2 A measure of dispersion

For a measure of dispersion we seek a single number to be indicative of the spread of a distribution. Here, we shall restrict consideration to just one such measure, which is the one most widely used.

First we define the variance V[X] of the distribution of the random variable X whose mean is μ, by

$$\mathrm{V}[X] = \mathrm{E}[(X-\mu)^2], \tag{1}$$

which is also denoted by σ^2, where σ is the small Greek letter 'sigma'. Since, from (1), $\sigma^2 = \mathrm{V}[X]$ is the average value of the squared deviation of X from μ, it is appropriate as a measure of the spread of the distribution around μ.

If X has range space $\{x_1, x_2, \ldots, x_k\}$ and $\mathrm{P}(X = x_i) = p_i$, for $i = 1, 2, \ldots, k$, then

$$\begin{aligned}\mathrm{V}[X] \equiv \mathrm{E}[(X-\mu)^2] &= \sum_{i=1}^{k} (x_i-\mu)^2 p_i \\ &= (x_1-\mu)^2 p_1 + (x_2-\mu)^2 p_2 + \ldots + (x_k-\mu)^2 p_k.\end{aligned} \tag{2}$$

EXAMPLE 1 *Find the variance of the distribution displayed in Table* 2.9. (*This is the distribution of the number of heads in three tosses of a fair coin derived in Example* 1, §2.2.)

Table 2.9

x	0	1	2	3
P($X = x$)	$\frac{1}{8}$	$\frac{3}{8}$	$\frac{3}{8}$	$\frac{1}{8}$

From Example 3 of §2.3, the mean of this distribution is

$$\mu \equiv \mathrm{E}[X] = 1\tfrac{1}{2}.$$

Hence, using (2), the variance of the distribution is

$$\begin{aligned}\sigma^2 \equiv \mathrm{V}[X] &= \frac{1}{8}(0-1\tfrac{1}{2})^2 + \frac{3}{8}(1-1\tfrac{1}{2})^2 + \frac{3}{8}(2-1\tfrac{1}{2})^2 + \frac{1}{8}(3-1\tfrac{1}{2})^2 \\ &= \frac{3}{4}.\end{aligned}$$

EXAMPLE 2 *Find the variance of the distribution displayed in Table* 2.10.

Table 2.10

x	0	1	2	3	4
$P(X=x)$	0·1	0·2	0·4	0·2	0·1

On observing that this distribution is symmetrical about the value 2, we have $\mu = 2$. Hence

$$V[X] = 0{\cdot}1(0-2)^2 + 0{\cdot}2(1-2)^2 + 0{\cdot}4((2-2)^2 + 0{\cdot}2(3-2)^2 + 0{\cdot}1(4-2)^2$$
$$= 1{\cdot}2.$$

For a distribution, such as that in Example 1, whose mean is not an integer (even though every possible value of X is an integer), the arithmetic involved in calculating a variance can be simplified using the following alternative formula for $V[X]$.

On expanding we have

$$\begin{aligned} V[X] &= E[(X-\mu)^2] \\ &= E[X^2 - 2\mu X + \mu^2] \\ &= E[X^2] - 2\mu E[X] + \mu^2, \end{aligned}$$

since μ is a constant. But $E[X] = \mu$, and consequently,

$$V[X] = E[X^2] - \mu^2. \tag{3}$$

Using (3) in preference to (1), only the possible x-values and μ have to be squared and this may be more easily accomplished than having to square each possible value of $(x-\mu)$. Applying (3) to the distribution in Example 1, we have

$$E[X^2] = 0^2 \times \frac{1}{8} + 1^2 \times \frac{3}{8} + 2^2 \times \frac{3}{8} + 3^2 \times \frac{1}{8} = 3,$$

and since $\mu = 1\frac{1}{2}$, it follows that

$$V[X] = 3 - (1\tfrac{1}{2})^2 = \tfrac{3}{4},$$

exactly as obtained earlier. The gain from using (3) in this example is only slight, but the reduction in arithmetical effort can be quite substantial, as illustrated in the following example.

EXAMPLE 3 Find the variance of the distribution in Table 2.11.

Table 2.11

x	0	1	2	3	4	5
$P(X=x)$	$\frac{1}{6}$	$\frac{5}{18}$	$\frac{2}{9}$	$\frac{1}{6}$	$\frac{1}{9}$	$\frac{1}{18}$

In Example 2 of Section 2.3 we showed that $\mu = \mathrm{E}[X] = \frac{35}{18}$. Using (2) we would need to square six numbers, each being a fraction with denominator 18, but using (3) we only have to square one such number. For this example

$$\mathrm{E}[X^2] = \frac{5}{18}+\frac{8}{9}+\frac{9}{6}+\frac{16}{9}+\frac{25}{18}=\frac{105}{18},$$

and, therefore,

$$\mathrm{V}[X] = \frac{105}{18}-\left(\frac{35}{18}\right)^2=\frac{665}{324}.$$

It follows from the definition of $\mathrm{V}[X]$ given in (1) that $\mathrm{V}[X]$ must be positive for every random variable X (provided X can take at least two possible values). Hence, from (3), with $\mu = \mathrm{E}[X]$, we must have

$$\mathrm{E}[X^2] > \{\mathrm{E}[X]\}^2$$

as stated in §2.3.1 (immediately before Example 5).

It also follows from (1) or (3) that the units of $\mathrm{V}[X]$ will be the square of the units of measurement of X. For a measure of dispersion having the same units as X we take the positive square root of $\mathrm{V}[X]$, which is called the *standard deviation* of the distribution and is denoted by $\mathrm{SD}[X]$ or by the Greek letter σ (sigma). Thus,

$$\mathrm{SD}[X] \equiv \sigma = \sqrt{\{\mathrm{E}[X-\mu)^2]\}} \tag{5}$$

EXERCISE 2.4B

Calculate the standard deviation, correct to 3 significant figures, of each of the following three distributions.

1

x	1	2	3
$P(X = x)$	0·4	0·2	0·4

2

x	0	1	2	3	4
$P(X = x)$	0·1	0·1	0·3	0·3	0·2

3

x	-10	10	20	25
$P(X = x)$	$\frac{1}{8}$	$\frac{1}{4}$	$\frac{3}{8}$	$\frac{1}{4}$

2.5 Mean and variance of a linear function

Consider $Y = aX + b$, where X is a discrete random variable whose distribution has mean μ_X and variance σ_X^2, and a, b are arbitrary constants ($a \neq 0$). Suppose we wish to find the mean and the variance of the distribution of Y. If we knew the distribution of X then we could use it to determine the distribution of Y and hence the mean and the variance of Y's distribution. However, the mean and the variance of Y can actually be determined without complete knowledge of the distribution of X; it is necessary to know only the mean and the variance of X, as is shown below.

Denoting the mean of the distribution of Y by μ_Y we have

$$\begin{aligned} \mu_Y \equiv \mathrm{E}[Y] &= \mathrm{E}[aX + b] \\ &= a\mu_X + b, \end{aligned} \tag{1}$$

on using the properties of E[ ] established in §2.3.1, and noting that $\mathrm{E}[X] = \mu_X$. Furthermore,

$$\begin{aligned} \mathrm{V}[Y] &\equiv \mathrm{E}[(Y - \mu_Y)^2] \\ &= \mathrm{E}[\{(aX + b) - (a\mu_X + b)\}^2] \\ &= \mathrm{E}[a^2(X - \mu)^2] \\ &= a^2\mathrm{V}[X]. \end{aligned} \tag{2}$$

Equivalently, (2) may be wrtten as

$$\mathrm{SD}[Y] = |a|\,\mathrm{SD}[X],$$

where $|a|$ denotes the absolute value of a, which simply means ignoring the sign of a if a is negative.

In particular, with $a = 1$ we have

$$\mathrm{E}[X + b] = \mu_X + b, \tag{4}$$

$$\mathrm{SD}[X + b] = \mathrm{SD}[X]. \tag{5}$$

Replacing X by $X + b$ is equivalent to shifting the distribution of X a distance b further to the right along the x-axis and it is clear that the effect of such a shift will be to increase the mean by the amount b and to leave the spread of the distribution unchanged, as implied by (4) and (5), respectively.

For the case when $b = 0$ we have

$$\mathrm{E}[aX] = a\mu_X, \tag{6}$$

$$\mathrm{SD}[aX] = |a|\mathrm{SD}[X]. \tag{7}$$

Replacing X by aX is equivalent to changing the scale of measurement (e.g. if X has centimetre units then $10X$ has millimetre units). It is clear that such a change of scale will change both the mean and the dispersion by the same factor (namely $|a|$), as indicated by (6) and (7), respectively.

EXERCISE 2.5

1 The discrete random variable X has mean 2 and standard deviation 3. Determine the mean and the standard deviation of (i) $X+1$, (ii) $2X$, (iii) $3X-1$, (iv) $\frac{1}{2}(X-2)$, (v) $9-3X$.

2 The discrete random variable X has mean 8 and standard deviation 4. Find values for a and b so that the random variable $Y = aX + b$ has zero mean and unit standard deviation.

3 A car salesman at a garage is paid a fixed weekly wage of £60 per week and a commission of £20 on each new car he sells. The number of new cars that the salesman sells per week is a discrete random variable whose mean is 1.96 and whose standard deviation is 1.34. Find the mean and the standard deviation of the salesman's weekly earnings.

4 Three balls are drawn at random without replacement from a box which contains three red and seven black balls. Let X denote the number of red balls that are drawn. Calculate the mean and the standard deviation of X. If a red ball scores 3 points and a black ball scores 1 point, deduce the mean and the standard deviation of the total score for the three balls.

2.6 The binomial distribution

Let X denote the number of successes that will be obtained in n independent Bernoulli trials, in each of which the probability of a success is p and the probability of a failure is $q = 1-p$. We showed in §1.11 that

$$P(X=r) = \binom{n}{r} p^r q^{n-r}, \qquad r = 0, 1, 2, \ldots, n. \tag{1}$$

Any random variable X having the probability distribution defined by (1) is said to be *binomially distributed with index n and probability parameter p*, a statement we shall abbreviate as $X \sim B(n, p)$, the symbol $\sim$ representing *is distributed as*. The calculation of binomial probabilities was discussed in §1.11.

We have already met such a distribution in Example 1 of §2.2, where X was the number of heads in three tosses of a fair coin and in that example, X has the distribution $B(n = 3, p = \frac{1}{2})$.

To study the shape of the distribution $B(n, p)$, we look at the relative values of the successive probabilities. For convenience, let us write p_r for $P(X=r)$ as given by (1). To see what happens when we go from r to the next possible value $r+1$, consider the ratio p_{r+1}/p_r, which is

$$\frac{p_{r+1}}{p_r} = \frac{\binom{n}{r+1} p^{r+1} q^{n-r-1}}{\binom{n}{r} p^r q^{n-r}} = \frac{(n-r)p}{(r+1)q}. \tag{2}$$

From (2) it follows that p_{r+1} will be greater than, equal to, or less than p_r, according to whether $(n-r)p$ is greater than, equal to, or less than $(r+1)q$.

Symbolically, we write

$$p_{r+1} \gtreqless p_r \quad \text{according as} \quad (n-r)p \gtreqless (r+1)q.$$

On setting $q = 1-p$ and solving for r, we find

$$p_{r+1} \gtreqless p_r \quad \text{according as} \quad r \lesseqgtr (n+1)p-1.$$

Thus, when we go from r to $r+1$, the probability will increase for any $r < (n+1)p-1$, will remain at the same value when $r = (n+1)p-1$ (provided of course that this value is an integer), and will decrease for any $r > (n+1)p-1$. Thus the general pattern of behaviour of the values of p_r ($r = 0, 1, 2, \ldots, n$) will be such that they initially start to increase and then decrease.

In particular, if $(n+1)p$ is an integer, so that $(n+1)p-1$ is also an integer, the $\mathrm{B}(n, p)$ distribution will have two equally most probable values at $(n+1)p-1$ and at $(n+1)p$.

However, *if* (n + 1)p *is not an integer, the distribution will have a unique mode* (most probable value) *occurring at the largest integer which is less than* (n + 1)p.

Figs. 2.3 and 2.4 show typical shapes of $\mathrm{B}(n, p)$ distributions, taking $n = 7$, and $p = 0{\cdot}25$ and $0{\cdot}4$, respectively. The former is an example where $(n+1)p = 2$ is an integer and is seen to have two equally most probable values 1 and 2, while the latter is an example where $(n+1)p = 3{\cdot}2$ is not an integer and has a unique mode at 3.

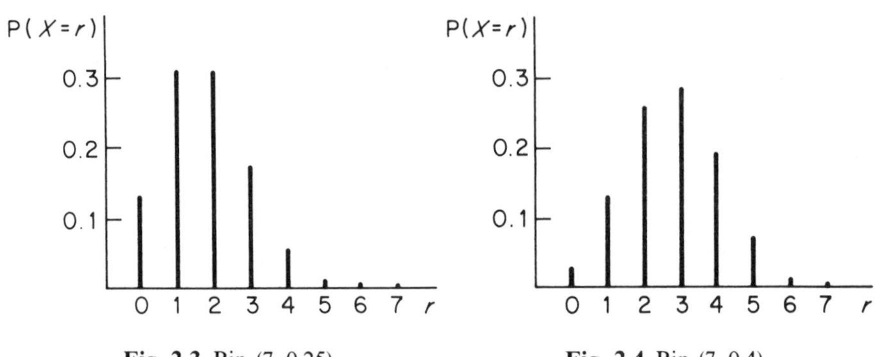

Fig. 2.3 Bin (7, 0·25)

Fig. 2.4 Bin (7, 0·4)

For the special case when $p = q = \frac{1}{2}$, the distribution (1) becomes

$$\mathrm{P}(X = r) = \binom{n}{r}\left(\frac{1}{2}\right)^n, \qquad r = 0, 1, 2, \ldots, n. \tag{3}$$

Since $\binom{n}{r} \equiv \binom{n}{n-r}$, this distribution is symmetrical, for any n, about the midvalue $r = \frac{1}{2}n$. If X is the number of heads in three tosses of a coin, then

$X \sim B(n = 3, p = \frac{1}{2})$ and the distribution of X is symmetrical about the value $3 \times \frac{1}{2} = 1\frac{1}{2}$. (See Table 2.1 or Fig. 2.1)

Mean and variance of a binomial distribution

The binomial distribution $B(n, p)$ has mean

$$\mu = np, \tag{4}$$

and variance

$$\sigma^2 = npq. \tag{5}$$

To illustrate these results, let X denote the number of heads in three tosses of a fair coin, so that $X \sim B(n = 3, p = \frac{1}{2})$. In Example 3 of §2.3 and Example 2 of §2.4, respectively, we showed that this distribution had mean $\mu = 1\frac{1}{2}$ and variance $\sigma^2 = \frac{3}{4}$, which agree with the results given by (4) and (5) on substituting $n = 3$ and $p = q = \frac{1}{2}$.

We now proceed to derive the results (4) and (5) for the general binomial distribution $B(n, p)$. The derivations given here are algebraically complicated, but in §4.5.2 we provide much simpler derivations. (Some readers may therefore prefer to accept (4) and (5) without proof for the present, deferring the derivations until §4.5.2.)

By definition, the mean of the distribution $B(n, p)$ given by (1) is

$$\begin{aligned}\mu \equiv E[X] &= \sum_{r=0}^{n} r\binom{n}{r} p^r q^{n-r} \\ &= \binom{n}{1} pq^{n-1} + 2\binom{n}{2} p^2 q^{n-2} + \ldots \\ &\quad + r\binom{n}{r} p^r q^{n-r} + \ldots + n\binom{n}{n} p^n. \end{aligned} \tag{6}$$

But

$$r\binom{n}{r} = r\frac{n!}{r!\,(n-r)!} = n\frac{(n-1)!}{(r-1)!\,(n-r)!} = n\binom{n-1}{r-1},$$

and therefore,

$$\begin{aligned}\mu &= npq^{n-1} + n\binom{n-1}{1} p^2 q^{n-2} + \ldots + n\binom{n-1}{r-1} p^r q^{n-r} + \ldots + np^n \\ &= np\left\{q^{n-1} + \binom{n-1}{1} pq^{n-2} + \ldots + \binom{n-1}{r-1} p^{r-1} q^{n-r} + \ldots \right. \\ &\quad \left. + p^{n-1}\right\} \\ &= np(q+p)^{n-1} \\ &= np, \quad \text{since } q + p = 1. \end{aligned}$$

We now proceed to find $\mathrm{E}[X^2]$.

$$\mathrm{E}[X^2] = \sum_{r=0}^{n} r^2 \binom{n}{r} p^r q^{n-r}$$

$$= 1^2 \binom{n}{1} pq^{n-1} + 2^2 \binom{n}{2} p^2 q^{n-2} + \ldots + r^2 \binom{n}{r} p^r q^{n-r} + \ldots + n^2 \binom{n}{n} p^n.$$

Now use the identity

$$r^2 \equiv r(r-1) + r, \qquad r = 1, 2, 3, \ldots,$$

for each term in the above series to get

$$\mathrm{E}[X^2] = \left\{0\binom{n}{1} pq^{n-1} + 2\binom{n}{2} p^2 q^{n-2} + \ldots + r(r-1)\binom{n}{r} p^r q^{n-r} + \ldots + n(n-1)p^n\right\} + \left\{\binom{n}{1} pq^{n-1} + 2\binom{n}{2} p^2 q^{n-2} + \ldots + r\binom{n}{r} p^r q^{n-r} + \ldots + np^n\right\}. \tag{7}$$

Reference to (6) shows that the second series in (7) is equal to $\mu = np$. To evaluate the first series in (7) we use the result

$$r(r-1)\binom{n}{r} \equiv r(r-1)\frac{n!}{r!(n-r)!} = n(n-1).\frac{(n-2)!}{(r-2)!(n-r)!}$$

$$= n(n-1)\binom{n-2}{r-2},$$

and the first series in (7) then becomes

$$n(n-1)\binom{n-2}{0} p^2 q^{n-2} + n(n-1)\binom{n-2}{1} p^3 q^{n-3} + \ldots + n(n-1)\binom{n-2}{r-2} p^r q^{n-r} + \ldots + n(n-1)p^n$$

$$= n(n-1)p^2 \left\{q^{n-2} + \binom{n-2}{1} pq^{n-3} + \ldots + \binom{n-2}{r-2} p^{r-2} q^{n-r} + \ldots + p^{n-2}\right\}$$

$$= n(n-1)p^2 (q+p)^{n-2}$$

$$= n(n-1)p^2.$$

Hence,

$$\mathrm{E}[X^2] = n(n-1)p^2 + np,$$

and

$$\begin{aligned} V[X] &= E[X^2] - \mu^2 \\ &= n(n-1)p^2 + np - n^2p^2 \\ &= np(1-p) = npq. \end{aligned}$$

EXAMPLE 1 *Find the mode of the binomial distribution whose mean is* 3·2 *and whose variance is* 2·56.

Suppose the distribution has index n and probability parameter p. Then from the given information,

$$np = 3{\cdot}2, \qquad npq = 2{\cdot}56.$$

Hence $q = 2{\cdot}56/3{\cdot}2 = 0{\cdot}8$, and $p = 1 - 0{\cdot}8 = 0{\cdot}2$. It follows that $n = 3{\cdot}2/p = 16$.
Since $(n+1)p = 3{\cdot}4$ is not an integer the mode of the distribution is at 3, the largest integer which is less than 3.4.

EXERCISE 2.6

1 Let X denote the number of 6s obtained in four throws of a fair die. Identify the distribution of X and write down the values of its mode, mean and variance. Verify your answers by compiling a table for the probability distribution of X.

2 In each trial of a certain random experiment the probability of a success is equal to 0·2. Find the number of independent trials that should be conducted if the mean of the distribution of the number of successes in the n trials is to be equal to its standard deviation.

3 The random variable X has a binomial distribution with unknown index n and probability parameter $p = 0{\cdot}8$. Given that

$$P(X = 3) = 8P(X = 2)$$

find the mean of the distribution.

4 A door-to-door salesman is paid a weekly basic salary of £40 and a commission of £2 on each sale he makes. Suppose the salesman makes 100 calls per week and that the probability that a call results in a sale is equal to 0·2. Identify the distribution of the number of sales made per week and write down its mean and its variance. Deduce the mean and the standard deviation of the salesman's weekly earnings (basic salary plus commission). Also find his most probable earnings in a week.

5 Find the maximum value of the variance for all binomial distributions having a given index n.

2.7* The Poisson distribution

In this section we shall make considerable use of the exponential series expansion

$$e^{\alpha} = 1 + \alpha + \frac{\alpha^2}{2!} + \frac{\alpha^3}{3!} + \ldots + \frac{\alpha^r}{r!} + \ldots. \tag{1}$$

Consider a random variable X whose range space is the set of all non-negative integers $\{0, 1, 2, 3, \ldots\}$, and suppose that

$$P(X = r) = \frac{e^{-\alpha}\alpha^r}{r!}, \qquad r = 0, 1, 2, 3, \ldots, \tag{2}$$

where α is a positive number. Observe that $P(X = r)$ is > 0 for every r, and that

$$\begin{aligned}\sum_{r=0}^{\infty} P(X = r) &= \sum_{r=0}^{\infty} e^{-\alpha}\frac{\alpha^r}{r!} \\ &= e^{-\alpha}\left(1 + \alpha + \frac{\alpha^2}{2!} + \ldots + \frac{\alpha^r}{r!} + \ldots\right) \\ &= e^{-\alpha}e^{\alpha} = 1.\end{aligned}$$

Hence for any $\alpha > 0$, (2) satisfies the conditions to be a probability distribution.

A random variable X having the distribution (2) is said to have the *Poisson distribution with parameter* α, a statement we shall abbreviate as $X \sim \text{Po}(\alpha)$.

If X denotes the number of occasions that some phenomenon occurs in a fixed interval of time or space, then it may be shown (using mathematics beyond the level of this text) that (2) is a reasonable model (for some α) for the distribution of X provided that:

(i) the phenomenon occurs at random (in time or space);
(ii) simultaneous occurrences of the phenomenon are not possible;
(iii) the average number of occurrences of the phenomenon in intervals (of time or space) of a specified size is directly proportional to the size of those intervals;
(iv) occurrences of the phenomenon are independent; that is, the occurrence of the phenomenon does not affect the probability of the phenomenon occurring subsequently (in time or space).

Some examples of random variables satisfying the above conditions (at least approximately) are as follows.

(i) The number of emissions from a radioactive source in a given time period.
(ii) The number of incoming calls to a telephone switchboard during a specified time period.
(iii) The number of cars passing over a bridge in a specified time period.
(iv) The number of weak points along a specified length of cable.
(v) The number of defects in a specified area of cloth material.
(vi) The number of blood cells that are visible under a microscope (the visible surface area under the microscope being a constant).

(vii) The number of organic particles suspended in a specified volume of liquid.

When $X \sim \text{Po}(\alpha)$ and α is known, probabilities such as $\text{P}(X = r)$ and $\text{P}(X \leqslant r)$ with r specified, may be computed on a calculator having the exponential function facility. Also, denoting $\text{P}(X = r)$ by p_r, we have

$$\frac{p_{r+1}}{p_r} = \frac{\text{e}^{-\alpha}\alpha^{r+1}/(r+1)!}{\text{e}^{-\alpha}\alpha^r/r!} = \frac{\alpha}{r+1},$$

so that

$$p_{r+1} = \frac{\alpha}{r+1}\, p_r,$$

which is a useful recursive formula when evaluating successive Poisson probabilities on a calculator. Tables of the Poisson distribution also exist and these give the values of at least one of $\text{P}(X = r)$, $\text{P}(X \leqslant r)$ and $\text{P}(X \geqslant r)$ for selected values of α. (It is assumed that such a table is available to the reader and that it will be used in the exercises whenever it is appropriate to do so; observe that when tabulated entries are added or multiplied the result may not be accurate to the same number of figures as a table entry.)

EXAMPLE 1 *The switchboard of a small business handles both incoming and outgoing telephone calls. During the lunch-hour on any day, the numbers of incoming and outgoing calls are independent and have Poisson distributions with parameters* 5 *and* 3, *respectively. Find the probabilities that during the lunch-hour of a randomly chosen day, there will be (i) exactly three outgoing calls, (ii) at least six incoming calls, (iii) a combined number of three calls through to the switchboard.*

(i) Let X denote the number of outgoing calls during a lunch-hour. Then, $X \sim \text{Po}(\alpha)$ with $\alpha = 3$, so that

$$\text{P}(X = r) = \text{e}^{-3}\,3^r/r!, \qquad r = 0, 1, 2, 3, \ldots .$$

Hence

$$\text{P}(X = 3) = \text{e}^{-3}\,3^3/3! = 27\text{e}^{-3}/6 = 0{\cdot}2240, \text{ to 4 decimal places.}$$

(ii) Let Y denote the number of incoming calls during a lunch-hour. Then $Y \sim \text{Po}(\alpha)$ with $\alpha = 5$, so that

$$\text{P}(Y = r) = \text{e}^{-5}\,5^r/r!, \qquad r = 0, 1, 2, 3, \ldots .$$

Hence

$$\text{P}(Y \geqslant 6) = \text{P}(Y = 6) + \text{P}(Y = 7) + \text{P}(Y = 8) + \ldots .$$

This requires evaluating an infinite number of terms, but since the terms become progressively smaller only a limited number need be evaluated for an answer to some specified degree of accuracy. However, there is some advantage in evaluating the probability of the event complementary to $(Y \geqslant 6)$, which is the event $(Y \leqslant 5)$.

Thus

$$\begin{aligned}P(Y \geqslant 6) &= 1 - P(Y \leqslant 5)\\ &= 1 - \{P(Y=0)+P(Y=1)+P(Y=2)+P(Y=3)\\ &\quad +P(Y=4)+P(Y=5)\}\\ &= 1 - e^{-5}\left(1+5+\frac{5^2}{2!}+\frac{5^3}{3!}+\frac{5^4}{4!}+\frac{5^5}{5!}\right)\\ &= 1-\frac{1097}{12}e^{-5} = 0{\cdot}3840 \text{ to 4 decimal places.}\end{aligned}$$

(Alternatively, the answer to (ii) may be obtainable more directly from a table of cumulative Poisson probabilities.)
(iii) With X and Y as defined above, the combined number of calls into the switchboard is $Z = X+Y$ and we need to find $P(Z = 3)$.
We have

$$\begin{aligned}\{Z=3) = \{(X=0)\cap(Y=3)\}\cup\{(X=1)\cap(Y=2)\}\\ \cup\{(X=2)\cap(Y=1)\}\cup\{(X=3)\cap(Y=0)\}.\end{aligned}$$

Since the events on the right-hand side are mutually exclusive,

$$\begin{aligned}P(Z=3) = P\{(X=0)\cap(Y=3)\}+P\{(X=1)\cap(Y=2)\}\\ +P\{(X=2)\cap(Y=1)\}+P\{(X=3)\cap(Y=0)\}.\end{aligned}$$

Further, since the numbers of incoming and outgoing calls are independent, the events $(X = r)$ and $(Y = s)$ are independent, and consequently,

$$\begin{aligned}P(Z=3) &= P(X=0)P(Y=3)+P(X=1)P(Y=2)+P(X=2)P(Y=1)\\ &\quad +P(X=3)P(Y=0)\\ &= e^{-3}\left(\frac{5^3}{3!}e^{-5}\right)+3e^{-3}\left(\frac{5^2}{2!}e^{-5}\right)+\frac{3^2}{2!}e^{-3}(5e^{-5})\\ &\quad +\frac{3^3}{3!}e^{-3}(e^{-5})\\ &= e^{-8}\left(\frac{125}{6}+\frac{75}{2}+\frac{45}{2}+\frac{27}{6}\right)\\ &= 256e^{-8}/3 = 0{\cdot}0286 \text{ to 4 decimal places.}\end{aligned}$$

(This is an instance where the use of a table of Poisson probabilities given correct to 4 decimal places would not give the answer correct to 4 decimal places. However, we shall later consider a property of Poisson distributions which will enable us to obtain the above answer more simply and, if tables are used, to the same accuracy as the tabulated entries.)

EXAMPLE 2 *A small garage has three cars available for daily hire. The daily demand for these cars has a Poisson distribution with parameter $\alpha = 2$. The owner* *charges £10 per day per car hired and his total outgoings on the three cars amount to £6 per day, irrespective of the number of cars that are actually hired. Find the expected daily profit from the hire of these cars.*

Let X denote the number of cars hired on a day. Then $X \sim \text{Po}(\alpha = 2)$, so that

$$P(X = x) = e^{-2}2^x/x!, \qquad x = 0, 1, 2, 3, \ldots.$$

Let £Y denote the profit made on a day. Then

$$Y = 10X - 6, \qquad \text{for } X = 0, 1, 2,$$

and

$$Y = 24, \qquad \text{for } X = 3, 4, 5, \ldots.$$

Hence, using the definition of the expected value of $h(X) \equiv Y$ given in §2.3.1, we have

$$E[Y] = \sum_{x=0}^{2} (10x - 6)P(X = x) + \sum_{x=3}^{\infty} 24P(X = x).$$

The first sum on the right-hand side is

$$\sum_{x=0}^{2} (10x - 6)e^{-2}2^x/x! = e^{-2} \sum_{x=0}^{2} (10x - 6)2^x/x!$$
$$= e^{-2}(-6 + 8 + 28) = 30e^{-2},$$

and the second sum is

$$\sum_{x=3}^{\infty} 24P(X = x) = 24P(X \geqslant 3)$$
$$= 24\{1 - P(X \leqslant 2)\}$$
$$= 24\{1 - e^{-2} \sum_{x=0}^{2} 2^x/x!\}$$
$$= 24\{1 - 5e^{-2}\} = 24 - 120e^{-2}.$$

Hence

$$E[Y] = 30e^{-2} + 24 - 120e^{-2} = 24 - 90e^{-2} = 11{\cdot}82, \quad \text{to decimal places.}$$

It follows that the expected daily profit from the hire of the cars is £11·82 correct to the nearest penny.

Mean and variance of the Poisson distribution

We now show that the distribution $\text{Po}(\alpha)$ has mean α and variance α. Let $X \sim \text{Po}(\alpha)$, so that

$$P(X = r) = e^{-\alpha}\alpha^r/r!, \qquad r = 0, 1, 2, 3, \ldots.$$

The mean μ is given by

$$\mu = \mathrm{E}[X] = \sum_{r=0}^{\infty} r\,\mathrm{e}^{-\alpha}\alpha^r/r!$$

$$= \mathrm{e}^{-\alpha}\left\{0+\alpha+\frac{2\alpha^2}{2!}+\frac{3\alpha^3}{3!}+\frac{4\alpha^4}{4!}+\ldots+\frac{r\alpha^r}{r!}+\ldots\right\}$$

$$= \alpha\mathrm{e}^{-\alpha}\left\{1+\alpha+\frac{\alpha^2}{2!}+\frac{\alpha^3}{3!}+\ldots+\frac{\alpha^{r-1}}{(r-1)!}+\ldots\right\}$$

$$= \alpha\mathrm{e}^{-\alpha}\,\mathrm{e}^{\alpha} = \alpha,$$

on using the series result (1) above. Also,

$$\mathrm{E}[X^2] = \sum_{r=0}^{\infty} r^2\frac{\mathrm{e}^{-\alpha}\alpha^r}{r!}$$

$$= \alpha\mathrm{e}^{-\alpha}\sum_{r=1}^{\infty}\frac{r^2\alpha^{r-1}}{r!}, \text{ since the first term } (r=0) \text{ is zero}$$

$$= \alpha\mathrm{e}^{-\alpha}\left\{1+2\alpha+\frac{3\alpha^2}{2!}+\frac{4\alpha^3}{3!}+\ldots+\frac{r\alpha^{r-1}}{(r-1)!}+\ldots\right\}$$

$$= \alpha\mathrm{e}^{-\alpha}\left[\left\{1+\alpha+\frac{\alpha^2}{2!}+\frac{\alpha^3}{3!}+\ldots+\frac{\alpha^{r-1}}{(r-1)!}+\ldots\right\}\right.$$
$$\left.+\left\{\alpha+\frac{2\alpha^2}{2!}+\frac{3\alpha^3}{3!}+\ldots+\frac{(r-1)\alpha^{r-1}}{(r-1)!}+\ldots\right\}\right]$$

From (1) the series in the upper line is equal to e^{α}. The series in the lower line is

$$\alpha+\alpha^2+\frac{\alpha^3}{2!}+\frac{\alpha^4}{3!}+\ldots+\frac{\alpha^{r-1}}{(r-1)!}+\ldots$$

$$= \alpha\left\{1+\alpha+\frac{\alpha^2}{2!}+\frac{\alpha^3}{3!}+\ldots+\frac{\alpha^{r-2}}{(r-2)!}+\ldots\right\}$$

$$= \alpha\mathrm{e}^{\alpha},$$

on using (1). Hence,

$$\mathrm{E}[X^2] = \alpha\mathrm{e}^{-\alpha}\{\mathrm{e}^{\alpha}+\alpha\mathrm{e}^{\alpha}\} = \alpha+\alpha^2.$$

Since $\mathrm{E}[X] = \alpha$ we have

$$\mathrm{V}[X] \equiv \mathrm{E}[X^2]-\{\mathrm{E}[X]\}^2 = \alpha+\alpha^2-\alpha^2 = \alpha.$$

EXERCISE 2.7A

1 The number of bacteria per ml of inoculum has a Poisson distribution with mean 2·5. If at least three bacteria are needed for a dose to be infective, show

that the probability of a dose of 1 ml being infective is equal to 0·456 to three decimal places.

2 There are two types of flaws that may occur in a length of manufactured material. The numbers of the two types that occur in a given length are independent and have Poisson distributions, the one type of flaw occurring on average once every 10 metre length of the material, and the other occurring on average once every 20 metre length of the material. Calculate correct to 3 decimal places the probabilities that a length of 1 metre of the material will (i) contain no flaw, (ii) contain only one flaw.

3 The number of errors made per page by a copytypist has a Poisson distribution with mean 0·2. Calculate, correct to three significant figures, the probabilities that in a particular assignment by this copytypist, (i) the first page typed will contain no error, (ii) the first error will appear on the third page she types, (iii) exactly two of the first five pages typed will contain no error, (iv) the total number of errors in the first two pages is 2 or less.

4 A dealer has a stock of six similar television sets which he rents out to customers on a weekly basis. The weekly demand for these sets is known to have a Poisson distribution with mean 4·5. Find the probabilities, correct to 3 decimal places, that in a given week (i) at least two of the sets will not be rented out, (ii) the demand exceeds the stock available.

5 The switchboard of a small business concern has three outside lines A, B and C. When an outside line is requested the choice is made randomly from the lines that are available (if any) at the time. The number of outside lines requested at any instant has a Poisson distribution with mean 2.
(i) Express, in terms of e, the probabilities that at a given instant, (a) none of the three lines is in use, (b) all three lines are in use, (c) line A is not in use.
(ii) The number of outside lines is to be increased so that the probability of all lines being in use at any instant is approximately 0·05. Find the number of outside lines that are necessary to meet this requirement.

6 The random variable X has the Poisson distribution with mean α. Show that

$$\sum_{x=0}^{r} x\,\mathrm{P}(X=x) = \alpha P(X \leqslant r-1).$$

The daily demand for a certain item at a particular shop has the Poisson distribution with mean 10. Use tables to find, to 3 decimal places in each case, the probability that on a given day the demand for the item will be (i) 21 or more, (ii) 19 or fewer.

The shop receives delivery of the items every morning and accepts as many items as are necessary to bring the stock level up to 20 items. The shop makes a profit of 50 p on each item sold. Show that the expected daily profit from the sale of these items is almost £5.

7 If $X \sim \mathrm{Po}(\alpha)$ and $p_r = \mathrm{P}(X=r)$ for $r = 0, 1, 2, \ldots$, show that

$$\frac{p_{r+1}}{p_r} = \frac{\alpha}{r+1}.$$

Hence show that if α is not an integer, the distribution $\mathrm{Po}(\alpha)$ has a unique mode and determine this mode in terms of α. Also determine the most probable value (or values) of X when α is an integer. (Hint: follow the argument used in §2.6 for the binomial distribution.)

2.7.1 The Poisson approximation to a binomial distribution

Suppose $X \sim \mathrm{B}(n, p)$, so that

$$\mathrm{P}(X = r) = \binom{n}{r} p^r (1-p)^{n-r}, \qquad r = 0, 1, 2, \ldots, n.$$

Let n increase indefinitely and *at the same time* let p decrease in such a way that the product np is kept constant at some value α. Setting $p = \alpha/n$ in the above expression, we have

$$\mathrm{P}(X = r) = \frac{n(n-1)(n-2)\ldots(n-r+1)}{r!} \frac{\alpha^r}{n^r}\left(1 - \frac{\alpha}{n}\right)^{n-r}$$

$$= \frac{\alpha^r}{r!}(1)\left(1 - \frac{1}{n}\right)\left(1 - \frac{2}{n}\right)\ldots\left(1 - \frac{r-1}{n}\right)\left(1 - \frac{\alpha}{n}\right)^{-r}\left(1 - \frac{\alpha}{n}\right)^{n}.$$

As n increases indefinitely each of the factors $(1-1/n)$, $(1-2/n)$, ..., $\left(1 - \frac{r-1}{n}\right)$, and $(1-\alpha/n)^{-r}$ will tend to the value 1, and the factor $(1-\alpha/n)^n$ will tend to $e^{-\alpha}$, since

$$\lim_{n \to \infty}\left(1 - \frac{x}{n}\right)^n = e^{-x}.$$

Thus, the limiting value of $\mathrm{P}(X = r)$ under the conditions described will be $e^{-\alpha}\alpha^r/r!$, which is seen to be $\mathrm{P}(Y = r)$ if $Y \sim \mathrm{Po}(\alpha)$ with $\alpha = np$.

This result indicates that *when n is very large and p is very small* binomial probabilities may be approximated by the corresponding Poisson probabilities with $\alpha = np$. The approximation should be very good when $n \geqslant 100$ and $p \leqslant 0{\cdot}01$; for smaller values of n the smaller p must be for a reasonably good approximation. To illustrate the order of accuracy of the approximation, Table 2.12 gives, for some selected values of n and p, the values of $\mathrm{P}(X \leqslant 3)$ to 4 decimal places when $X \sim \mathrm{B}(n, p)$, and the corresponding values using the Poisson approximation.

Table 2.12

n	p	$\mathrm{P}(X \leqslant 3)$	$\alpha = np$	Approx.
50	·02	0·9822	1	0·9810
50	·01	0·9984	0·5	0·9982
100	·02	0·8590	2	0·8571
100	·01	0·9816	1	0·9810

EXAMPLE 3 *A manufactured item has probability* 0·003 *of being defective. The*

items are boxed in cartons, each containing 1000 *of the items. Purchasers of these cartons will return any carton that contains three or more defective items. Use a Poisson approximation to calculate (i) the proportion of cartons that will not be returned, (ii) the conditional probability that a carton which has not been returned does not contain a defective item.*

Let X denote the number of defective items in a carton. Thus

$$X \sim \mathrm{B}(n = 1000,\ p = 0{\cdot}003).$$

Since n is very large and p is very small, we may approximate the distribution of X by the distribution of Y, where $Y \sim \mathrm{Po}(\alpha)$ with $\alpha = np = 3$.

(i) Proportion of cartons not returned $= \mathrm{P}(X \leqslant 2) \simeq \mathrm{P}(Y \leqslant 2)$

$$= \mathrm{e}^{-3}\left(1 + 3 + \frac{3^2}{2!}\right)$$

$$= 8{\cdot}5\,\mathrm{e}^{-3}$$

$$= 0{\cdot}4232 \text{ to 4 decimal places}$$

(ii) Here we require

$$\mathrm{P}(\text{no defective in carton} \mid \text{carton not returned})$$

$$= \mathrm{P}(X = 0 \mid X \leqslant 2)$$

$$= \frac{\mathrm{P}(X = 0)}{\mathrm{P}(X \leqslant 2)} \simeq \frac{\mathrm{P}(Y = 0)}{\mathrm{P}(Y \leqslant 2)}$$

$$= \frac{\mathrm{e}^{-3}}{8{\cdot}5\mathrm{e}^{-3}} = \frac{2}{17} = 0{\cdot}1176 \text{ to 4 decimal places}$$

The Poisson approximation may also be used for evaluating a binomial probability when p is close to 1 and n is large, as illustrated in the following example.

EXAMPLE 4 In Example 3, use a Poisson approximation to calculate the probability that a carton will contain at least 995 non-defective items.

Let X denote the number of non-defective items in the carton. Then $X \sim \mathrm{B}(n, p)$ with $n = 1000$ and $p = 0{\cdot}997$, and we need to evaluate $\mathrm{P}(X \geqslant 995)$. Let $X' = 100 - X$ denote the number of defective items in the carton; then $X' \sim \mathrm{B}(n, q)$ where $n = 1000$ and $q = 0{\cdot}003$, and $\mathrm{P}(X \geqslant 995) \equiv \mathrm{P}(X' \leqslant 5)$. Since $n(= 1000)$ is large and $q(= 0{\cdot}003)$ is small we can use the Poisson approximation with $\alpha = nq = 3$ to evaluate $\mathrm{P}(X' \leqslant 5)$. We then find

$$\mathrm{P}(X' \leqslant 5) \simeq \mathrm{e}^{-3}\left(1 + 3 + \frac{3^2}{2} + \frac{3^3}{6} + \frac{3^4}{24}\right) = \frac{131}{8}\mathrm{e}^{-3} \simeq 0{\cdot}8153.$$

EXERCISE 2.7B

1 On average, one in every 10,000 people contracts a certain non-contagious disease in a year. Use a distributional approximation to calculate the probability that in a town of 20,000 people at least three of the people will contract the disease in a given year.

2 The probability of a baby being stillborn is 0·0001. Find the probabilities that of the next 5000 babies (i) none will be stillborn, (ii) there will be exactly one stillborn baby, (iii) there will be at least two stillborn babies.

3 The probability that a typist will mistype a character is 0·01. Write down an expression for the probability that of 500 characters typed by this typist exactly r will be incorrect. Write down the corresponding Poisson approximation to this probability. Hence find the probabilities that of the 500 characters (i) at most two of them will be incorrect, (ii) between three and five (inclusive) of them will be incorrect.

4 A steel cable of a certain maximum strength has probability 0·005 of snapping under a specified load. Find an approximate value for the probability that of 600 cables subjected to that load at least 597 of them will not snap.

It is known that when a similar type of cable is subjected to a load of s units its probability of snapping is e^{-s}. Write down an expression for the probability that when 100 such cables are subjected to a load of s units none of them will snap. Find the minimum cable strength s if there is to be a probability of at least 0·95 that when 100 cables are subjected to a load of s units, none of them will snap.

2.8* The geometric distribution

In this section we shall need to use the negative binomial series expansions

$$(1-q)^{-1} = 1 + q + q^2 + q^3 + \dots + q^r + \dots, \tag{1}$$

$$(1-q)^{-2} = 1 + 2q + 3q^2 + 4q^3 + \dots + rq^{r-1} + \dots, \tag{2}$$

which are valid for $0 < q < 1$. (Observe that (2) may be derived by differentiating (1)).

EXAMPLE 1

In Example 2, §2.1 we defined the random variable Z to be the number of times a fair die would have to be tossed if tossing is to stop when a 6 is obtained. As indicated in that example, the range space of Z is $\{1, 2, 3, \dots\}$, the set of all positive integers (contrast this with the range space of a random variable having a Poisson distribution which also includes the value 0).

To determine the probability distribution of Z we need to evaluate $P(Z = r)$ for $r = 1, 2, 3, \dots$. We have, on denoting a score other than 6 by $\bar{6}$,

$$P(Z = 1) = P(6 \text{ on 1st toss}) = \frac{1}{6},$$

$$P(Z = 2) = P(\bar{6} \text{ on 1st, 6 on 2nd}) = \left(\frac{5}{6}\right)\left(\frac{1}{6}\right),$$

$$P(Z = 3) = P(\bar{6} \text{ on 1st, } \bar{6} \text{ on 2nd, 6 on 3rd}) = \left(\frac{5}{6}\right)^2\left(\frac{1}{6}\right),$$

and generally for any $r \geqslant 2$,

$$\begin{aligned}\mathrm{P}(Z=r) &= \mathrm{P}(\bar{6} \text{ on each of the first } r-1 \text{ tosses and 6 on the } r\text{th toss})\\ &= \left(\frac{5}{6}\right)^{r-1}\left(\frac{1}{6}\right).\end{aligned}$$

Hence, the probability distribution of Z is given by

$$\mathrm{P}(Z=r)=\frac{1}{6}\left(\frac{5}{6}\right)^{r-1}, \qquad r=1, 2, 3, \ldots.$$

Summing these probabilities we have

$$\begin{aligned}\sum_{r=1}^{\infty} \mathrm{P}(Z=r) &= \frac{1}{6}+\frac{1}{6}\left(\frac{5}{6}\right)+\frac{1}{6}\left(\frac{5}{6}\right)^2+\ldots+\frac{1}{6}\left(\frac{5}{6}\right)^{r-1}+\ldots\\ &= \frac{1}{6}\left\{1+\frac{5}{6}+\left(\frac{5}{6}\right)^2+\ldots+\left(\frac{5}{6}\right)^{r-1}+\ldots\right\}.\end{aligned}$$

From (1),

$$1+\frac{5}{6}+\left(\frac{5}{6}\right)^2+\ldots+\left(\frac{5}{6}\right)^{r-1}+\ldots=\left(1-\frac{5}{6}\right)^{-1}=6,$$

so that

$$\sum_{r=1}^{\infty} \mathrm{P}(Z=r)=\frac{1}{6}\times 6=1,$$

as it should be.

Let us now generalise the above example. Suppose that independent Bernoulli trials, in each of which the probability of a success is p, are carried out until a success is obtained. Let X denote the number of trials that will be conducted; then X has range space $\{1, 2, 3, \ldots\}$ and for any $r=1, 2, 3, \ldots$,

$$\begin{aligned}\mathrm{P}(X=r) &= \mathrm{P}\{\text{each of the first } (r-1) \text{ trials yields a failure and the } r\text{th trial yields a success}\}\\ &= q^{r-1}p,\end{aligned}$$

where $q=1-p$. Hence the probability distribution of X is given by

$$\mathrm{P}(X=r)=pq^{r-1}, \qquad r=1, 2, 3, \ldots. \tag{3}$$

A random variable X with probability distribution of the form (3) is said to have the *geometric distribution with probability parameter p*, a statement we shall abbreviate as $X \sim \mathrm{Geo}(p)$. With Z defined as in Example 1 we see that $Z \sim \mathrm{Geo}\left(\frac{1}{6}\right)$.

Using (1), it is readily verified that the sum of the probabilities defined by

(3) is equal to one. Denoting $P(X = r)$ defined in (3) by p_r, we have

$$\frac{p_{r+1}}{p_r} = \frac{pq^r}{pq^{r-1}} = q,$$

so that

$$p_{r+1} = qp_r, \tag{4}$$

for $r = 1, 2, 3, \ldots$, which is a useful recursive formula for computing the successive values of the probabilities given by (3). Further, since each probability is q times the preceding probability and $q < 1$, it follows that the mode of every geometric distribution is equal to 1.

Mean and variance

The mean of the geometric distribution (3) is given by

$$\begin{aligned}\mu \equiv E[X] &= \sum_{r=1}^{\infty} rpq^{r-1} \\ &= p(1 + 2q + 3q^2 + 4q^3 + \ldots) \\ &= p(1-q)^{-2}, \text{ using (2).}\end{aligned}$$

Since $(1-q)^{-2} = p^{-2} = 1/p^2$, we have

$$\mu = \frac{1}{p}. \tag{5}$$

Also

$$\begin{aligned}E[X^2] &= \sum_{r=1}^{\infty} r^2 pq^{r-1} \\ &= p(1 + 2^2 q + 3^3 q^2 + 4^2 q^3 + \ldots + r^2 q^{r-1} + \ldots).\end{aligned} \tag{6}$$

On multiplying (2) by q we have

$$q(1-q)^{-2} = q + 2q^2 + 3q^3 + 4q^4 + \ldots + rq^r + \ldots,$$

and on differentiating both sides with respect to q, we obtain

$$(1+q)(1-q)^{-3} = 1 + 2^2 q + 3^2 q^2 + 4^2 q^3 + \ldots + r^2 q^{r-1} + \ldots,$$

which is precisely the series appearing in (6). Hence,

$$E[X^2] = p(1+q)(1-q)^{-3}.$$

But since $1 - q = p$, this reduces to

$$E[X^2] = (1+q)/p^2.$$

We then have

$$\begin{aligned}V[X] &= E[X^2] - \mu^2 \\ &= \frac{1+q}{p^2} - \frac{1}{p^2} = \frac{q}{p^2} = \frac{1-p}{p^2}.\end{aligned} \tag{7}$$

EXAMPLE 2 *Independently for each shot he fires at a target, a boy has probability* 0·8 *of hitting the target. Suppose that in each practice period the boy fires shots until he hits the target. Find the mean and the standard deviation of the number of shots fired per practice period. Also find* (i) *the probability that the boy will need to take at least five shots to hit the target,* (ii) *the smallest value of n for which there is a probability of at least* 0·99 *that the boy will need only n or fewer shots to hit the target.*

Let X denote the number of shots for the first hit. Since the probability of a hit is 0·8, then $X \sim \text{Geo}(p)$ with $p = 0{\cdot}8$, and from (3),

$$P(X = r) = 0{\cdot}8\,(0{\cdot}2)^{r-1}, \qquad r = 1, 2, 3, \ldots.$$

From (5), the mean number of shots for a hit is $1/0{\cdot}8 = 1{\cdot}25$, and from (6), the standard deviation is $\sqrt{\{(1-0{\cdot}8)/0{\cdot}8^2\}} = 0{\cdot}5590$, correct to four decimal places.
(i) Here we require

$$\begin{aligned} P(X \geqslant 5) &= \sum_{r=5}^{\infty} 0{\cdot}8\,(0{\cdot}2)^{r-1} \\ &= (0{\cdot}8)\,(0{\cdot}2)^4\,\{1 + 0{\cdot}2 + 0{\cdot}2^2 + 0{\cdot}2^3 + \ldots\} \\ &= (0{\cdot}8)\,(0{\cdot}2)^4\,(1-0{\cdot}2)^{-1} \\ &= (0{\cdot}2)^4 = 0{\cdot}0016. \end{aligned}$$

(ii) We need to find the smallest integer n for which

$$P(X \leqslant n) \geqslant 0{\cdot}99.$$

One method for finding n is to add successive probabilities until the total first exceeds 0·99. More elegantly, we can proceed as follows.

$$\begin{aligned} P(X \leqslant n) &= 1 - P(X \geqslant n+1) \\ &= 1 - \sum_{r=n+1}^{\infty} (0{\cdot}8)\,(0{\cdot}2)^{r-1} \\ &= 1 - 0{\cdot}2^n. \end{aligned}$$

Thus, n must be the smallest integer such that

$$1 - 0{\cdot}2^n \geqslant 0{\cdot}99;$$

that is,

$$0{\cdot}2^n \leqslant 0{\cdot}01,$$

or

$$n \geqslant \log 0{\cdot}01/\log 0{\cdot}2 = 2{\cdot}86.$$

Hence the smallest integer value of n is 3.

EXERCISE 2.8

1 During a practice session a rugby player takes kicks at goal from the same place until he succeeds. Suppose that independently for each attempt, his

probability of kicking a goal is 0·6. Let X denote the number of attempts he makes to his first success.
(i) Write down the probability distribution of X and identify it by name.
(ii) Calculate the probability that he will need at least four attempts to his first success.
(iii) Assuming that the time in minutes he will take over his practice session (kicking from one place) is given by $Y = 10+3X$, calculate the mean and the variance of Y.

2 A fair coin is tossed until the same face shows twice in succession. Define the random variable X to be the number of tosses required. Show that

$$P(X = r) = 1/2^{r-1}, \qquad r = 2, 3, 4, \ldots.$$

(i) Verify that these probabilities sum to unity.
(ii) Find the probabilities that: (a) fewer than six tosses will be required; (b) the number of tosses required will be an exact multiple of 3.

3 In an investigation of animal behaviour, rats have to choose between four doors, one of which leads to food and the others lead to the rat having a mild electric shock. If a rat receives a shock it is returned to the starting point for another run, this being repeated until the rat locates the food. Let X denote the number of runs made by a rat when it locates the food. Determine the distribution of X and its mean in each of the cases when (i) independently on each run, a rat is equally likely to choose any one of the four doors, (ii) a rat is equally likely to choose any one door on its first run but on each subsequent run it chooses a door at random from the three doors which it did not choose on the immediately preceding run, independently of its choice before the preceding run.

Why is it not surprising that the expected number of runs by a rat in (ii) is less than that in (i)?

4 In a game of 'odd one out', $n \geqslant 3$ persons simultaneously toss a fair coin each. If one coin turns up differently from the other $(n-1)$ coins, then the tosser of that coin is the 'odd one out'. Tossing continues until there is an 'odd one out'. Let X denote the number of times the coins have to be tossed to get an 'odd one out'. Find the probability distribution of X and identify it by name. For the case when $n = 8$ deduce the expected number of times the coins will have to be tossed to get an 'odd one out'.

5 Given that X has the geometric distribution with parameter p, and that m and n are two positive integers, prove that

$$P(X > m+n \mid X > m) = P(X > n).$$

REVIEW PROBLEMS ON CHAPTER 2

1 A random variable X has the probability distribution given in the table, and $Y = 2X-18$. Find $E[Y]$ and $E[Y^2]$. Deduce the values of $E[X]$ and $\mathrm{Var}[X]$.

x	12	16	18	20	24
$P(X = x)$	1/15	4/15	1/3	1/5	2/15

(*L 1981*)

2 A sample of four mice is to be chosen at random from a litter of ten mice, of which six are male and four are female. Let X denote the number of male mice in the sample. Calculate the values of $P(X = r)$ for $r = 0, 1, 2, 3, 4$. Hence find the mean and the standard deviation of X. Deduce the mean and the standard deviation of the number of female mice in the sample. (*WJEC 1977*)

3 When N children are vaccinated it is known that each child may experience an adverse reaction. Let X be the number of children who react adversely. Given that the probability distribution of X is

$$P(X = r) = A/2^r, \qquad r = 0, 1, 2, \ldots, N,$$

where A is a positive constant, show that $A = 2^N/(2^{N+1} - 1)$. Find in terms of A and M, the probability that at least M of the children react adversely. Show that when $N = 4$, the probability of there being at least one adverse reaction is 15/31. (*L 1979*)

4 An employee motors daily to car park A in the town in which he works. If there is a space for his car he parks there and he then has a five minute walk to his office. If car park A is full he drives to car park B which always has parking spaces available. It takes him five minutes to drive from A to B and a further fifteen minutes to walk from car park B to his office. On any day the probability that car park A will be full when he arrives there is 1/5. If on any day it takes the employee T minutes to reach his office after arriving at car park A, find the mean and the standard deviation of T. (*JMB 1982*)

5 A bag contains six blue discs and five red discs. Three discs are randomly selected without replacement. Find the probability that the three selected discs (i) are all of the same colour, (ii) consist of two blue discs and one red disc. Find the mean and the variance of the number of blue discs that will be selected. If instead the three discs are selected with replacement, write down the new mean and variance of the number of blue discs selected. (*JMB 1982*)

6 Let X denote the number of heads obtained when a fair coin is tossed three times. Write down the mean and the variance of X.

A pack of six cards consists of three cards labelled H and the other three labelled T. Three cards are drawn at random without replacement from the pack. Let Y denote the number of Hs obtained. Calculate the probabilities that Y takes the values 0, 1, 2 and 3, respectively. Show that the mean of Y is equal to the mean of X, and express the variance of Y as a percentage of the variance of X. (*JMB 1978*)

7 A batch of 20 items is inspected as follows. A random sample of five items is drawn from the batch without replacement and the number of defective items in the sample is counted. If this number is two or more the batch is rejected; if there is no defective item in the sample the batch is accepted; if there is exactly one defective item in the sample, then a further random sample of five items is drawn without replacement from the remaining 15 items in the batch. If this second sample includes at least one defective item then the batch is rejected; otherwise the batch is accepted. Suppose that a batch to be inspected consists of exactly two defective items and 18 non-defective items. (i) Calculate the probabilities that (a) the batch will be accepted on the basis of the first sample, (b) a second sample will be taken and the batch will then be accepted, (c) the batch will be rejected. (ii) Find the expected number of items that will have to be sampled to reach a decision on the batch. (*WJEC 1981*)

8 An electrical circuit contains five components, one of which is faulty. To isolate the fault, the components are tested one by one until the faulty one is found. The random variable X denotes the number of tests required to locate the fault; the test of the faulty component itself is always included, so that X takes the values from 1 to 5, inclusive. Given that any one of the five components is equally likely to be the faulty one, find the expectation and variance of X. The cost C (in suitable units) of locating a fault depends in part on the number of tests required and is given by the formula $C = 5+2X$. Find the expectation and variance of C. (*C 1982*)

9 Breakdowns in an electricity supply system occur on average once in every 50 days. The probability distribution of the number of breakdowns occurring is given by a Poisson distribution. Show that the probability that a period of 200 days will pass without any breakdown is approximately 0·018. Show also that the probability of one and only one breakdown in a year of 365 days is approximately 0·005. Find the probability that two or more breakdowns occur in a month of 30 days. (*L 1978*)

10 The monthly demand for a certain magazine at a small newsagent's shop has a Poisson distribution with mean 3. The newsagent always orders four copies of the magazine for sale each month; any demand for the magazine in excess of four is not met. (i) Calculate the probability that the newsagent will not be able to meet the demand in a given month. (ii) Find the most probable number of magazines *sold* in one month. (iii) Find the expected number of magazines *sold* in one month. (iv) Determine the least number of copies of the magazine that the newsagent should order each month so as to meet the demand with a probability of at least 0·95. (*JMB 1979*)

11 Packets of fruit gums contain 12 fruit gums altogether, and two flavours, orange and lime, are manufactured. The filling machine mixes the two flavours randomly in the overall proportion of two orange to one lime. Packets are regarded as acceptable provided they contain at least one lime and at least three orange flavours. Calculate the probability that a randomly chosen packet will not be acceptable. The packets are delivered to shops in boxes of 200 packets. Use a Poisson distribution to calculate the probability that a box will contain at least two unacceptable packets. (*C 1981*)

12 Bacteria are distributed independently of one another in a solution, and it is known that the number of bacteria per ml follows a Poisson distribution with mean 2. (i) Show that the probability of a sample of 1 ml of solution containing three or more bacteria is 0·32 approximately. (ii) Five samples, each of 1 ml of solution, are taken. Find the probability that less than two of these samples contain three or more bacteria. (*L 1979*)

13 A college's switchboard handles both internal and external calls. In any half-hour period the number of internal and external calls are independent and have Poisson distributions with means λ and μ, respectively. (i) Find expressions, in terms of λ and μ, for the probabilities that during a half-hour period there will be (a) no call at all, (b) 2 internal calls and 1 external call, (c) a total of 3 calls. (ii) Given that $\lambda = 3$ and $\mu = 5$, obtain the probabilities that during a half-hour period there will be (a) at least 10 internal calls, (b) exactly 3 external calls. (c) Given that a total of 3 calls arrived during a half-hour period, find the conditional probability that exactly 2 of them were internal calls. (*WJEC 1980*)

14 Show that the mean and the variance of the Poisson distribution are equal. From a long period of observation, it is known that the mean number of cars on the hard shoulder of a motorway is three cars for every 10 km of motorway. Assuming that the Poisson distribution is applicable, find the probability that on a 30 km stretch of motorway, fewer than four cars will be on the hard shoulder. Obtain the probability that at least one car will be on the hard shoulder on each of 10 separate 10 km stretches of motorway. (*L 1981*)

15 (i) The random variable X has a Poisson distribution and is such that $P(X = 2) = 3P(X = 4)$. Find, correct to three decimal places, the values of (a) $P(X = 0)$, (b) $P(X \leqslant 4)$.
(ii) The number of characters that are mistyped by a copytypist in any assignment has a Poisson distribution, the average number of mistyped characters per page being 0·8. In an assignment of 80 pages calculate, to three decimal places, (i) the probability that the first page will contain exactly two mistyped characters, (ii) the probability that the first mistyped character will appear on the third page. (*WJEC 1982*)

16 As part of its sales campaign for a new beauty preparation, a cosmetics manufacturer has a counter in a large store at which each prospective customer is given a free 10-minute individual session with a personal assistant to try the preparation. The store opens at 09.00. The first 10-minute session commences at 09.10 and, from then on, there are 50 sessions which run continuously through the day. It is estimated that the number of customers arriving at the counter per hour has a Poisson distribution with a mean of 15. Evaluate, to the nearest integer in each case, the expected number of 10-minute sessions in the day during which 0, 1, 2, 3, more than 3, customers arrive at the counter. Any assistant who has no customer waiting at the beginning of a 10-minute session is allowed to have the whole of that session as a rest period. It is found that any customer who would have to wait longer than the start of the next 10-minute session goes away, that no customers buy the preparation without a trial, and that 50% of the customers who do have a trial buy the preparation. The manufacturer makes a profit of £1.60 for each sale and a loss on materials of £0.10 for every trial where no sale results. The daily wage of an assistant is £20. Prove that, if the counter has two assistants, then the expected daily profit is £21.50. Find the expected daily profit if the counter has three assistants. (*C 1981*)

17 Derive the mean and the variance of the Poisson distribution.
Two types of flaw A and B may occur in manufactured cloth. The numbers of flaws of type A and of type B occurring per metre length of the cloth are independent random variables having Poisson distributions with means 0·5 and 1, respectively. (i) Find the probabilities, to three significant figures, that a length of 1 metre of the cloth will have (a) two or fewer flaws of type A, (b) no flaw of either type. (ii) Show that the probability of a length of 1 metre of the cloth containing one flaw only is *exactly* three times that of it containing one flaw of each type.

18 A car ferry plies between jetties at A and B. Cars arrive at random at each jetty at an average of one per five minutes. The ferry will accommodate three cars and departs when it is full or half an hour after arrival, whichever is the sooner. Find (i) the probability that, if the jetty is empty when the ferry arrives, it does not depart until the half hour is up, (ii) the probability that the ferry has exactly three cars waiting for it when it arrives at A if it has waited 10 minutes to load at B, the journey takes 5 minutes each way and the jetty at A was empty when it left there, (iii) the probability that, if one car is waiting at A when the ferry arrives, the ferry will depart again in less than 10 minutes. (*C 1980*)

19 In a large school, 60 % of the children receive more than £1 per week pocket money, but only 4 % of the children receive more than £2 per week. Find the probability that a random group of 10 children of this school would contain at most one child who receives £1 or less per week. Calculate also an approximate value for the probability that a random group of 100 children from the school would contain more than one child whose pocket money exceeds £2 per week. (*L 1982*)

20 A fair penny is thrown until at least two heads and at least two tails have been thrown. Obtain the probability that this occurs at the Rth throw. Find (i) the most probable value of R, (ii) the mean of R. [$(1-y)^{-2} = 1+2y+3y^2+4y^3 + \ldots, (1-y)^{-3} = 1+3y+6y^2+10y^3+\ldots$]. (*C 1981*)

21 The number X of customers per day requiring a copy of a particular newspaper at a newsagent's shop is a discrete random variable having the distribution

$$P(X = k) = pq^{k-30}, \qquad k = 30, 31, 32, \ldots,$$

where $p = 0{\cdot}02$ and $q = 1-p = 0{\cdot}98$. (i) Assuming that on each day the newsagent has an unlimited supply of copies of the newspaper, calculate the mean number of copies sold per day. (ii) If the newsagent has only N copies of the newspaper available for sale each day, find the smallest value of N for there to be a probability of at least 0·8 that the daily demand will be met. (iii) The newsagent makes a profit of 4 p on every copy of the newspaper that he sells, and loses 6 p on every copy left unsold at the end of the day. If the newsagent has N copies available for sale each day and the number of customers requiring the paper is x, write down expressions for the daily profit in the cases when $x < N$ and $x \geqslant N$, respectively. By considering the additional daily profit in each of these cases if the newsagent had $(N+1)$ copies available each day, or otherwise, find the value of N which will maximise the newsagent's mean daily profit from the sale of this newspaper. (*JMB 1980S*)

3 Continuous Random Variables

3.1 Introduction

In §2.1 we defined a random variable as being a numerically valued characteristic associated with the outcomes of a random experiment, or more formally as being a function which assigns a numerical value to every element of a sample space. We also defined the range space of a random variable as being the set of all possible values that it may take.

In Chapter 2 we restricted consideration to random variables whose range space elements could be listed individually. Determining the probability distribution of such a random variable then consisted of assigning a probability to each element of its range space.

In the present chapter we extend consideration to random variables whose range space elements cannot be listed individually. The following example illustrates such a random variable.

EXAMPLE 1 Suppose a string of length 10 cm is cut at an arbitrary point and the length of the longer of the two pieces is measured. Let X cm denote the length of the longer piece. Then, since the longer piece must be more than 5 cm long, the range space of X is

$$R_X = \{x : 5 < x < 10\}$$

In practice, of course, any measurement of the longer piece of string will be of limited accuracy, in which case the range space for the measurement will consist of a finite number of elements only. For instance, if the longer piece is measured correct to the nearest millimetre, then the set of all possible measurements will be $\{5.0, 5.1, 5.2, \ldots, 9.9, 10.0\}$, consisting of 51 elements. Nevertheless, we shall find it more convenient to suppose that the length of the longer piece may take any value between 5 cm and 10 cm.

We define a random variable whose range space elements cannot be listed individually as being *continuous*. Here we shall restrict consideration to continuous random variables whose range spaces are intervals of values.

Some other examples of continuous random variables are as follows:

(i) The time T hours showing on a clock when it stops has range space

$$R_T = \{t : 0 < t \leqslant 12\}.$$

(ii) The operational lifetime, X hours, of an electric light bulb has range space

$$R_X = \{x : x > 0\}$$

In this example, there is clearly an upper bound on the lifetime but since it is unknown to us we cannot specify it in the range space.
(iii) The weight W g of the contents of a packet of powder which is guaranteed to contain at least 100 g of powder has range space

$$R_W = \{w : w \geqslant 100\}.$$

Since the elements of the range space of a continuous random variable cannot be listed individually a method different from that used in chapter 2 is necessary for describing how the one unit of probability is to be distributed over the range space.

3.2 Probability density function

Suppose X is a continuous random variable having range space $R_X = \{x : a \leqslant x \leqslant b\}$. We need a description of how the one unit of probability is to be shared among the elements of R_X. Imagining the one unit of probability as being powder which is in a jug, we can envisage pouring the powder over the line segment defined by the interval $a \leqslant x \leqslant b$. This will give us a pictorial representation of how the one unit of probability has been distributed over R_X. Three examples are given in the Figs. 3.1, 3.2 and 3.3, each of which shows the shape of the mound of probability on the interval $a \leqslant x \leqslant b$. Note that the total area of each mound in the figures must equal unity (the total probability).

For a mathematical description of a probability distribution, let $f(x)$ be the height of the mound above the value x in R_X, as indicated in Fig. 3.4.

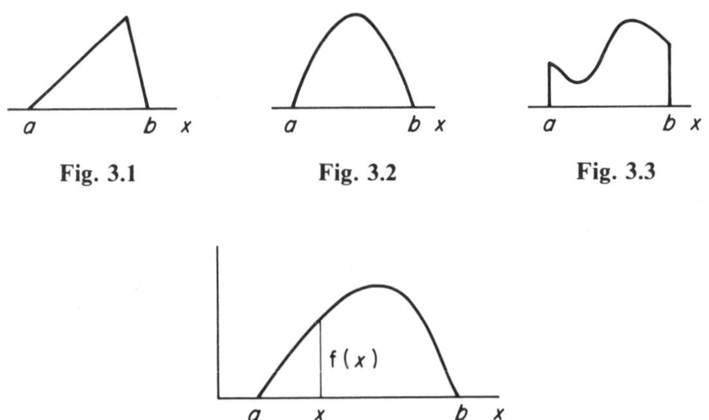

Fig. 3.1 Fig. 3.2 Fig. 3.3

Fig. 3.4

Since the total area of the mound is unity it follows that

$$\int_a^b f(x)dx = 1. \tag{1}$$

Furthermore, as illustrated in Fig. 3.5, the amount of probability allocated to any subinterval $[c, d]$ where $a \leqslant c < d \leqslant b$, is the area of the mound above the subinterval $[c, d]$. Thus, the probability of the event $\{c \leqslant X \leqslant d\}$ is given by

$$P(c \leqslant X \leqslant d) = \int_c^d f(x)dx. \tag{2}$$

The function f defined above is called *the probability density function of the random variable X* and it provides us with a mathematical description of how the one unit of probability has been distributed over the range space. It is important to observe that $f(x)$ itself does not represent a probability; only when it is integrated between two limits do we get a probability; the value $f(x)$ merely represents the *density* of concentration of the probability in the vicinity of the value x.

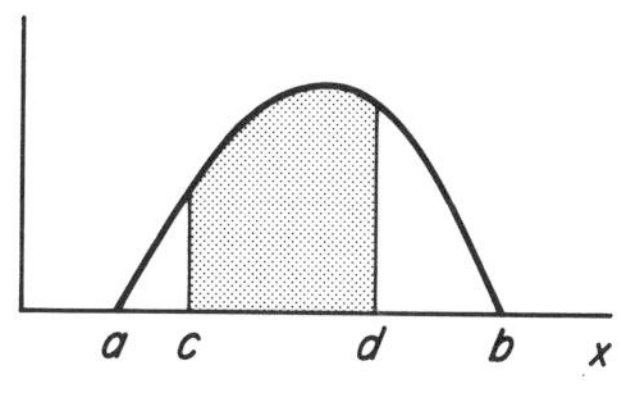

Fig. 3.5

Definition: Any function f such that

$$f(x) \geqslant 0, \text{ for } a \leqslant x \leqslant b,$$

and

$$\int_a^b f(x)dx = 1,$$

may serve as the *probability density function* (p.d.f.) of a continuous random variable having range space $R_X = \{x : a \leqslant x \leqslant b\}$.

An interesting consequence of the above approach is that for any c in R_X, we have $P(X = c) = 0$. This follows from the fact that in the present context, probability is measured by means of area, but the line $x = c$ has no thickness and consequently its area is zero. In particular it follows that

$$P(c \leqslant X \leqslant d) = P(c < X \leqslant d) = P(c \leqslant X < d) = P(c < X < d).$$

Thus, unlike the case when X is discrete, we need not distinguish between strong ($\leqslant$ and $\geqslant$) and weak ($<$ and $>$) inequalities when evaluating probabilities such as those displayed above.

That $P(X = c)$ is zero does not pose any real practical problems. For example, consider an event such as $\{X = 2.4\}$: while it is true that this event has probability zero, if we interpret the value 2.4 as being the observed value of X recorded correct to one decimal place, then the event $\{X = 2.4\}$ is really the event $\{2.35 < X \leqslant 2.45\}$ and this event will have a non-zero probability.

EXAMPLE 1 *The continuous random variable X is distributed with probability density function f defined by*

$$f(x) = cx(16 - x^2), \qquad 0 < x < 4.$$

Evaluate (i) c, (ii) $P(1 < X < 2)$, *(iii)* $P(X \geqslant 3)$, *(iv)* $P(X < 2 | 1 < X < 3)$.

(In this textbook we adopt the convention that $f(x)$ is always identically zero for all values of x other than those specified; this convention is consistent with that we used for discrete random variables.)

(i) To determine c we use the fact that $\int_0^4 f(x)dx = 1$. Thus,

$$c\int_0^4 (16x - x^3)dx = 1$$

or

$$c[8x^2 - \tfrac{1}{4}x^4]_0^4 = 1,$$

from which we find $64c = 1$, giving $c = 1/64$.

(ii) $$P(1 < X < 2) = \int_1^2 f(x)dx$$

$$= \frac{1}{64}\int_1^2 (16x - x^3)dx = \frac{81}{256}.$$

(iii) $$P(X \geqslant 3) = \frac{1}{64}\int_3^4 (16x - x^3)dx = \frac{49}{256}$$

(iv) $$P(X < 2 | 1 < X < 3) = \frac{P\{(X < 2) \cap (1 < X < 3)\}}{P(1 < X < 3)} = \frac{P(1 < X < 2)}{P(1 < X < 3)}.$$

$$P(1 < X < 2) = \frac{1}{64}\int_1^2 (16x - x^3)dx = 81/256.$$

$$P(1 < X < 3) = \frac{1}{64}\int_1^3 (16x - x^3)dx = 44/64.$$

Hence

$$P(X < 2 | 1 < X < 3) = \frac{81/256}{44/64} = \frac{81}{176}.$$

EXAMPLE 2 *The continuous random variable* X *has range space* $R_X = \{x: 0 \leqslant x \leqslant 3\}$ *and probability density function* f *where*

$$f(x) = \frac{1}{4}, \qquad 0 \leqslant x < 1,$$

$$f(x) = \frac{3}{8}(3-x), \qquad 1 \leqslant x \leqslant 3.$$

Sketch the graph of $f(x)$ and verify that it satisfies the conditions to be a probability density function. Evaluate (i) $P(X < 2{\cdot}5)$, (ii) $P(|X-2| \leqslant 0{\cdot}5)$.

The two 'parts' of $f(x)$ are seen to be straight lines and the graph is as shown in Fig. 3.6. Observe that $f(x)$ has a discontinuity at $x = 1$. We note that $f(x) \geqslant 0$ for all x in R_X, being one of the conditions to be satisfied by a p.d.f. We also need the area under $f(x)$ to be equal to unity. This area consists of the area of the rectangle above $0 \leqslant x < 1$ which is 0·25, and the area of the right-angled triangle above $1 \leqslant x \leqslant 3$ which is $\frac{1}{2} \times 2 \times 0{\cdot}75 = 0{\cdot}75$. Thus, the total area under $f(x)$ is $0{\cdot}25 + 0{\cdot}75 = 1$, as required.

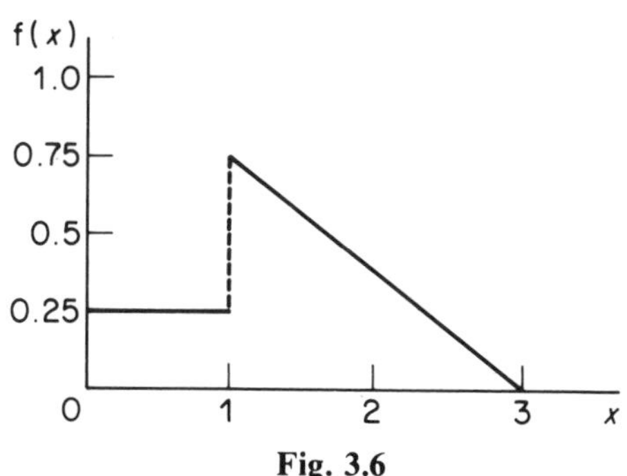

Fig. 3.6

(i) To evaluate $P(X < 2{\cdot}5)$ we need the area of the region under $f(x)$ above the interval $0 \leqslant x < 2{\cdot}5$, which consists of the rectangle above $0 \leqslant x < 1$ and the trapezium above $1 \leqslant x < 2{\cdot}5$. However, it is easier here to use the result $P(X < 2{\cdot}5) = 1 - P(X \geqslant 2{\cdot}5)$. The region under $f(x)$ to the right of $x = 2{\cdot}5$ is seen to be a right-angled triangle whose area is $\frac{1}{2}(3-2{\cdot}5) \times \frac{3}{8}(3-2{\cdot}5) = 3/64$. Hence, $P(X < 2{\cdot}5) = 1 - \frac{3}{64} = \frac{61}{64}$.

Alternatively, by direct integration, we have

$$P(X < 2{\cdot}5) = \int_0^{2\cdot5} f(x)\,dx$$

$$= \int_0^1 \frac{1}{4}\,dx + \int_1^{2\cdot5} \frac{3}{8}(3-x)\,dx = \frac{1}{4} + \frac{45}{64} = \frac{61}{64}.$$

(ii) $$P(|X-2| \leqslant 0{\cdot}5) = P(-0{\cdot}5 \leqslant X-2 \leqslant 0{\cdot}5)$$

$$= P(1{\cdot}5 \leqslant X \leqslant 2{\cdot}5) = \int_{1\cdot5}^{2\cdot5} \frac{3}{8}(3-x)\,dx = \frac{3}{8}.$$

EXERCISE 3.2A

1 The operational lifetimes in hours of certain batteries are distributed with probability density function f, where

$$f(x) = \frac{c}{x^2}, \qquad 100 \leqslant x \leqslant 400.$$

Find the value of c and the probability that the operational lifetime of such a battery will lie between 150 and 200 hours.

2 A continuous random variable X has range space $R_X = \{x: -a < x < a\}$ and probability density function f, where

$$f(x) = k(a^2 - x^2), \qquad -a < x < a.$$

(i) Find k in terms of a.
(ii) For $a = 1$, sketch the graph of $f(x)$ and in this case calculate the probability that X will take a value in the interval $(-\frac{1}{2}, \frac{1}{2})$.

3 The continuous random variable X is distributed with probability density function

$$f(x) = kx(4 - x), \qquad 0 \leqslant x \leqslant 4.$$

Find (i) the value of k, (ii) the probability, to three significant figures, that at least two of five independently observed values of X will exceed 3.

4 A continuous random variable X has probability density function f, where

$$f(x) = \frac{5}{8}(1 - x^4), \qquad -1 < x < 1.$$

(i) Check that this f is a valid probability density function. (ii) Calculate $P(X > \frac{1}{2})$ and $P(X^2 > \frac{1}{4})$.

5 Let A and B denote the left-hand and right-hand end-points of the line segment defined by the interval $0 \leqslant x \leqslant 1$. A point P is chosen on AB in such a way that X, the distance of P from A, has probability density function f, where

$$f(x) = \frac{c}{(x+1)^2}, \qquad 0 \leqslant x \leqslant 1.$$

Determine the value of c and calculate the probability that P will be in the line-segment defined by the interval $(0, \frac{1}{4})$.

Another point Q is chosen on AB in such a way that Y, the distance of Q from A, has probability density function g, where

$$g(y) = 2y, \qquad 0 \leqslant y \leqslant 1.$$

Calculate the probability that both P and Q will be in $(0, \frac{1}{4})$.

6 The duration, X minutes, of a telephone call by a certain person to a friend, is a continuous random variable having probability density function f defined by

$$f(x) = x^{-2}, \qquad x \geqslant 1.$$

(i) Find the probability that the duration of such a call will (a) lie between 5 minutes and 10 minutes, (b) be less than 3 minutes.
(ii) Given that a call has already lasted 3 minutes, calculate the conditional probability that its total duration will be less than 5 minutes.

7 A garage is supplied with petrol every Monday morning and its weekly sales in thousands of litres is a random variable X whose probability density function f is given by

$$\mathrm{f}(x) = \frac{3}{125}(5-x)^2, \qquad 0 < x < 5$$

Find: (i) the probability that the garage's sales in a week will be less than 3000 litres; (ii) the probability that the garage will not be able to meet the demand in a week given that the capacity of its supply tanks is 4000 litres. (Continued in Exercise 3.3 question 1).

8 A man fires a rifle at a circular target of radius 4 cm on which are drawn circles of radii 1 cm, 2 cm and 3 cm, all centred at the centre of the target. The distance X cm of the point of impact of a shot from the centre of the target is a continuous random variable having probability density function f, where

$$\mathrm{f}(x) = 0{\cdot}03(x^2+3), \qquad 0 \leqslant x \leqslant 4.$$

(i) Calculate the probability that a shot will hit the target inside the innermost circle.
(ii) A shot inside the innermost circle scores 4 points; a shot between the innermost and middle circles scores 2 points; a shot between the middle and outermost circles scores 1 point; and a shot outside the outermost circle scores nothing. Calculate (a) the most probable score from one shot, (b) the mean score per shot.

9 A continuous random variable X has range space $R_X = \{x: 4 \leqslant x \leqslant 8\}$ and probability density function f, where

$$\begin{aligned} \mathrm{f}(x) &= cx + k, \qquad & 4 \leqslant x \leqslant 6, \\ \mathrm{f}(x) &= 0{\cdot}3, \qquad & 6 \leqslant x \leqslant 8. \end{aligned}$$

Given that f(x) is continuous at $x = 6$, find the values of c and k.

10 A continuous random variable X has probability density function f, where

$$\begin{aligned} \mathrm{f}(x) &= (a+x)/a^2, \qquad & -a \leqslant x \leqslant 0, \\ \mathrm{f}(x) &= (a-x)/a^2, \qquad & 0 \leqslant x \leqslant a. \end{aligned}$$

Find the values of (i) $\mathrm{P}(X < \tfrac{1}{2}a)$, (ii) $\mathrm{P}(X^2 > \tfrac{1}{4}a^2)$.

3.2.1 The uniform distribution

Consider the random experiment in which a string of length 10 cm is to be cut into two pieces. Let X cm denote the distance of the point at which the cut is made from one end of the string. Then, clearly,

$$R_X = \{x : 0 < x < 10\}.$$

Suppose further that the point at which the string is to be cut is chosen at random, so that every possible point of the string is equally likely to be chosen. Using the analogy introduced in §3.2 of regarding the one unit of probability as powder in a jug, then it is clear that the probability should be distributed evenly over R_X, as shown in Fig. 3.7. Since the area of the

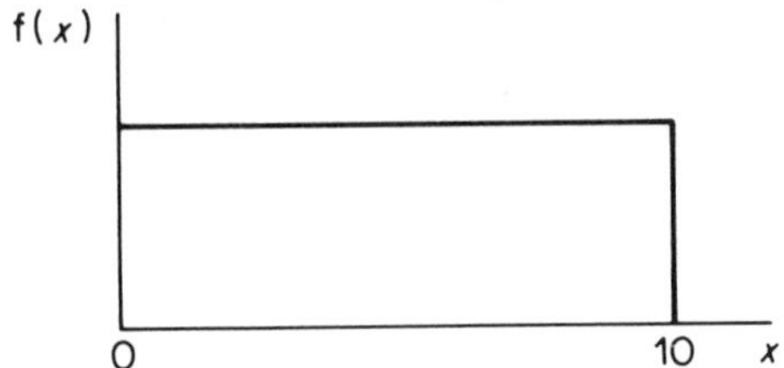

Fig. 3.7 Uniform distribution

mound, in this case a rectangle, must equal unity it follows that the height of the rectangle is 0·1. Thus, the probability density function f of X is given by

$$f(x) = 0{\cdot}1, \qquad 0 < x < 10,$$

and X is said to have the *uniform* (or *rectangular*) *distribution* over the interval (0, 10).

Generalising the above, if X denotes a randomly chosen value from $R_X = \{x : a \leqslant x \leqslant b\}$, then X will have the uniform distribution over the interval (a, b) and its p.d.f. will be f, where

$$f(x) = (b-a)^{-1}, \qquad a \leqslant x \leqslant b.$$

For this distribution, for any subinterval (c, d) of (a, b), the probability that X will have a value in (c, d) is the area of the mound above (c, d) and is given by

$$P(c < X < d) = \frac{d-c}{b-a},$$

from which it follows that X is equally probable to take a value in any one of several intervals of *equal* widths. We shall abbreviate the statement that X has a uniform distribution over the interval (a, b) as $X \sim U(a, b)$.

EXAMPLE 3 *A string of length* 10 *cm is cut at a randomly chosen point. Find the probabilities that* (i) *the longer piece will have length greater than* 7 *cm,* (ii) *the length of the longer piece will be at least twice the length of the shorter piece.*

Let X cm denote the distance of the cutting point from one end of the string. Since the cutting point is chosen randomly, X has the uniform distribution over the interval (0, 10), so that the p.d.f. of X is f, where

$$f(x) = 0{\cdot}1, \qquad 0 < x < 10.$$

(i) The lengths of the two pieces will be X cm and $(10 - X)$ cm. Let A denote the event that the longer piece has a length greater than 7 cm. Then, allowing for either piece having a length greater than 7 cm,

$$\begin{aligned} A &= \{X > 7\} \cup \{10 - X > 7\} \\ &= \{X > 7\} \cup \{X < 3\}. \end{aligned}$$

Hence $P(A) = P(X > 7) + P(X < 3) = \dfrac{10-7}{10} + \dfrac{3-0}{10} = 0{\cdot}6.$

(ii) Let B denote the event that the longer piece will be at least twice the length of the shorter piece. Then

$$B = \{X \geqslant 2(10-X)\} \cup \{10 - X \geqslant 2X\} = \{X \geqslant 6\tfrac{2}{3}\} \cup \{X \leqslant 3\tfrac{1}{3}\},$$

and

$$P(B) = P(X \geqslant 6\tfrac{2}{3}) + P(X \leqslant 3\tfrac{1}{3}) = \frac{10 - 6\frac{2}{3}}{10} + \frac{3\frac{1}{3} - 0}{10} = \frac{2}{3}.$$

EXAMPLE 4 *A semicircle of radius r has diameter AOB, and OC is the radius perpendicular to AOB. A point P is chosen at random on OC and a chord is drawn through P parallel to AOB. Find the probability that the length of the chord will be greater than r.*

The semicircle and a possible chord QPR are shown in Fig. 3.8.

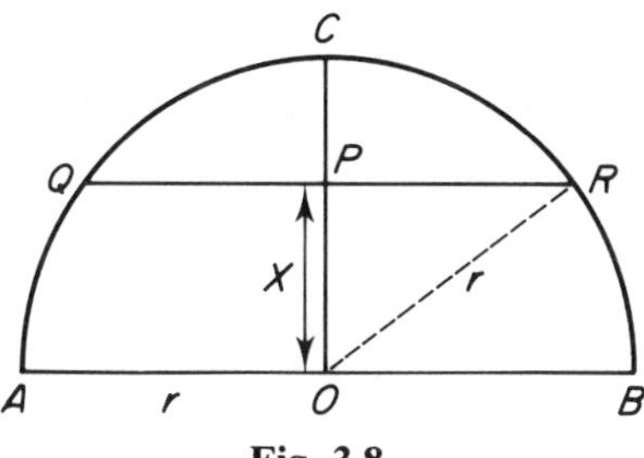

Fig. 3.8

Denote the length of OP by X. Since P is a random choice on OC it follows that X is uniformly distributed over $(0, r)$, so that the p.d.f. of X is f, where

$$f(x) = \frac{1}{r}, \qquad 0 < x < r.$$

Let Y denote the length of the chord QR. Using Pythagoras's theorem we have

$$Y = 2(r^2 - X^2)^{1/2}.$$

We require

$$\begin{aligned} P(Y > r) &= P\{2(r^2 - X^2)^{1/2} > r\} \\ &= P\{4(r^2 - X^2) > r^2\} \\ &= P\left\{X^2 < \frac{3}{4}r^2\right\} \\ &= P\left\{X < \frac{\sqrt{3}}{2}r\right\} \\ &= \frac{\frac{\sqrt{3}}{2}r}{r} = \frac{\sqrt{3}}{2} \simeq 0{\cdot}866 \text{ to three decimal places.} \end{aligned}$$

EXERCISE 3.2B

1 A point P is chosen at random on a line AB of length $2a$. Calculate the probability that the area of the rectangle having adjacent sides AP and BP is greater than $\frac{3}{4}a^2$.

2 A measuring device for determining the length of a line will give the length correct to the nearest millimetre. It may be assumed that the deviation of the recorded length from the true length is equally likely to be anywhere in the range from $-0{\cdot}5$ mm to $+0{\cdot}5$ mm. Calculate the probability that the deviation between the true and recorded lengths of a line is less than 0·4 mm.

3 During the peak hour from 17.00 to 18.00 on a Friday, buses leave a town's bus station for a certain suburban area at 17.00, 17.05, 17.15, 17.20, 17.30, 17.35, 17.45 and 18.00. Find the probability that a person who arrives at the bus station at a random time during the peak hour will not have to wait longer than 2 minutes for the departure of one of these buses. Given that a person arrives within 4 minutes after the departure of a bus, find the conditional probability that he will not have to wait more than 2 minutes for the next bus.

4 AT is the tangent at the fixed point A on a circle of radius r. AP is a chord to the circle which has been drawn in a random direction from A; that is, the angle PAT may be regarded as a random variable which is uniformly distributed over the interval $(0, \pi)$. Find the probability that the length of the chord will be greater than r. (Continued in Exercise 3.3, question 5.)

5 Suppose that in the quadratic equation in a given by

$$a^2 - 2a - X = 0,$$

the value of X is chosen at random from the interval $(-1, 1)$. Calculate the probability that the larger root of the equation will exceed 1·5.

If, instead, the value of X is taken to be the largest of three randomly chosen values from $(-1, 1)$, calculate the probability that the larger root will exceed 2.

3.3 Expected value

Let $h(X)$ denote a function of the continuous random variable X whose range space is R_X and whose p.d.f. is $f(x)$. As an extension to the definition given in §2.3.1 for a discrete random variable, we define the *expected value* or *expectation* of $h(X)$ by

$$E[h(X)] = \int_{R_X} h(x)f(x)dx. \qquad (1)$$

As for the case when X was discrete, $E[h(X)]$ as defined above is the average value of $h(X)$ in an indefinitely large number of trials of the random experiment with respect to which X is defined.

As particular examples of (1) above when $R_X = \{x : a \leqslant x \leqslant b\}$ we have

$$E[X] = \int_a^b x f(x)dx,$$

$$E[X^2] = \int_a^b x^2 f(x)dx,$$

$$E[X^3 - 1] = \int_a^b (x^3 - 1)f(x)dx.$$

The properties of E[ ] derived in §2.3.1 for discrete random variables are equally valid for continuous random variables, as may be readily verified on using properties of integrals. In particular, for any constants c_1, c_2 and any functions $h_1(X)$, $h_2(X)$ of a continuous random variable X,

$$E[c_1 h_1(X) + c_2 h_2(X)] = c_1 E[h_1(X)] + c_2 E[h_2(X)]. \qquad (2)$$

For particular forms of this general result, refer back to §2.3.1.

EXAMPLE 1 *The continuous random variable X has the p.d.f.* f, *where*

$$f(x) = x + \tfrac{1}{2}, \qquad 0 \leqslant x \leqslant 1.$$

Find the expected value of (*i*) X, (*ii*) $Y = 12X + 1$, (*iii*) $Z = (1 - X)^{1/2}$, (*iv*) U, where $U(X) = 2X + 1$ *for* $X \leqslant \frac{1}{2}$ *and* $U(X) = 2$ *for* $X > \frac{1}{2}$.

(i) From (1) above

$$E[X] = \int_0^1 x f(x)dx = \int_0^1 (x^2 + \tfrac{1}{2}x)dx = \frac{7}{12}.$$

(ii) $E[Y] = E[12X + 1] = 12E[X] + 1 = 7 + 1 = 8$.
Alternatively, from (1),

$$E[12X + 1] = \int_0^1 (12x + 1)(x + \tfrac{1}{2})dx = 8.$$

(iii) $E[Z] = E[(1 - X)^{1/2}] = \int_0^1 (1 - x)^{1/2}(x + \tfrac{1}{2})dx.$

To evaluate this integral we get rid of the square root term $(1 - x)^{1/2}$ by making a change of variable to $t = (1 - x)^{1/2}$, so that

$$x = 1 - t^2, \qquad dx = -2t\,dt.$$

Since $t = 1$ when $x = 0$, and $t = 0$ when $x = 1$,

$$E[Z] = \int_1^0 t\left(\frac{3}{2} - t^2\right)(-2t)\,dt = 2\int_0^1 \left(\frac{3}{2}t^2 - t^4\right)dt.$$

on noting that interchanging the limits of an integral merely changes the sign of the result. We then find

$$\mathrm{E}[Z] = 2\left[\frac{1}{2}t^3 - \frac{1}{5}t^5\right]_0^1 = \frac{3}{5}.$$

(Note well that $\mathrm{E}[(1-X)^{1/2}] \neq \{\mathrm{E}[1-X]\}^{1/2}$, the former having the value $\frac{3}{5}$ and the latter the value $\sqrt{(5/12)}$.)
(iv) From (1)

$$\mathrm{E}[\mathrm{U}(X)] = \int_0^1 \mathrm{U}(x)\mathrm{f}(x)\mathrm{d}x.$$

Allowing for the different forms that $\mathrm{U}(X)$ may take we have

$$\begin{aligned}\mathrm{E}[\mathrm{U}(X)] &= \int_0^{1/2} (2x+1)(x+\tfrac{1}{2})\mathrm{d}x + \int_{1/2}^1 2(x+\tfrac{1}{2})\mathrm{d}x \\ &= \int_0^{1/2} (2x^2+2x+\tfrac{1}{2})\mathrm{d}x + \int_{1/2}^1 (2x+1)\mathrm{d}x \\ &= \left[\frac{2}{3}x^3 + x^2 + \tfrac{1}{2}x\right]_0^{1/2} + [x^2+x]_{1/2}^1 = \frac{7}{12} + \frac{5}{4} = 1\tfrac{5}{6}.\end{aligned}$$

EXERCISE 3.3

1 In Exercise 3.2A question 7 find the expected number of litres of petrol sold per week by the garage if the capacity of its supply tanks is (i) 5000 litres, (ii) 4000 litres.

2 The percentage content of lead in a certain alloy is a continuous random variable X having probability density function f, where

$$\mathrm{f}(x) = 6x(100-x)/10^6, \qquad 0 \leqslant x \leqslant 100.$$

The net profit in pounds made per kg of the alloy is given by $Y = 5+9X$. Calculate the expected net profit per kg of the alloy.

3 The continuous random variable X has probability density function f, where

$$\begin{aligned}\mathrm{f}(x) &= (a+x)/a^2, \qquad -a \leqslant x < 0 \\ \mathrm{f}(x) &= (a-x)/a^2, \qquad 0 \leqslant x \leqslant a.\end{aligned}$$

Find the expected value of (i) X, (ii) $Y = 2a - X$, (iii) Z, where $Z(X) = a+X$ for $-a \leqslant X < 0$ and $Z(X) = a - X$ for $0 \leqslant X \leqslant a$.

4 If $Y = c+mX$, where c and m are constants and X is a continuous random variable having range space $R_X = \{x\colon a \leqslant x \leqslant b\}$, use properties of integrals to show that $\mathrm{E}[Y] = c + m\mathrm{E}[X]$.

5 Find the expected length of the chord in (i) Example 4 §3.2, (ii) Exercise 3.2B question 4.

6 The quality X of a manufactured item is a continuous random variable having probability density function f, where

$$\mathrm{f}(x) = 2x/\lambda^2, \qquad 0 < x < \lambda,$$

and λ is a positive constant whose value may be controlled by the manufacturer.

(i) Find the expected quality of such an item.

(ii) Each item is inspected before being sold. Any item for which X is 8 or more is passed for selling and any item for which X is less than 8 is scrapped. The manufacturer makes a profit of £$(27-\lambda)$ on every item sold and suffers a loss of £$(5+\lambda)$ on every item scrapped. Find the value of λ which should be set by the manufacturer in order to maximise his expected profit per item manufactured and calculate this maximum value of the expected profit per item.

3.4 Mean and variance of a continuous distribution

In this section we proceed as in §2.4 to consider quantitative assessments or summary measures for two particular features of a continuous distribution, namely, its location and its dispersion.

Recall from §2.4.1 that we defined the mean of a discrete distribution to be the expected value of the random variable having that distribution. In this form, the definition is equally valid for a continuous distribution. If X is a continuous random variable having range space $R_X = \{x : a \leqslant x \leqslant b\}$ and probability density function f, then the *mean* of the distribution of X is defined by

$$\mu \equiv \mathrm{E}[X] = \int_a^b x\mathrm{f}(x)\,\mathrm{d}x. \tag{1}$$

Observe that μ must be an element of the range space, $\{x : a \leqslant x \leqslant b\}$, a property which was not always the case for a discrete distribution (see §2.4.1).

Again, as for a discrete variable (see §2.4.2), we define the *variance* $\mathrm{V}[X]$ of the distribution of a continuous random variable X by

$$\begin{aligned}\sigma^2 \equiv \mathrm{V}[X] &= \mathrm{E}[(X-\mu)^2]\\ &= \int_a^b (x-\mu)^2\mathrm{f}(x)\,\mathrm{d}x.\end{aligned} \tag{2}$$

Using properties of expectation, an alternative form for $\mathrm{V}[X]$ is

$$\mathrm{V}[X] = \mathrm{E}[X^2] - \mu^2, \tag{3}$$

as shown earlier ((3) in §2.4.2). The *standard deviation* $\sigma = \mathrm{SD}\ [X]$ is again defined to be the positive square root of σ^2.

EXAMPLE 1 *Determine the mean and the standard deviation of the distribution whose probability density function* f *is given by*

$$\mathrm{f}(x) = x + \tfrac{1}{2}, \qquad 0 \leqslant x \leqslant 1.$$

The mean μ of this distribution is given by

$$\mu = \int_0^1 x\mathrm{f}(x)\,\mathrm{d}x = \int_0^1 (x^2 + \tfrac{1}{2}x)\,\mathrm{d}x$$
$$= \left[\frac{1}{3}x^3 + \frac{1}{4}x^2\right]_0^1 = \frac{7}{12}.$$

Also,

$$\mathrm{E}[X^2] = \int_0^1 x^2\mathrm{f}(x)\,\mathrm{d}x = \int_0^1 (x^3 + \tfrac{1}{2}x^2)\,\mathrm{d}x$$
$$= \left[\frac{1}{4}x^4 + \frac{1}{6}x^3\right]_0^1 = \frac{5}{12}.$$

Hence, from (3), the variance σ^2 of the distribution is given by

$$\sigma^2 \equiv \mathrm{E}[X^2] - \mu^2 = \frac{5}{12} - \left(\frac{7}{12}\right)^2 = \frac{11}{144},$$

and its standard deviation is

$$\sigma = \frac{\sqrt{11}}{12} = 0{\cdot}276, \qquad \text{to 3 decimal places.}$$

If X is a continuous random variable whose range space R_X is a finite interval and whose distribution is symmetrical about some value μ in R_X, then μ is the mean of the distribution of X (compare with the corresponding result for a discrete distribution given in §2.4.1). This is illustrated in the following example.

EXAMPLE 2 *Find the mean and the standard deviation of the distribution whose probability density function is* f, *where*

$$\mathrm{f}(x) = 1 + x, \qquad -1 \leqslant x \leqslant 0,$$
$$\mathrm{f}(x) = 1 - x, \qquad 0 < x \leqslant 1.$$

From the graph of f(x) shown in Fig. 3.9 it is seen that f(x) is symmetrical about zero, and hence the mean of the distribution is zero.

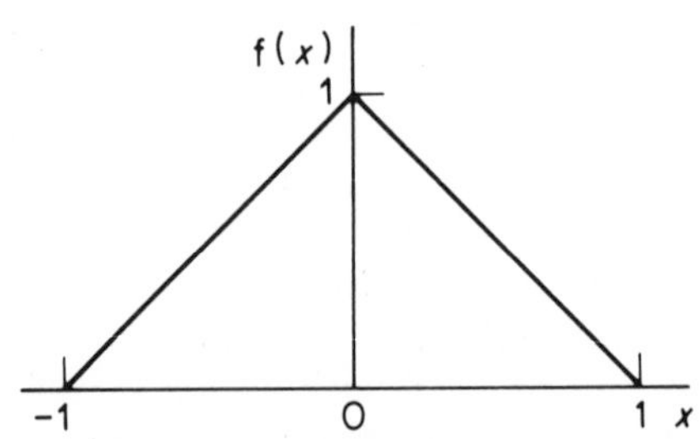

Fig. 3.9

To verify this, using (1), we have

$$\mu = \int_{-1}^{1} x\mathrm{f}(x)\mathrm{d}x = \int_{-1}^{0} x(1+x)\mathrm{d}x + \int_{0}^{1} x(1-x)\mathrm{d}x$$

$$= \left[\frac{1}{2}x^2 + \frac{1}{3}x^3\right]_{-1}^{0} + \left[\frac{1}{2}x^2 - \frac{1}{3}x^3\right]_{0}^{1}$$

$$= -\frac{1}{2} + \frac{1}{3} + \frac{1}{2} - \frac{1}{3} = 0.$$

Since $\mu = 0$, it follows from (3) that the variance σ^2 of the distribution is given by

$$\sigma^2 = \mathrm{E}[X^2]$$

$$= \int_{-1}^{0} x^2(1+x)\mathrm{d}x + \int_{0}^{1} x^2(1-x)\mathrm{d}x$$

$$= \left[\frac{1}{3}x^3 + \frac{1}{4}x^4\right]_{1}^{0} + \left[\frac{1}{3}x^3 - \frac{1}{4}x^4\right]_{0}^{1}$$

$$= \frac{1}{3} - \frac{1}{4} + \frac{1}{3} - \frac{1}{4} = \frac{1}{6}.$$

Hence the standard deviation is

$$\sigma = 1/\sqrt{6} = 0{\cdot}408 \text{ to 3 decimal places}$$

EXERCISE 3.4

Determine the mean and the variance of each of the following distributions.

1 $\mathrm{f}(x) = 5(1-x^4)/8, \quad -1 \leqslant x \leqslant 1.$

2 $\mathrm{f}(x) = 0{\cdot}3x(3-x), \quad 1 \leqslant x \leqslant 3.$

3 $\mathrm{f}(x) = cx(10-x), \quad 5 \leqslant x \leqslant 10.$

4 $\mathrm{f}(x) = \dfrac{1}{b-a}, \quad a \leqslant x \leqslant b.$

5 $\mathrm{f}(x) = 0{\cdot}1x - 0{\cdot}3, \quad 4 \leqslant x \leqslant 6$
$\mathrm{f}(x) = 0{\cdot}3, \quad 6 \leqslant x \leqslant 8$

6 $\mathrm{f}(x) = kx^3, \quad 0 \leqslant x \leqslant 1$
$\mathrm{f}(x) = k\ , \quad 1 \leqslant x \leqslant 2.$

3.5 Mean and variance of a function

Let $Y = \mathrm{h}(X)$, where X is a continuous random variable having range space $R_X = \{x : a \leqslant x \leqslant b\}$ and probability density function $\mathrm{f}(x)$. Observe that Y is also a continuous random variable whose distribution can be deduced from that of X using the method to be described in §3.7. Here, we shall consider the determination of the mean and the variance of Y directly from the distribution of X without actually first determining the distribution of Y. All we need are properties of expectation and variance, as illustrated in the following example.

EXAMPLE 1 *Given that X has the probability density function* f, *where*

$$f(x) = x+\tfrac{1}{2}, \qquad 0 \leqslant x \leqslant 1,$$

find the mean and the variance of (*i*) $Y = 12X+1$, (*ii*) $Z = (1-X)^{1/2}$.

The means of Y and Z were found in Example 1, §3.3 to be

$$\mu_Y \equiv \mathrm{E}[Y] = 8, \qquad \mu_Z \equiv \mathrm{E}[Z] = \frac{3}{5}.$$

(i) Now $\mathrm{V}[Y] = \mathrm{E}[Y]^2 - \mu_Y^2$, but

$$\mathrm{E}[Y^2] = \mathrm{E}[(12X+1)^2] = \mathrm{E}[144X^2+24X+1] = 144\mathrm{E}[X^2]+24\mathrm{E}[X]+1.$$

From Examples 1, §3.3 and 1, §3.4

$$\mathrm{E}[X] = \frac{7}{12} \quad \text{and} \quad \mathrm{E}[X^2] = \frac{5}{12}.$$

Hence

$$\mathrm{E}[Y^2] = 144\left(\frac{5}{12}\right)+24\left(\frac{7}{12}\right)+1 = 75,$$

and it follows that

$$\mathrm{V}[Y] = 75-8^2 = 11.$$

(ii) The variance of Z is given by

$$\mathrm{V}[Z] = \mathrm{E}[Z^2]-\mu_Z^2.$$

But

$$\mathrm{E}[Z^2] = \mathrm{E}[1-X] = 1-\mathrm{E}[X] = 1-\frac{7}{12} = \frac{5}{12}.$$

Hence $\mathrm{V}[Z] = \dfrac{5}{12}-\left(\dfrac{3}{5}\right)^2 = \dfrac{17}{300}$.

In the particular case where $Y \equiv \mathrm{h}(X) = aX+b$, then from the derivations in §2.5 we have

$$\mu_Y \equiv \mathrm{E}[Y] = a\mu_X+b,$$
$$\sigma_Y^2 \equiv \mathrm{V}[Y] = a^2\sigma_X^2.$$

Applying these results to $Y = 12X+1$ in the above example we have

$$\mu_Y \equiv \mathrm{E}[Y] = 12\mathrm{E}[X]+1 = 7+1 = 8,$$
$$\sigma_Y^2 \equiv \mathrm{V}[Y] = 144\mathrm{V}[X].$$

From Example 1 of §3.4, $\mathrm{V}[X] = \frac{11}{144}$, and hence

$$\sigma_Y^2 = 11.$$

The results for μ_Y and σ_Y^2 agree with those obtained above.

EXERCISE 3.5

1 The random variable X is uniformly distributed over the interval $(-1, 1)$. Determine the mean and the variance of (i) $Y = 1-2X$, (ii) $Z = |X|$.

2 If X has the distribution given in Example 2 of §3.4, use the results obtained there to write down the mean and the variance of (i) $U = 2X-1$, (ii) $W = \frac{1}{2}(1-X)$, and find the values of a and b if $Y = aX+b$ is to have mean 1 and variance 1.

3 The continuous random variable X has probability density function f, where

$$f(x) = 2(1-x), \qquad 0 < x < 1.$$

Obtain an expression for $E[X^r]$. Hence find the mean and the variance of $Y = X(1-X)$.

4 Find the mean and the variance of the area of the rectangle having two adjacent sides AP and BP, where P is a point chosen at random on a line AB of length $2a$ (continuation of Exercise 3.2B question 1).

5 Find the mean and the variance of the distribution whose probability density function is f, where

$$f(x) = x, \qquad 0 \leqslant x \leqslant 1,$$
$$f(x) = 2-x, \qquad 1 < x \leqslant 2.$$

A rectangle is constructed with adjacent sides of lengths x cm and $(2-x)$ cm, where x is a random value from the above distribution. Find the mean value of the area of the rectangle.

3.6 Cumulative distribution function

Definition: For any random variable X, the function F such that for all x

$$F(x) = P(X \leqslant x)$$

is called the *cumulative distribution function* (c.d.f.), or sometimes, the *distribution function* of X.

Specifying $F(x)$ for all x provides an alternative to the probability density function as a mathematical description of the probability distribution of the random variable X. The c.d.f. is most useful when X is a continuous random variable.

If X is continuous with range space $R_X = \{x: a \leqslant x \leqslant b\}$ and probability density function f, then its c.d.f., F, is such that

$$F(x) = 0 \quad \text{for} \quad x \leqslant a,$$
$$F(x) = \int_a^x f(t)\,dt \quad \text{for} \quad a < x < b, \qquad (1)$$
$$F(x) = 1 \quad \text{for} \quad x \geqslant b.$$

Continuing with our earlier analogy, suppose the one unit of probability has been poured from a jug over the range space. Then, if we move a vacuum cleaner along the x-axis from left to right so as to pick up the probability cumulatively, the amount of probability that will have been picked up when we reach the value x is precisely $F(x)$.

EXAMPLE 1 *Determine the c.d.f. of the random variable X whose p.d.f. is f, where*

$$f(x) = \frac{1}{64}x(16-x^2), \qquad 0 < x < 4.$$

Since no probability has been assigned to values of $x \leqslant 0$, the c.d.f. $F(x)$ will be such that

$$F(x) = 0 \quad \text{for all} \quad x \leqslant 0.$$

For any x in the interval $(0, 4)$

$$F(x) \equiv P(X \leqslant x) = \int_0^x f(t)dt$$

$$= \frac{1}{64}\int_0^x (16t - t^3)dt = \frac{1}{64}(8x^2 - \tfrac{1}{4}x^4) = \frac{1}{256}x^2(32-x^2).$$

As a check, we note that when $x = 4$, $F(x) = 1$ as it should be since the entire one unit of probability is to the left of $x = 4$. Finally, for any $x \geqslant 4$,

$$F(x) = 1.$$

Combining these results, the c.d.f. is given by

$$F(x) = 0, \quad \text{for} \quad x \leqslant 0,$$

$$F(x) = \frac{1}{256}x^2(32-x^2), \quad \text{for} \quad 0 < x < 4,$$

$$F(x) = 1, \quad \text{for} \quad x \geqslant 4.$$

The graph of this $F(x)$ is shown in Fig. 3.10, and is typical of the general shape of the graph of a c.d.f.

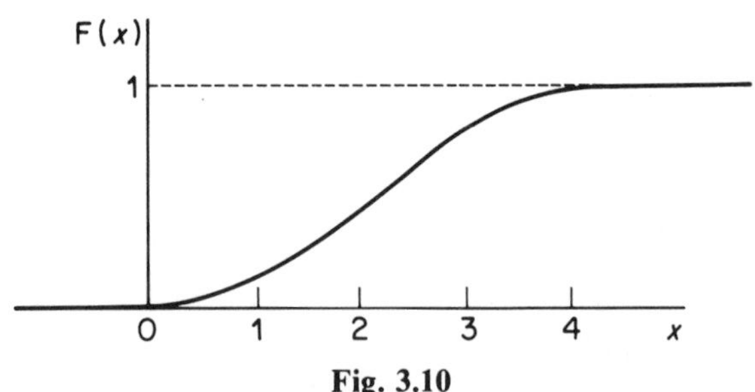

Fig. 3.10

EXAMPLE 2 *Find the c.d.f. of the distribution whose p.d.f. is f, where*

$$f(x) = \frac{1}{5}, \qquad 0 \leqslant x < 1,$$

$$f(x) = \frac{1}{25}x^3, \qquad 1 \leqslant x \leqslant 3.$$

Since the range space in this example is $R_X = \{x : 0 \leqslant x \leqslant 3\}$, it follows that F, the c.d.f., will be such that

$$F(x) = 0 \quad \text{for} \quad x < 0,$$

and

$$F(x) = 1 \quad \text{for} \quad x \geqslant 3.$$

For a value x in the interval $[0, 3]$, we have

$$F(x) = \int_0^x f(t)dt.$$

From the specification of $f(x)$ we must give separate consideration to values of x in $(0, 1)$ and values of x in $(1, 3)$.

For $0 \leqslant x < 1$,

$$F(x) = \int_0^x \frac{1}{5}dt = \frac{1}{5}x.$$

For $1 \leqslant x \leqslant 3$,

$$F(x) = \int_0^1 \frac{1}{5}dt + \int_1^x \frac{1}{25}t^3 dt = \frac{1}{5} + \frac{1}{100}(x^4 - 1) = (x^4 + 19)/100$$

As a check, we note that $F(3) = \dfrac{81}{100} + \dfrac{19}{100} = 1.$

Hence the c.d.f. in this case is given by

$$F(x) = 0 \quad \text{for} \quad x < 0,$$

$$F(x) = \frac{1}{5}x \quad \text{for} \quad 0 \leqslant x < 1,$$

$$F(x) = (x^4 + 19)/100 \quad \text{for} \quad 1 \leqslant x \leqslant 3,$$

$$F(x) = 1 \quad \text{for} \quad x > 3.$$

A sketch of $F(x)$ is shown in Fig. 3.11.

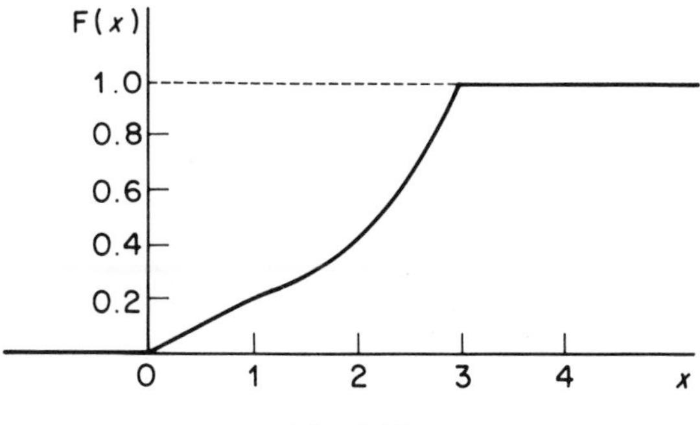

Fig. 3.11

EXERCISE 3.6A

Determine the c.d.f. of each of the following distributions

1 $f(x) = \frac{3}{32}x(4-x), \quad 0 \leqslant x \leqslant 4$

2 $f(x) = \frac{3}{4}(1-x^2), \quad -1 \leqslant x \leqslant 1$

3 $f(x) = \frac{4}{3x^2}, \quad 1 \leqslant x \leqslant 4$

4 $f(x) = 3(1-x)^2, \quad 0 \leqslant x \leqslant 1$

5 $f(x) = 0{\cdot}1x - 0{\cdot}3, \quad 4 \leqslant x \leqslant 6$
$f(x) = 0{\cdot}3, \quad 6 < x \leqslant 8$

6 $f(x) = kx^3, \quad 0 \leqslant x \leqslant 1$
$f(x) = k, \quad 1 < x \leqslant 2$

3.6.1 Quantiles of a continuous distribution

Let X denote a continuous random variable having range space $R_X = \{x: a \leqslant x \leqslant b\}$, probability density function f, and cumulative distribution function F. For any p between 0 and 1, there is a unique value ξ_p in R_X such that $F(\xi_p) = p$, as indicated in Fig. 3.12. Such a value ξ_p is called a *quantile* (or a *fractile*), of the distribution. With reference to Fig. 3.13, ξ_p is such that the area of the region under $f(x)$ to the left of ξ_p is equal to p. The particular quantile $\xi_{0\cdot5}$ is called the *median* of the distribution. Since $\xi_{0\cdot5}$ divides the probability distribution into two equal halves it is often taken as the location of the 'centre' of the distribution, and, for this reason, may be preferred to the mean as a measure of location. Observe that for a symmetrical distribution the mean and median are equal.

A continuous distribution may be divided into four equal parts, the points of division being $\xi_{0\cdot25}, \xi_{0\cdot5}, \xi_{0\cdot75}$, which are collectively called the *quartiles* of the distribution; the values $\xi_{0\cdot25}$ and $\xi_{0\cdot75}$ are generally referred to as the *lower* and *upper quartiles*, respectively, the middle quartile $\xi_{0\cdot5}$ being the median.

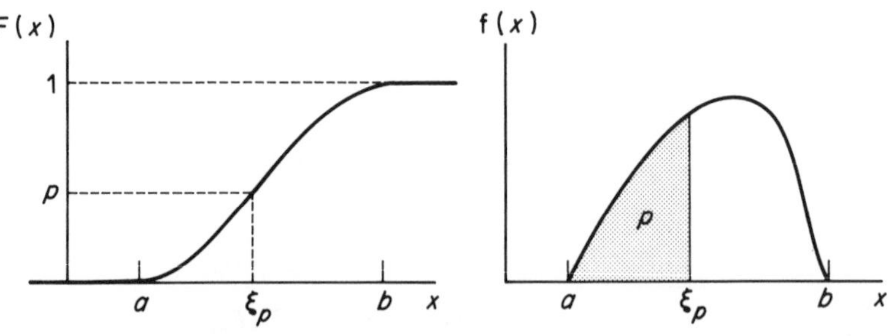

Fig. 3.12 **Fig. 3.13**

Similarly, a continuous distribution may be divided into 10 equal parts, the dividing points being the *deciles* $\xi_{0\cdot1}, \xi_{0\cdot2}, \ldots, \xi_{0\cdot9}$, or into 100 equal parts for which the dividing points will be the *percentiles* $\xi_{0\cdot01}$, $\xi_{0\cdot02}, \ldots, \xi_{0\cdot99}$.

Knowing the percentiles of a distribution provides considerable information and they are often quoted as a set of values to summarise a probability distribution. In an examination with a large entry, the ranges of marks for the various grades to be awarded are frequently determined from consideration of the percentiles of the distribution of the marks.

Quantiles may also be used to give some indication of the spread of a distribution. The most commonly used measures of dispersion based on quantiles are $\xi_{0\cdot75} - \xi_{0\cdot25}$, which is called the *interquartile range* (or *quartile deviation*) and $\frac{1}{2}(\xi_{0\cdot75} - \xi_{0\cdot25})$, which is called the *semi-interquartile range*. That these qualify as measures of spread is evident on noting that the inter-quartile interval $(\xi_{0\cdot25}, \xi_{0\cdot75})$ covers the middle 50% of the distribution. Either of the two quantities would be an appropriate choice of measure of dispersion when the median is used as the measure of location. Various inter-percentile ranges may also be used as measures of dispersion.

EXAMPLE 3 *Find an expression for the quantile ξ_p of the distribution whose p.d.f. is* f, *where*

$$f(x) = \frac{1}{64}x(16 - x^2), \qquad 0 \leqslant x \leqslant 4.$$

From Example 1, the c.d.f. of this distribution is F, where

$$F(x) = \frac{1}{256}x^2(32 - x^2), \qquad 0 \leqslant x \leqslant 4.$$

The quantile ξ_p is thus the solution of the equation

$$\frac{1}{256}x^2(32 - x^2) = p,$$

or

$$x^4 - 32x^2 + 256p = 0,$$

or

$$(x^2 - 16)^2 = 256(1 - p),$$

from which we find that

$$x = 4\{1 \pm (1 - p)^{1/2}\}^{1/2}.$$

Since $0 \leqslant x \leqslant 4$, the required solution is

$$\xi_p = 4\{1 - (1 - p)^{1/2}\}^{1/2}.$$

In particular, the quartiles of the distribution are

$$\xi_{0\cdot25} = 4\{1 - (0\cdot75)^{1/2}\}^{1/2} \simeq 1\cdot464,$$
$$\xi_{0\cdot5} = 4\{1 - (0\cdot5)^{1/2}\}^{1/2} \simeq 2\cdot165,$$
$$\xi_{0\cdot75} = 4\{1 - (0\cdot25)^{1/2}\}^{1/2} \simeq 2\cdot828.$$

EXAMPLE 4 *Find the semi-interquartile range, correct to three significant figures, of the distribution*

$$f(x) = \frac{1}{5}, \qquad 0 \leqslant x < 1,$$

$$f(x) = \frac{1}{25}x^3, \quad 1 \leqslant x \leqslant 3.$$

From Example 2, the c.d.f. of this distribution is given by

$$F(x) = \frac{1}{5}x, \qquad 0 \leqslant x < 1,$$

$$F(x) = (x^4 + 19)/100, \qquad 1 \leqslant x \leqslant 3.$$

On observing that $F(1) = 0{\cdot}2$, it follows that all three quartiles are in the interval $(1, 3)$. In fact, for any $p > 0{\cdot}2$, the quantile ξ_p will be the solution of the equation $F(x) = p$, which here is

$$(x^4 + 19)/100 = p,$$

from which we find that

$$\xi_p = (100p - 19)^{1/4}.$$

Hence, the lower and upper quartiles are

$$\xi_{0\cdot25} = 6^{1/4} \quad \text{and} \quad \xi_{0\cdot75} = 56^{1/4},$$

and the semi-interquartile range is

$$\tfrac{1}{2}(\xi_{0\cdot75} - \xi_{0\cdot25}) = \tfrac{1}{2}(56^{1/4} - 6^{1/4})$$
$$= 0{\cdot}585, \text{ correct to 3 significant figures.}$$

EXERCISE 3.6B

1–4 Calculate, correct to 3 significant figures, the median, the lower quartile and the upper quartile of each of the distributions given in Exercise 3.6A questions 3–6.

5 The random variable X has a distribution whose probability density function f is given by

$$f(x) = 2e^{-2x}, \qquad x > 0.$$

Show that the quantile ξ_p of this distribution is equal to $-\frac{1}{2}\ln(1-p)$. Hence determine, correct to 3 significant figures, the median and the semi-interquartile range of the distribution.

3.7* Distribution of a function

If X is a continuous random variable having range space $R_X = \{x : a \leqslant x \leqslant b\}$, probability density function f, and cumulative distribution function F, then from (1) of §3.6.

$$F(x) = \int_a^x f(t)\,dt \qquad \text{for } a \leqslant x \leqslant b. \tag{1}$$

Since integration is the inverse operation to differentiation it follows that

$$\mathrm{f}(x) = \frac{\mathrm{dF}(x)}{\mathrm{d}x} \tag{2}$$

for every x in R_X where $\mathrm{F}(x)$ has a derivative. This second relation connecting f and F can be extremely useful, especially for determining the p.d.f. of a function of a continuous random variable X whose distribution is known, as demonstrated in the following examples.

EXAMPLE 1 *Given that X has the distribution*

$$\mathrm{f}(x) = x + \tfrac{1}{2}, \qquad 0 \leqslant x \leqslant 1,$$

find the distribution of (i) $Y = 12X + 1$, (ii) $Z = (1 - X)^{1/2}$.

(i) Since the range space of X is $R_X = \{x\colon 0 \leqslant x \leqslant 1\}$, the range space of Y is

$$R_Y = \left\{ y\colon 0 \leqslant \frac{y-1}{12} \leqslant 1 \right\} = \{ y\colon 1 \leqslant y \leqslant 13 \}.$$

Denote the p.d.f. and c.d.f. of Y by g and G, respectively. Then, from the definition of a c.d.f.,

$$\begin{aligned}\mathrm{G}(y) &= \mathrm{P}(Y \leqslant y) = \mathrm{P}(12X + 1 \leqslant y) \\ &= \mathrm{P}\left(X \leqslant \frac{y-1}{12} \right) = \mathrm{F}\left(\frac{y-1}{12} \right),\end{aligned} \tag{a}$$

where $\mathrm{F}(x)$ is the c.d.f. of X. Now, for $0 \leqslant x \leqslant 1$,

$$\mathrm{F}(x) = \int_0^x \mathrm{f}(t)\,\mathrm{d}t = \int_0^x (t + \tfrac{1}{2})\,\mathrm{d}t = \tfrac{1}{2}(x^2 + x).$$

Hence, for $1 \leqslant y \leqslant 13$, the c.d.f. G of Y is such that

$$\mathrm{G}(y) = \tfrac{1}{2}\left[\frac{(y-1)^2}{144} + \frac{y-1}{12} \right] = \frac{1}{288}[(y-1)^2 + 12(y-1)].$$

Using (2), the p.d.f. of Y is g, where

$$\mathrm{g}(y) = \frac{\mathrm{dG}(y)}{\mathrm{d}y} = \frac{1}{288}[2(y-1) + 12], \qquad 1 \leqslant y \leqslant 13,$$

or

$$\mathrm{g}(y) = \frac{y+5}{144}, \qquad 1 \leqslant y \leqslant 13.$$

(It is left as an exercise to carry out the advisable check that this p.d.f. does integrate to unity, and that the mean and the variance of the distribution of Y agree with the answers obtained in Example 1, §3.5.)

(ii) Since the range space of X is $R_X = \{x\colon 0 \leqslant x \leqslant 1\}$ and $Z = (1 - X)^{1/2}$, or equivalently, $X = 1 - Z^2$, it follows that the range space of Z is

$$R_Z = \{ z\colon 0 \leqslant 1 - z^2 \leqslant 1 \} = \{ z\colon 0 \leqslant z \leqslant 1 \},$$

noting that only the positive square root is taken, since Z is restricted to be the positive square root of $1-X$.

Denoting the c.d.f. of Z by H, we have

$$\begin{aligned} \mathrm{H}(z) &= \mathrm{P}(Z \leqslant z) = \mathrm{P}\{(1-X)^{1/2} \leqslant z\} = \mathrm{P}\{X \geqslant 1-z^2\} \\ &= 1-\mathrm{F}(1-z^2) \end{aligned} \qquad \text{(b)}$$

where F is the c.d.f. of X. We showed above that for $0 \leqslant x \leqslant 1$,

$$\mathrm{F}(x) = \tfrac{1}{2}(x^2+x).$$

Hence, for $0 \leqslant z \leqslant 1$,

$$\mathrm{H}(z) = 1 - \tfrac{1}{2}[(1-z^2)^2 + (1-z^2)].$$

Differentiating $\mathrm{H}(z)$ and simplifying the resultant expression gives the p.d.f. h of Z as

$$\mathrm{h}(z) = z(3-2z^2), \qquad 0 \leqslant z \leqslant 1.$$

(Again, it is left as an exercise to check that this is a legitimate p.d.f. and that the mean and the variance of the distribution agree with the results obtained in Example 1, §3.5.)

In the above solutions we determined $\mathrm{F}(x)$ in order to determine $\mathrm{G}(y)$ and $\mathrm{H}(z)$. This was not necessary. In (i), having reached the stage (a), namely

$$\mathrm{G}(y) = \mathrm{F}\left(\frac{y-1}{12}\right),$$

we could proceed directly to finding the p.d.f. of Y as follows. Differentiating $\mathrm{F}(y-1/12)$, using the chain rule, gives the p.d.f. of Y as

$$\mathrm{g}(y) = \frac{1}{12}\mathrm{f}\left(\frac{y-1}{12}\right),$$

where

$$\mathrm{f}(x) = x + \tfrac{1}{2}, \qquad 0 \leqslant x \leqslant 1.$$

Hence

$$\mathrm{g}(y) = \frac{1}{12}\left(\frac{y-1}{12} + \tfrac{1}{2}\right), \qquad 1 \leqslant y \leqslant 13,$$

i.e.

$$\mathrm{g}(y) = \frac{1}{144}(y+5), \qquad 1 \leqslant y \leqslant 13,$$

exactly as obtained earlier.

Similarly, from (b) in (ii), the c.d.f. of Z is given by

$$\mathrm{H}(z) = 1 - \mathrm{F}(1-z^2),$$

which, on differentiating, gives the p.d.f. of Z as

$$\mathrm{h}(z) = 2z\mathrm{f}(1-z^2),$$

Substituting for $f(1-z^2)$ then gives

$$h(z) = 2z(1-z^2+\tfrac{1}{2}), \qquad 0 \leqslant z \leqslant 1$$
$$= z(3-2z^2), \qquad 0 \leqslant z \leqslant 1,$$

again agreeing with the result obtained earlier.

The conversion of an event such as $\{Y \leqslant y\}$ into the corresponding event in terms of X in the above example was fairly straightforward. This is not always so, and particular care is needed in carrying out such a conversion when Y is not a one-to-one function of X, as illustrated in the following example.

EXAMPLE 2 *Find the distribution of $Y = X^2$ given that X is uniformly distributed over the interval $(-1, 2)$.*

Since X is uniformly distributed over $(-1, 2)$ its p.d.f. is f, where

$$f(x) = \tfrac{1}{3}, \qquad -1 < x < 2.$$

We first determine the range space R_Y corresponding to $R_X = \{x\colon -1 < x < 2\}$. This will be the set of values that X^2 can take when $-1 < X < 2$. Fig. 3.14 shows the graph of $y = x^2$ for $-1 < x < 2$.

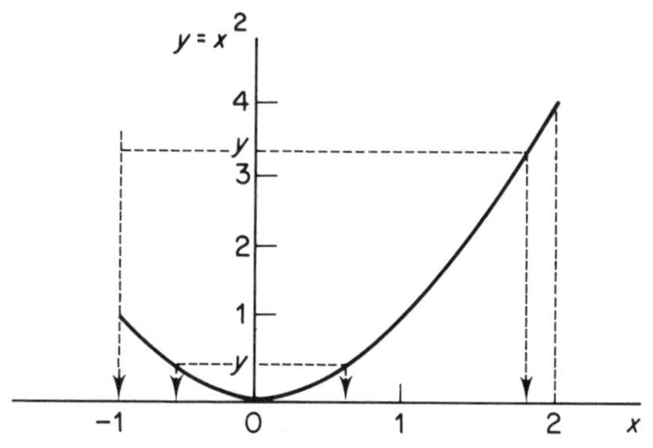

Fig. 3.14

We see from the graph that y can take any value from 0 to 4, so that

$$R_Y = \{y\colon 0 < y < 4\}.$$

Let G denote the c.d.f. of Y. Then, for any y in R_Y,

$$G(y) = P(Y \leqslant y) = P(X^2 \leqslant y).$$

From Fig. 3.14, for $0 < y \leqslant 1$,

$$(X^2 \leqslant y) = (-y^{1/2} \leqslant X \leqslant y^{1/2}),$$

while, for $1 < y < 4$,

$$(X^2 \leqslant y) = (-1 \leqslant X \leqslant y^{1/2}).$$

Thus, for $0 < y \leqslant 1$,

$$G(y) = P(-y^{1/2} \leqslant X \leqslant y^{1/2}) = F(y^{1/2}) - F(-y^{1/2}),$$

and for the same range of values of y, the p.d.f. of Y is given by

$$\begin{aligned} g(y) &= \frac{d}{dy}[F(y^{1/2}) - F(-y^{1/2})] \\ &= \tfrac{1}{2}y^{-1/2}[f(y^{1/2}) + f(-y^{1/2})] \\ &= \tfrac{1}{2}y^{-1/2}(\tfrac{1}{3} + \tfrac{1}{3}) = \tfrac{1}{3}y^{-1/2}. \end{aligned}$$

But, for $1 < y < 4$, we have

$$G(y) = P(-1 \leqslant X \leqslant y^{1/2}) = F(y^{1/2}) - F(-1),$$

and the p.d.f. for the same range of values of y is given by

$$g(y) = \tfrac{1}{2}y^{-1/2}f(y^{1/2}) = \tfrac{1}{6}y^{-1/2}.$$

(Observe that $F(-1)$ is a constant so that its derivative with respect to y is zero.)

Combining the above results, the p.d.f. g of Y is thus

$$\begin{aligned} g(y) &= \tfrac{1}{3}y^{-1/2}, \qquad 0 < y \leqslant 1, \\ g(y) &= \tfrac{1}{6}y^{-1/2}, \qquad 1 < y < 4. \end{aligned}$$

(Alternatively, we could have used the result $F(x) = \frac{1}{3}(x+1)$ for $-1 < x < 2$ to replace $F(y^{1/2})$ and $F(-y^{1/2})$ in the above before differentiating with respect to y.)

EXERCISE 3.7

1 The continuous random variable X has probability density function f, where

$$f(x) = 2(1-x), \qquad 0 \leqslant x \leqslant 1.$$

(i) Find the cumulative distribution function of X.
(ii) Hence find the probability density function of (a) $Y = 1 - X$, (b) $Z = X^{-1}$.

2 The time, X minutes, that a bus takes to cover a specified journey of 20 km, is uniformly distributed over the interval [20, 30]. Let Y denote the average speed, in kilometres per hour, of the bus on such a journey. Find an expression for $P(Y \leqslant y)$, where y is an arbitrary value between 40 and 60. Hence, or otherwise, find (i) the probability density function of the distribution of Y, (ii) the probability that on such a journey the average speed of the bus will exceed 50 km per hour, (iii) the median speed for the journey.

3 AB is the diameter of a semicircle of radius r. A chord is drawn parallel to AB at a randomly chosen distance X from AB (so that X is uniformly distributed over the interval from 0 to r). Find the probability density function of the distribution of the length of the chord (reference to Example 4, §3.2 might be found helpful).

4 Given that the probability density function of X is

$$f(x) = 2e^{-2x}, \qquad x > 0,$$

show that $Y = e^{-2X}$ has a uniform distribution over an interval which should be specified.

5 The random variable X has probability density function f, where

$$f(x) = \frac{2}{x^3}, \qquad x \geqslant 1.$$

Find the probability density function of $W = \ln(X)$.

6 Given that X has the probability density function f, where

$$f(x) = 1 + x, \qquad -1 \leqslant x \leqslant 0$$

$$f(x) = 1 - x, \qquad 0 < x \leqslant 1,$$

determine the probability density function of (i) $U = 2X - 1$, (ii) $W = \frac{1}{2}(1 - X)$. Use the results to find the means and the variances of U and W, checking your answers with those you obtained in Exercise 3.5 question 2.

7 Given that X is uniformly distributed over the interval $(-1, 1)$ find the probability density function of (i) $Y = X^2$, (ii) $Z = |X|$, (iii) $W = (X+2)^{-1}$.

3.8 The normal distribution

3.8.1 The standard normal distribution

Consider the function φ defined by

$$\varphi(z) = \frac{1}{\sqrt{(2\pi)}} \mathrm{e}^{-\frac{1}{2}z^2}, \qquad -\infty < z < \infty, \qquad (1)$$

a sketch of which is shown in Fig. 3.15.

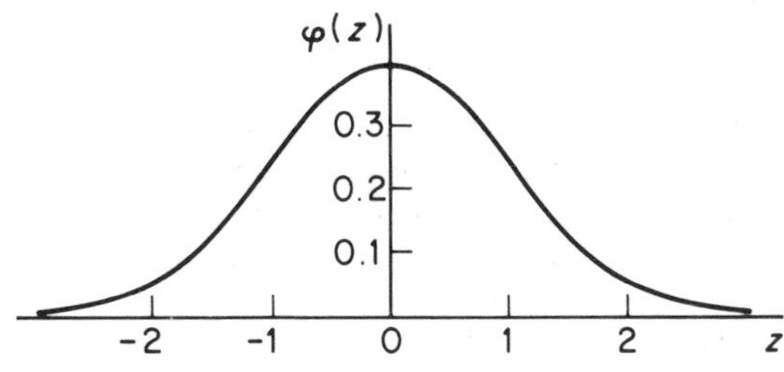

Fig. 3.15

Using mathematics beyond the level assumed in this text it may be shown that

$$\int_{-\infty}^{\infty} \varphi(z)\,\mathrm{d}z = 1. \qquad (2)$$

This result and the property $\varphi(z) > 0$ for all z, indicate that φ can serve as a p.d.f. A random variable Z having the p.d.f. φ is said to have the *standard normal distribution.*

The mean of such a random variable Z is given by

$$\mathrm{E}[Z] = \frac{1}{\sqrt{(2\pi)}} \int_{-\infty}^{\infty} z\mathrm{e}^{-\frac{1}{2}z^2}\,\mathrm{d}z.$$

Since $\dfrac{\mathrm{d}}{\mathrm{d}z}(\mathrm{e}^{-\frac{1}{2}z^2}) = -z\mathrm{e}^{-\frac{1}{2}z^2}$, it follows that

$$\mathrm{E}[Z] = \frac{1}{\sqrt{(2\pi)}}\left[-\mathrm{e}^{-\frac{1}{2}z^2}\right]_{-\infty}^{\infty} = 0.$$

Since the mean is zero, the variance is given by

$$\mathrm{V}[Z] = \mathrm{E}[Z^2] = \frac{1}{\sqrt{(2\pi)}} \int_{-\infty}^{\infty} z^2\mathrm{e}^{-\frac{1}{2}z^2}\,\mathrm{d}z.$$

Integrating by parts we have

$$\mathrm{V}[Z] = \frac{1}{\sqrt{(2\pi)}}\left[-z\mathrm{e}^{-\frac{1}{2}z^2}\right]_{-\infty}^{\infty} + \frac{1}{\sqrt{(2\pi)}} \int_{-\infty}^{\infty} \mathrm{e}^{-\frac{1}{2}z^2}\,\mathrm{d}z.$$

The first term on the right-hand side is zero since $z\mathrm{e}^{-\frac{1}{2}z^2}$ tends to zero as z tends to plus infinity and as z tends to minus infinity. Using (2) above the second term on the right-hand side is seen to be equal to one. Hence $\mathrm{V}[Z] = 1$, or equivalently, $\mathrm{SD}[Z] = 1$. It follows that a random variable Z whose p.d.f. is the function φ given by (1) above has zero mean and unit standard deviation. We shall abbreviate this statement as $Z \sim N(0, 1)$.

The cumulative distribution function Φ corresponding to (1) is

$$\Phi(z) = \int_{-\infty}^{z} \varphi(t)\,\mathrm{d}t = \frac{1}{\sqrt{(2\pi)}} \int_{-\infty}^{z} \mathrm{e}^{-\frac{1}{2}t^2}\,\mathrm{d}t. \tag{3}$$

This cannot be evaluated explicitly for a value of z which is non-zero. When $z = 0$ it is clear from the symmetry of the distribution about the value zero that $\Phi(0) = 0{\cdot}5$. For a non-zero value of z, the integral in (3) can be evaluated only by means of numerical methods. The results of such evaluations have been extensively tabulated. It will be assumed that a table

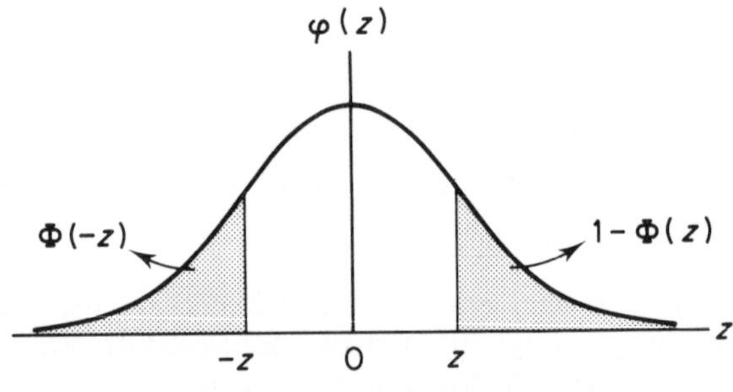

Fig. 3.16

of $\Phi(z)$ or of $1-\Phi(z)$ is available to the reader. Most such tables only provide for positive values of z, since it follows from the symmetry of the distribution that for any positive z

$$\Phi(-z) = 1 - \Phi(z). \tag{4}$$

This is illustrated in Fig. 3.16.

EXAMPLE 1 *Given that* $Z \sim N(0, 1)$, *use tables to evaluate* (*i*) $P(Z < 0{\cdot}5)$, (*ii*) $P(Z < 1{\cdot}64)$, (*iii*) $P(Z < 1{\cdot}562)$, (*iv*) $P(Z < -0{\cdot}25)$, (*v*) $P(Z > -0{\cdot}5)$, (*vi*) $P(1{\cdot}24 < Z < 2{\cdot}36)$, (*vii*) $P(-0{\cdot}2 < Z < 0{\cdot}2)$, (*viii*) *the value c for which* $P(Z < c) = 0{\cdot}68$.

Let Φ as defined by (3) above denote the c.d.f. of Z. Use your tables to verify the following answers. You may find it useful to draw a diagram in each case.

(i) $P(Z < 0{\cdot}5) = \Phi(0{\cdot}5) = 0{\cdot}6915$

(ii) $P(Z < 1{\cdot}64) = \Phi(1{\cdot}64) = 0{\cdot}9495$

(iii) $P(Z < 1{\cdot}562) = \Phi(1{\cdot}562)$

Assuming that your table only provides for values of z to two decimal places (which is commonly the case), we find

$$\Phi(1{\cdot}56) = 0{\cdot}9406 \quad \text{and} \quad \Phi(1{\cdot}57) = 0{\cdot}9418.$$

To obtain an approximate value for $\Phi(1{\cdot}562)$ we shall use linear interpolation (or proportional parts), to get

$$\begin{aligned}\Phi(1{\cdot}562) &= \Phi(1{\cdot}56) + \frac{0{\cdot}002}{0{\cdot}01}[\Phi(1{\cdot}57) - \Phi(1{\cdot}56)] \\ &\simeq 0{\cdot}9406 + 0{\cdot}0002 \simeq 0{\cdot}9408.\end{aligned}$$

(iv) $P(Z < -0{\cdot}25) = \Phi(-0{\cdot}25)$.

Assuming that negative values of z are not tabulated we use the result

$$\Phi(-0{\cdot}25) = 1 - \Phi(0{\cdot}25) = 1 - 0{\cdot}5987 = 0{\cdot}4013.$$

(v) $P(Z > -0{\cdot}5) = 1 - P(Z < -0{\cdot}5) = 1 - \Phi(-0{\cdot}5) = \Phi(0{\cdot}5) = 0{\cdot}6915$,
or more directly by making use of the symmetry of the distribution, the area of the region under $\varphi(z)$ to the right of $z = -0{\cdot}5$ is equal to the area of the region to the left of $z = 0{\cdot}5$, and therefore $P(Z > -0{\cdot}5) = P(Z < 0{\cdot}5) = \Phi(0{\cdot}5) = 0{\cdot}6915$.

(vi)
$$\begin{aligned}P(1{\cdot}24 < Z < 2{\cdot}36) &= P(Z < 2{\cdot}36) - P(Z < 1{\cdot}24) \\ &= \Phi(2{\cdot}36) - \Phi(1{\cdot}24) \\ &= 0{\cdot}9909 - 0{\cdot}8925 = 0{\cdot}0984.\end{aligned}$$

(vii)
$$\begin{aligned}P(-0{\cdot}2 < Z < 0{\cdot}2) &= P(Z < 0{\cdot}2) - P(Z < -0{\cdot}2) \\ &= \Phi(0{\cdot}2) - \Phi(-0{\cdot}2) = \Phi(0{\cdot}2) - \{1 - \Phi(0{\cdot}2)\} \\ &= 2\Phi(0{\cdot}2) - 1 = 0{\cdot}1586\end{aligned}$$

(viii) Here, we need to find c such that $P(Z < c) = 0{\cdot}68$, that is such that $\Phi(c) = 0{\cdot}68$. Searching through the table of Φ for successive values of z for which the corresponding values of Φ straddle 0·68, we find

$$\Phi(0{\cdot}46) = 0{\cdot}6772 \quad \text{and} \quad \Phi(0{\cdot}47) = 0{\cdot}6808.$$

Thus c lies between 0·46 and 0·47. Using linear interpolation to find an approximate value of c, we have

$$c = 0{\cdot}46 + \frac{0{\cdot}68 - 0{\cdot}6772}{0{\cdot}6808 - 0{\cdot}6772}(0{\cdot}47 - 0{\cdot}46)$$

$$= 0{\cdot}46 + 0{\cdot}0078 = 0{\cdot}468 \text{ to 3 decimal places.}$$

EXERCISE 3.8A

Given that Z has the standard normal distribution, evaluate the following, correct to 3 significant figures.

1 $P(Z < 2{\cdot}26)$.
2 $P(Z > 1{\cdot}05)$.
3 $P(Z > 0{\cdot}036)$.
4 $P(Z > -2{\cdot}165)$.
5 $P(Z < -0{\cdot}33)$.
6 $P(0{\cdot}12 < Z < 1{\cdot}34)$.
7 $P(-1{\cdot}26 < Z < -0{\cdot}35)$.
8 $P(-0{\cdot}464 < Z < 1{\cdot}368)$.
9 The value c such that $P(Z > c) = 0{\cdot}4$.
10 The value c such that $P(Z < c) = 0{\cdot}37$.

3.8.2 General normal distribution

Suppose we now relocate the distribution given by (1) above so that it is symmetrical about some arbitrary value μ, and introduce a new scale of measurement so that one unit becomes σ units, for some arbitrary $\sigma > 0$. All this can be achieved by introducing a new variable X defined by

$$X = \mu + \sigma Z, \tag{5}$$

where $Z \sim N(0, 1)$. Observe that, from the results obtained in §3.5, and recalling that $E[Z] = 0$, $V[Z] = 1$, X will have mean

$$E[X] = \mu + \sigma E[Z] = \mu,$$

and variance

$$V[X] = \sigma^2 V[Z] = \sigma^2.$$

Denoting the c.d.f. of X by F,

$$F(x) = P(X \leqslant x) = P\left(Z \leqslant \frac{x-\mu}{\sigma}\right) = \Phi\left(\frac{x-\mu}{\sigma}\right).$$

Hence the p.d.f. of X is f, where

$$f(x) = \frac{1}{\sigma}\varphi\left(\frac{x-\mu}{\sigma}\right)$$

$$= \frac{1}{\sigma\sqrt{(2\pi)}} e^{-(x-\mu)^2/(2\sigma^2)}, \qquad -\infty < x < \infty. \tag{6}$$

A random variable X having the p.d.f. given by (6) is said to have the *normal distribution with mean μ and variance σ^2*, which we abbreviate as $X \sim N(\mu, \sigma^2)$. The graph of (6) is similar to that shown in Fig. 3.15 but with mean = median = μ (instead of 0); the larger the value of σ the more dispersed the distribution will be, resulting in the graph having a flatter hump.

The transformation (5) allows us to reduce any $N(\mu, \sigma^2)$ distribution to $N(0, 1)$, the standard normal distribution, and consequently the latter may be used to evaluate probabilities relating to the $N(\mu, \sigma^2)$ distribution. This is illustrated in the following example.

EXAMPLE 2 *Given that X is normally distributed with mean 5 and standard deviation 2*
(i) *find the values of* (*a*) $P(X < 6)$, (*b*) $P(X < 2{\cdot}56)$, (*c*) $P(3{\cdot}4 < X < 5{\cdot}5)$;
(ii) *find the values c such that* (*a*) $P(X < c) = 0{\cdot}63$, (*b*) $P(X > c) = 0{\cdot}2$, (*c*) $P(X < c) = 0{\cdot}3$.

Here $X \sim N(5, 2^2)$, and therefore from (5),

$$Z = \frac{X-5}{2} \sim N(0, 1).$$

(i) (a) $P(X < 6) \equiv P\left(Z < \dfrac{6-5}{2}\right) = \Phi(0{\cdot}5) = 0{\cdot}6915.$

(b) $P(X < 2{\cdot}56) \equiv P\left(Z < \dfrac{2{\cdot}56-5}{2}\right) = \Phi(-1{\cdot}22) = 1 - \Phi(1{\cdot}22) = 0{\cdot}1112.$

(c)
$$\begin{aligned} P(3{\cdot}4 < X < 5{\cdot}5) &\equiv P\left(\frac{3{\cdot}4-5}{2} < Z < \frac{5{\cdot}5-5}{2}\right) \\ &= \Phi(0{\cdot}25) - \Phi(-0{\cdot}8) \\ &= \Phi(0{\cdot}25) - \{1 - \Phi(0{\cdot}8)\} \\ &= 0{\cdot}5987 - 0{\cdot}2119 = 0{\cdot}3868. \end{aligned}$$

(ii) (a) $P(X < c) \equiv P\left(Z < \dfrac{c-5}{2}\right) = \Phi\left(\dfrac{c-5}{2}\right).$

We need to find c such that $\Phi\left(\dfrac{c-5}{2}\right) = 0{\cdot}63$. From the tables we find

$$\Phi(0{\cdot}33) = 0{\cdot}6293 \quad \text{and} \quad \Phi(0{\cdot}34) = 0{\cdot}6331.$$

Using linear interpolation we obtain

$$\frac{c-5}{2} \simeq 0{\cdot}33 + \frac{(0{\cdot}63 - 0{\cdot}6293)}{(0{\cdot}6331 - 0{\cdot}6293)} \times 0{\cdot}01 \simeq 0{\cdot}3318,$$

and $c \simeq 5 + 2 \times 0{\cdot}3318 \simeq 5{\cdot}664$

(b) $P(X > c) \equiv P\left(Z > \dfrac{c-5}{2}\right) = 1 - \Phi\left(\dfrac{c-5}{2}\right).$

Hence c is the solution of the equation

$$1-\Phi\left(\frac{c-5}{2}\right)=0{\cdot}2 \quad\text{or}\quad \Phi\left(\frac{c-5}{2}\right)=0{\cdot}8.$$

From tables, $\Phi(0{\cdot}84)=0{\cdot}7995$, $\Phi(0{\cdot}85)=0{\cdot}8023$. Hence

$$\frac{c-5}{2}\simeq 0{\cdot}84+\frac{(0{\cdot}8-0{\cdot}7995)}{(0{\cdot}8023-0{\cdot}7995)}\times 0{\cdot}01\simeq 0{\cdot}8418$$

and $c\simeq 6{\cdot}684$.

(c) As in (a), $P(X<c)=\Phi\left(\dfrac{c-5}{2}\right)$ and we need to solve

$$\Phi\left(\frac{c-5}{2}\right)=0{\cdot}3.$$

Since the right-hand side is less than 0·5, the value of $\dfrac{c-5}{2}$ must be negative. To enable us to use the table of $\Phi(z)$ with $z\geqslant 0$, we can replace the above equation by

$$1-\Phi\left(\frac{5-c}{2}\right)=0{\cdot}3, \quad\text{or}\quad \Phi\left(\frac{5-c}{2}\right)=0{\cdot}7.$$

From tables, $\Phi(0{\cdot}52)=0{\cdot}6985$, $\Phi(0{\cdot}53)=0{\cdot}7019$.
Hence

$$\frac{5-c}{2}\simeq 0{\cdot}52+\frac{(0{\cdot}7-0{\cdot}6985)\times 0{\cdot}01}{(0{\cdot}7019-0{\cdot}6985)}\simeq 0{\cdot}5244$$

and $\quad c\simeq 5-2\times 0{\cdot}5244\simeq 3{\cdot}951$.

Some tables, such as those used by WJEC and JMB, include a table giving the solution z_α to the equation $P(Z>z_\alpha)=\alpha$ for some selected values of α. Such a table can be used for questions such as those in (ii) above only if the relevant probability value α is included in the table. Table 6.1 in Chapter 6 is such a table, where the chosen values of α are particularly relevant to topics discussed in Chapters 6 and 7.

EXERCISE 3.8B

1 Given that X is normally distributed with mean 2 and standard deviation 1 (i) evaluate (a) $P(X<2)$, (b) $P(X<3{\cdot}64)$, (c) $P(X>2{\cdot}07)$, (d) $P(0<X<3)$, (e) $P(1{\cdot}5<X<2{\cdot}5)$, (f) $P(|X-1|<1)$; (ii) find the values of c to 3 significant figures, such that (a) $P(X>c)=0{\cdot}05$, (b) $P(X<c)=0{\cdot}1$.

2 Given that X is normally distributed with mean 2·86 and standard deviation 1·2, find approximate values, to 3 decimal places, for (i) $P(X<3{\cdot}5)$, (ii) $P(X>1{\cdot}72)$, (iii) $P(3{\cdot}1<X<3{\cdot}5)$, (iv) $P(1{\cdot}66<X<3{\cdot}08)$.

3.8.3 Some problems involving normal distributions

The normal distribution is a very important one in both statistical theory and practice. Histograms of data collected on random variables from a wide variety of scientific disciplines have suggested that normal distributions would serve as good approximations to the underlying distributions. Furthermore, in Chapter 5 we shall consider conditions under which a normal distribution may be used to advantage as an approximation to a sampling distribution.

EXAMPLE 3 *A machine produces cylindrical rods whose diameters are normally distributed with mean* 1 *cm and standard deviation* 0·01 *cm. A rod is satisfactory for a specific purpose only if its diameter lies between* 0·993 *cm and* 1·017 *cm.*

(i) *Find the probability that a randomly chosen rod is satisfactory. Deduce the expected number of satisfactory rods in one day's production of* 1000 *rods.*

(ii) *Given that a rod has a diameter greater than* 1 *cm, find, to three significant figures, the probability that the rod is satisfactory.*

(iii) *Find the mean value, correct to three significant figures, of the cross-sectional areas of the rods.*

Let X cm denote the diameter of a randomly chosen rod. Then $X \sim N(1, 0{\cdot}01^2)$, and

$$Z = \frac{X-1}{0{\cdot}01} \sim N(0, 1).$$

$$\text{(i) P (rod is satisfactory)} = \mathrm{P}(0{\cdot}993 < X < 1{\cdot}017)$$
$$= \mathrm{P}\left(\frac{0{\cdot}993-1}{0{\cdot}01} < Z < \frac{1{\cdot}017-1}{0{\cdot}001}\right)$$
$$= \Phi(1{\cdot}7) - \Phi(-0{\cdot}7) = 0{\cdot}9554 - 0{\cdot}2420 = 0{\cdot}7134.$$

Let R denote the number of the 1000 rods that will be satisfactory. Then

$$R \sim \mathrm{B}(n = 1000, p = 0{\cdot}7134).$$

Hence the expected number of satisfactory rods $= np = 713{\cdot}4$.

(ii) Here we require

$$\mathrm{P}(0{\cdot}993 < X < 1{\cdot}017 \mid X > 1) = \frac{\mathrm{P}(1 < X < 1{\cdot}017)}{\mathrm{P}(X > 1)}.$$

$$\mathrm{P}(1 < X < 1{\cdot}017) = \mathrm{P}\left(\frac{1-1}{0{\cdot}01} < Z < \frac{1{\cdot}017-1}{0{\cdot}01}\right).$$
$$= \Phi(1{\cdot}7) - \Phi(0) = 0{\cdot}9554 - 0{\cdot}5 = 0{\cdot}4554.$$

$$\mathrm{P}(X > 1) = \mathrm{P}\left(Z > \frac{1-1}{0{\cdot}01}\right) = \mathrm{P}(Z > 0) = 0{\cdot}5.$$

Hence the required answer is $\dfrac{0{\cdot}4554}{0{\cdot}5} = 0{\cdot}911$ to three significant figures.

(iii) Let Y cm^2 denote the cross-sectional area of a rod of diameter X cm. Then

$$Y = \tfrac{1}{4}\pi X^2,$$

and the mean cross-sectional area of the rod is

$$E[Y] = \tfrac{1}{4}\pi\, E[X^2].$$

Since $X \sim N(1, 0{\cdot}01^2)$,

$$E[X] = 1 \quad \text{and} \quad V[X] = (0{\cdot}01)^2.$$

Hence $E[X^2] \equiv V[X] + \{E[X]\}^2 = (0{\cdot}01)^2 + 1^2 = 1{\cdot}0001$.
Thus, the mean cross-sectional area of the rods is $1{\cdot}0001\,\pi/4 = 0{\cdot}785\ \text{cm}^2$, correct to three significant figures.

Note: Since the diameter of a rod cannot be negative it might appear strange to assume that the diameters are normally distributed, since this allows for all possible values from $-\infty$ to $+\infty$. However, in the above example, the probability that a rod will have a negative diameter is

$$P(X < 0) = P\left(Z < \frac{0-1}{0{\cdot}01}\right) = \Phi(-100),$$

which is negligibly small.

EXERCISE 3.8C

1 A weighing device is such that the recorded weights in repeated weighings of an object are normally distributed with a mean equal to the true weight of the object and a standard deviation of 0·02 g. If the device is used once to determine the weight of an object whose true weight is 10 g, calculate the probability that the recorded weight will be in the range from 9·99 g to 10·02 g.

2 Suppose that the time X that an athlete will take to run 1500 m is a normally distributed random variable having mean 4 minutes and standard deviation 20 seconds. Calculate the probability that this athlete will run 1500 m in (i) less than 4 minutes, (ii) less than 3·25 minutes.

3 Two electronic devices A and B have life-lengths in months of X and Y, respectively, where $X \sim N(40, 6^2)$ and $Y \sim N(45, 3^2)$. Determine which of the two devices is the more likely to last for (i) at least 48 months, (ii) at least 52 months.

4 Large-scale testing by means of a standardised test on children of a certain age-group gave scores which could be assumed to be normally distributed with mean 74 and standard deviation 15. This test is recommended for grading purposes and the following system is adopted. The top grade 'A' is to be awarded to 10% of the children, the next highest grade 'B' to 30% of the children, the third highest grade 'C' to 40% of the children, and the lowest grade 'D' to the remaining 20% of the children. Determine the range of scores for each grade.

5 The error made by a certain length-measuring instrument is known to be normally distributed with mean zero and standard deviation 0·5 mm. Find the probability that the error in a measurement will be (i) numerically greater than 1 mm, (ii) numerically greater than 0·5 mm.

6 The operational life times in hours of manufactured light bulbs are normally distributed with mean 1060. Determine, to two decimal places, the standard deviation of the life times if 80% of the bulbs have a life time greater than 1050 hours.

7 The inside diameter X cm of a nozzle has a normal distribution with mean

4 cm and standard deviation 0·1 cm. The specification for the inside diameter of a nozzle is 4 cm. If the inside diameter of a nozzle differs from specification by more than 0·05 cm but less than 0·08 cm, then the loss to the manufacturer is 50 p. If the inside diameter of a nozzle differs from specification by more than 0·08 cm then the loss to the manufacturer is £1. The manufacturer makes a profit of £2 on each nozzle whose inside diameter is within 0·05 cm of specification. Calculate, to the nearest penny, the manufacturer's expected profit per nozzle.

8 An automatic filling device is used for putting a liquid product into containers. When the device is set to put μ cm^3 into each container, the actual volume put in a container is normally distributed with mean μ cm^3 and standard deviation 0.1 cm^3.
(i) If the device is set to put 12 cm^3 into each container, calculate the proportion, to three decimal places, of the containers that will contain between 11·8 cm^3 and 12·1 cm^3 of liquid.
(ii) Determine the value of μ, to two decimal places, that should be set if it is required that only 10% of the containers will contain less than 12 cm^3.

9 A certain ingredient may be extracted from raw material by either one of two methods A and B. For a fixed volume of raw material, the amount X cm^3 of ingredient extracted using method A is normally distributed with mean 13 and standard deviation 2, and the amount Y cm^3 extracted using method B is distributed with probability density function g, where

$$g(y) = 0{\cdot}08\ (y-10), \qquad 10 \leqslant y \leqslant 15.$$

Determine which of the two methods (i) has the greater probability of extracting more than 14 cm^3, (ii) extracts, on average, the greater amount.

The cost of applying method A is 3 p per cm^3 extracted and that of applying method B is $(15+2Y)$ p. If the extracted ingredient is sold at 5 p per cm^3, determine which of the two methods gives the higher expected profit.

3.9 Normal approximations to binomial and Poisson distributions

Given any distribution which is unimodal and symmetrical about its mode (or approximately so), it may be advantageous for some purposes to approximate that distribution by a normal distribution of the same mean and variance. In this section we shall consider such approximations to binomial and Poisson distributions. Before discussing the conditions under which such approximations are appropriate, we should first observe that a discrete distribution (restricted to integer values) is being approximated by a continuous distribution. To allow for this it is necessary to regard an integer k as equivalent to any value in the interval $(k-0{\cdot}5, k+0{\cdot}5)$ on a continuous scale of measurement; this is known as the *continuity correction.* Let X denote a discrete random variable which is restricted to integer values only and let Y denote a continuous random variable. Suppose that the distribution of X is to be approximated by the distribution of Y. Then, allowing for the continuity correction we have,

$$P(X = k) \simeq P(k-0{\cdot}5 < Y < k+0{\cdot}5),$$
$$P(X \leqslant k) \simeq P(Y < k+0{\cdot}5),$$
$$P(X \geqslant k) \simeq P(Y > k-0{\cdot}5).$$

3.9.1 Normal approximation to a binomial distribution

For the reason stated at the outset above, a normal approximation to the binomial distribution $B(n, p)$ will be appropriate only when the binomial distribution is symmetrical, or approximately so. In §2.6 we showed that the distribution $B(n, p)$ is symmetrical only when $p = 0{\cdot}5$. It follows that the normal approximation should be reasonably good for any $B(n, p = 0{\cdot}5)$ distribution; the larger the value of n the better the approximation should be. Furthermore, for any given p, the larger the value of n the more nearly symmetrical the distribution $B(n, p)$ becomes. This suggests that even when $p \neq 0{\cdot}5$, the normal approximation could be quite good provided n is large; in such a case the further p deviates from 0·5 the larger n will need to be for a good approximation.

A working rule to use in practice can be derived as follows. Since the normal distribution extends from $-\infty$ to $+\infty$, but the $B(n, p)$ distribution is limited to the range from 0 to n, it is clearly desirable that the normal distribution probability in the range from 0 to n should be close to 1. For the $N(\mu, \sigma^2)$ distribution, the interval $(\mu - 4\sigma, \mu + 4\sigma)$ has probability 0·99994, which is close enough to the value 1 for practical purposes. Since our normal approximation has mean $\mu = np$ and variance $\sigma^2 = npq$, where $q = 1-p$, it is therefore desirable that

$$np - 4\sqrt{(npq)} > 0 \quad \text{and} \quad np + 4\sqrt{(npq)} < n,$$

from which we find that n must exceed the larger of $(16p/q)$ and $(16q/p)$, that is

$$n > \max\left(\frac{16p}{q}, \frac{16q}{p}\right). \tag{1}$$

This provides a reasonably good rule-of-thumb to use for determining whether a $B(n, p)$ can be approximated reasonably well by the normal distribution having mean np and variance npq. For example, if $p = \frac{1}{2}$, the above rule requires n to be at least 17. (A less conservative rule has 9 instead of 16 in the above condition on n, and is derived in a similar way on noting that for the $N(\mu, \sigma^2)$ distribution, the interval $(\mu - 3\sigma, \mu + 3\sigma)$ has probability 0·9973.)

EXAMPLE 1 *If* $X \sim B(n = 100, \; p = 0{\cdot}4)$, *evaluate* (*i*) $P(X = 50)$, (*ii*) $P(X \geqslant 55)$, (*iii*) $P(X < 46)$.

These probabilities would require very heavy computation to evaluate exactly unless one had access to a table of binomial probabilities for the case when $n = 100$ and $p = 0{\cdot}4$. The normal approximation provides a fairly easy way of evaluating the probabilities approximately. With $p = 0{\cdot}4$, condition (1) above requires that

$$n > \max\left\{\frac{16 \times 0{\cdot}4}{0{\cdot}6}, \frac{16 \times 0{\cdot}6}{0{\cdot}4}\right\} = 24.$$

Since here we have $n = 100$, the normal approximation should give reasonably good approximations for the probabilities required.

Let $Y \sim N(\mu, \sigma^2)$ with $\mu = np = 40$ and $\sigma^2 = npq = 24$.

(i) $\mathrm{P}(X = 50) = \mathrm{P}(49{\cdot}5 < X < 50{\cdot}5)$, on using the continuity correction

$$\simeq \mathrm{P}(49{\cdot}5 < Y < 50{\cdot}5), \text{ on using the normal approximation}$$

$$\simeq \Phi\left(\frac{50{\cdot}5 - 40}{\sqrt{24}}\right) - \Phi\left(\frac{49{\cdot}5 - 40}{\sqrt{24}}\right) \simeq \Phi(2{\cdot}1433) - \Phi(1{\cdot}9392)$$

$$\simeq 0{\cdot}0105.$$

From binomial tables the exact probability, to four decimal places, is 0·0103, so that the above approximation is very close to the correct answer.

(ii) $\mathrm{P}(X \geqslant 55) = \mathrm{P}(X > 54{\cdot}5)$, on using the continuity correction,

$$\simeq \mathrm{P}(Y > 54{\cdot}5) \simeq 1 - \Phi\left(\frac{54{\cdot}5 - 40}{\sqrt{24}}\right) \simeq 1 - \Phi(2{\cdot}9598) \simeq 0{\cdot}0015,$$

as compared with the answer 0·0017 obtained from binomial tables.

(iii) $\mathrm{P}(X < 46) = \mathrm{P}(X \leqslant 45) = \mathrm{P}(X < 45{\cdot}5) \simeq \mathrm{P}(Y < 45{\cdot}5) = \Phi\left(\frac{45{\cdot}5 - 40}{\sqrt{24}}\right)$

$$\simeq \Phi(1{\cdot}1227) \simeq 0{\cdot}8692,$$

as compared with the answer 0·8689 obtained from binomial tables.

EXAMPLE 2 *Independently for each seed of a certain type that is sown under specified conditions there is a probability of* 0·8 *that it will germinate and produce a plant. Determine the minimum number of seeds that should be sown under the specified conditions to ensure with a probability of at least* 0·9 *that* 60 *or more plants will be produced.*

Suppose n seeds are sown. Then

$$X = \text{Number that will produce plants} \sim \mathrm{B}(n, p = 0{\cdot}8).$$

We require the smallest n satisfying $\mathrm{P}(X \geqslant 60) \geqslant 0{\cdot}9$. Let us assume that n is large enough to justify using a normal approximation to the distribution of X (this can be checked having obtained the value of n). Let $Y \sim N(\mu, \sigma^2)$ with $\mu = np = 0{\cdot}8n$, $\sigma^2 = npq = 0{\cdot}16n$. Then on applying the continuity correction and the normal approximation, we have

$$\mathrm{P}(X \geqslant 60) = \mathrm{P}(X > 59{\cdot}5) \simeq \mathrm{P}(Y > 59{\cdot}5)$$

$$\simeq 1 - \Phi\left(\frac{59{\cdot}5 - 0{\cdot}8n}{\sqrt{(0{\cdot}16n)}}\right).$$

For this to be at least 0·9, we must have

$$\Phi\left\{\frac{59{\cdot}5-0{\cdot}8n}{\sqrt{(0{\cdot}16n)}}\right\} \leqslant 0{\cdot}1,$$

or

$$\frac{59{\cdot}5-0{\cdot}8n}{\sqrt{(0{\cdot}16n)}} \leqslant -1{\cdot}2816. \tag{a}$$

Since (a) will be satisfied only if the left-hand side is negative, it follows that we must have

$$59{\cdot}5-0{\cdot}8n<0, \quad \text{or} \quad n>\frac{59{\cdot}5}{0{\cdot}8}=74{\cdot}375.$$

We could now proceed to solve the inequality (a) for n by squaring both sides and solving the resulting quadratic inequality in n, the required root being determined by the condition that $n > 74{\cdot}375$. However, it is probably quicker with the aid of a calculator to evaluate the left-hand side of (a) for varying n. The following table summarises the application of this iterative procedure. Starting with $n = 75$ the left-hand side of (a) has the value $-0{\cdot}144$, which is greater than $-1{\cdot}2816$ and means that we should next try a larger value of n, taken to be 80 in the table. With $n = 80$ we find that the left-hand side of (a) has the value $-1{\cdot}258$ which is still greater than $-1{\cdot}2816$. So, we next try the slightly greater value $n = 81$, leading to $-1{\cdot}472$ which is less than $-1{\cdot}2816$.

$n =$	75	80	81
L.H.S. of (a) =	$-0{\cdot}144$	$-1{\cdot}258$	$-1{\cdot}472$.

Hence, to satisfy the specified requirements, we must have $n \geqslant 81$; that is, at least 81 seeds should be sown. (Observe that with $p = 0{\cdot}8$, our rule-of-thumb given by (1) requires n to be at least $16 \times 0{\cdot}8/0{\cdot}2 = 64$ and this condition is certainly satisfied by our answer.)

EXERCISE 3.9A

1 An electronic device consists of 100 components and will function throughout a given time period only if at least 80 of the components function throughout the period. Independently for each component there is a probability of 0·25 that a component will fail during the specified time period. Use tables of the normal distribution to find an approximate value for the probability that the device will function throughout the time period.

2 If two fair dice are tossed together 180 times, find an approximate value for the probability that a score of 7 (being the sum of the scores on the two dice) will be obtained at least 25 times.

3 The random variable X has the $B(n, p)$ distribution. Using appropriate approximations when necessary evaluate $P(X = np)$ in each of the cases when (i) $n = 400$, $p = 0{\cdot}5$, (ii) $n = 550$, $p = 0{\cdot}8$, (iii) $n = 200$, $p = 0{\cdot}01$, (iv) $n = 50$, $p = 0{\cdot}75$ (be alert when answering (iv)).

4 Of the population of England and Wales, 22% have blood group A. In a random sample of 150 people, find approximate values for the probabilities that (i) 20 or fewer are of blood group A, (ii) 30 or more are of blood group A.

Find also the smallest integer r if there is a probability of at least 0·95 that the sample of 150 people will include r or fewer of blood group A.

5 In a certain district the dental profession recommended that fluoride be added to the domestic water supplies in order to reduce the incidence of tooth decay. The authorities agreed to carry out the recommendation provided that at least 55% of the adult population in the district favoured the action. To assess public opinion, it was decided to carry out a sample survey. Given that the true percentage of adults in the district favouring fluoridation is 60%, how large a sample should be taken in the survey if there is to be a probability of about 0·001 that fewer than 55% of the adults in the sample favour fluoridation?

3.9.2 Normal approximation to a Poisson distribution

A Poisson distribution with mean α becomes more and more symmetrical as α increases. It follows that a normal approximation is reasonable only when α is very large.

Suppose $X \sim \text{Po}(\alpha)$ and α is large. Since X has mean α and variance α the appropriate approximating normal distribution will also have mean α and variance α. Suppose $Y \sim N(\alpha, \alpha)$. Since the Poisson distribution extends to $+\infty$, the argument used in §3.9.1 leads to the condition

$$\alpha - 4\sqrt{\alpha} > 0 \quad \text{or} \quad \alpha > 16,$$

for the normal approximation to be a reasonable one to use in the case of a Poisson distribution with mean α.

EXAMPLE 3 *If* $X \sim \text{Po}(36)$ *find approximate values for* (*i*) $\text{P}(X \geqslant 30)$, (*ii*) $\text{P}(X = 35)$.

Let $Y \sim N(\mu, \sigma^2)$ with $\mu = \sigma^2 = 36$.

(i) $\text{P}(X \geqslant 30) = \text{P}(X > 29{\cdot}5) \simeq \text{P}(Y > 29{\cdot}5)$

$$= 1 - \Phi\left(\frac{29{\cdot}5 - 36}{\sqrt{36}}\right) = \Phi(1{\cdot}0833) \simeq 0{\cdot}8606.$$

(From Poisson tables the answer to four decimal places is 0·8621)

(ii) $\text{P}(X = 35) = \text{P}(34{\cdot}5 < X < 35{\cdot}5) \simeq \text{P}(34{\cdot}5 < Y < 35{\cdot}5)$

$$\simeq \Phi(-0{\cdot}0833) - \Phi(-0{\cdot}25)$$

$$\simeq 0{\cdot}4668 - 0{\cdot}4013 \simeq 0{\cdot}0655$$

(From Poisson tables the answer to four decimal places is 0·0595.)

EXERCISE 3.9B

1 The number of incoming calls to a switchboard in a certain hour of each day has a Poisson distribution with mean 120. Find approximate values for the probabilities that during that hour on a given day the number of incoming calls will be (i) exactly 100, (ii) more than 150.

2 The number of accidents occuring along a certain stretch of motorway has a

Poisson distribution, the average number of accidents per week being 1·8. Find an approximate value for the probability that in a year (52 weeks) the number of accidents along this stretch of motorway will be less than 100.

3 In a certain city an average of 35 babies are born per day. Stating clearly any assumptions you make, calculate the probabilities that on a given day the number of babies born in this city will be (i) 25 or fewer, (ii) 30 or more. Also find the least number of days during which there is a probability of at least 0·95 that 1000 or more babies will be born.

3.10* The exponential distribution

A continuous random variable X whose p.d.f. is of the form

$$f(x) = \alpha e^{-\alpha x}, \qquad x > 0, \tag{1}$$

where $\alpha > 0$ is a constant, is said to have the *exponential distribution* with parameter α; we shall abbreviate this statement as $X \sim \text{Exp}(\alpha)$.

The corresponding c.d.f., for any $x > 0$, is given by

$$F(x) = \int_0^x \alpha e^{-\alpha t}\,dt = 1 - e^{-\alpha x}. \tag{2}$$

Observe that $F(\infty) = 1$, as it should be for f to be a p.d.f. Sketches of the graphs of $f(x)$ and $F(x)$ are given in Figs. 3.17a and b.

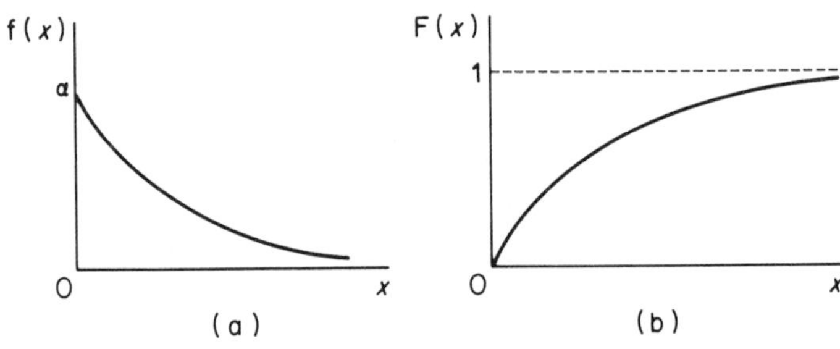

Fig. 3.17

The mean of the distribution is

$$E[X] = \int_0^\infty \alpha x e^{-\alpha x}\,dx,$$

and, on integrating by parts, we find

$$E[X] = [-xe^{-\alpha x}]_0^\infty + \int_0^\infty e^{-\alpha x}\,dx = [-xe^{-\alpha x}]_0^\infty + \left[-\frac{1}{\alpha}e^{-\alpha x}\right]_0^\infty.$$

Since $\alpha > 0$, it follows that $e^{-\alpha x}$ and $xe^{-\alpha x}$ tend to zero as x tends to infinity. Hence

$$E[X] = \frac{1}{\alpha}. \tag{3}$$

To determine the variance of the distribution, let us first find $E[X^2]$.

$$\begin{aligned} E[X^2] &= \int_0^\infty \alpha x^2 e^{-x} dx, \\ &= [-x^2 e^{-\alpha x}]_0^\infty + 2\int_0^\infty x e^{-\alpha x} dx = 2/\alpha^2. \end{aligned}$$

Hence

$$V[X] \equiv E[X^2] - \{E[X]\}^2 = \frac{2}{\alpha^2} - \frac{1}{\alpha^2} = \frac{1}{\alpha^2}. \tag{4}$$

If follows that the mean and the standard deviation of the distribution $\text{Exp}(\alpha)$ are both equal to α^{-1}.

It is readily verified from (2) above that the quantile ξ_p of the $\text{Exp}(\alpha)$ distribution is given by

$$\xi_p = -\{\ln(1-p)\}/\alpha.$$

(compare Exercise 3.6B question 5 in which α was equal to 2).

The exponential distribution has been found to be relevant in many situations, particularly as a description of the distribution of the operational lifetimes of certain types of electronic components. It also arises in a natural way from a Poisson distribution. Suppose that the number Y of incidents of a certain type that may occur in a time period t units has the Poisson distribution $\text{Po}(\alpha t)$. Now let X denote the time between successive occurrences of the incident. It is clear that X is a continuous random variable with range space $R_X = \{x:x > 0\}$. Denote its p.d.f. by f and its c.d.f. by F. Then, for any $x > 0$,

$$F(x) = P(X \leqslant x) = P(Y \geqslant 1), \quad \text{where} \quad Y \sim \text{Po}(\alpha x).$$

Thus,

$$F(x) = 1 - P(Y = 0) = 1 - e^{-\alpha x},$$

and

$$f(x) = \alpha e^{-\alpha x},$$

so that

$$X \sim \text{Exp}(\alpha).$$

An unusual property of the exponential distribution is its 'lack of memory' in the following sense. For any $a > 0$ and $b > 0$, consider the conditional probability,

$$P(X > a+b \mid X > a) = \frac{P(X > a+b)}{P(X > a)} = \frac{1-F(a+b)}{1-F(a)}.$$

If $X \sim \text{Exp}(\alpha)$, then it follows from (2) that

$$P(X > a+b \mid X > a) = \frac{e^{-(a+b)\alpha}}{e^{-a\alpha}} = e^{-b\alpha}$$

$$= P(X > b).$$

Thus, for example, if X is the operational lifetime of a component, then at any time while it is still operational the probability that it will operate for a further time b is exactly the same as the probability that it will operate for time b from new.

EXERCISE 3.10

1 The duration, X minutes, of a telephone call made by a certain lady to her friend is a continuous random variable having probability density function f, where

$$f(x) = ce^{-x/5}, \qquad x > 0.$$

(i) Find the value of c. (ii) Calculate the probability that a call by this lady will last for (a) more than 10 minutes, (b) less than 5 minutes.

2 Fuses of a particular type are produced by two manufacturers, A and B. Those produced by A have lifetimes which are exponentially distributed with a mean of 100 hours, while those produced by B have lifetimes which are exponentially distributed with a mean of 150 hours. Each manufacturer offers a refund of the price for any fuse which lasts less than 50 hours. An electrical contractor purchases fuses in bulk. Manufacturer A charges 50 pence per fuse and manufacturer B charges 40 pence per fuse. From which manufacturer should the contractor purchase fuses in bulk in order to minimise the average cost per fuse?

3 If X is uniformly distributed over the interval (0, 2) and Y has the exponential distribution with mean λ, find the value of λ, correct to three significant figures, in each of the cases for which (i) $P(X < 1) = P(Y < 1)$, (ii) $V[X] = V[Y]$.

4 Given that X has an exponential distribution with mean 0·5, show that $Y = e^{-2X}$ has a uniform distribution.

5 The continuous random variable X has probability density function f, where

$$f(x) = ke^{-x}, \qquad x \geqslant 2.$$

(i) Express k in terms of e. (ii) Determine the probability density function of $Y = X^{-1}$.

REVIEW PROBLEMS ON CHAPTER 3

1 A greengrocer sells apples singly at 10 p each and by weight at 75 p per kilogramme. On any day the number, R, of apples sold singly is a discrete random variable having the binomial distribution

$$P(R = r) = \binom{10}{r}(0{\cdot}8)^r(0{\cdot}2)^{10-r}, \qquad r = 0, 1, 2, \ldots, 10,$$

and the weight, X kg, of apples sold by weight is a continuous random variable whose probability density function is given by

$$f(x) = 0{\cdot}08(x-5), \qquad 5 \leqslant x \leqslant 10.$$

Using tables, or otherwise, find, to two decimal places, the probabilities that in a day the number of apples sold singly will be (i) 8 or more, (ii) 8 or less, (iii) exactly 8.

Find the probabilities that in a day the weight of apples sold by weight will be (iv) 8 kg or more, (v) less than 6 kg.

Calculate the expected daily receipts from the sale of apples.

(*JMB 1982*)

2 The distribution of the salaries, in thousands of pounds, of persons in a certain profession can be approximated by a continuous distribution having probability density function f given by

$$f(x) = x(9-x)/90, \qquad 3 \leqslant x \leqslant 9.$$

(i) Find the mean salary and show that more than half the persons in the profession earn less than the mean salary. (ii) Each person in the profession has to contribute 5% of his/her salary towards a pension scheme. Find the mean amount contributed.

It is decided to raise this mean contribution to £305, by requiring each person earning more than £6000 to pay a fixed amount £C in addition to the 5% of his/her salary. Find the value of C. (*JMB 1980*)

3 The probability density function for the random variable X is given by

$$f(x) = \lambda \sin x, \qquad \text{for } 0 \leqslant x \leqslant \pi.$$

Find (i) the value of λ, (ii) $P(X \leqslant 1)$, (iii) the variance of the distribution.

(*L 1981*)

4 The continuous random variable X is distributed with probability density function

$$f(x) = cx^3(1-x^2), \qquad 0 < x < 1.$$

Find (i) the value of the constant c, (ii) the value of $E[X^2]$, (iii) the cumulative distribution function of X, (iv) the probability density function of $Y = 1 - X^2$, and verify that $E[Y] = 1 - E[X^2]$. (*WJEC 1981*)

5 The continuous random variable X has probability density function f given by

$$f(x) = k(3-x)^2, \qquad 0 \leqslant x \leqslant 3.$$

(i) Show that $k = 1/9$, and sketch the graph of f. (ii) Calculate $E[X]$ and prove that $V[X] = 27/80$. (iii) Obtain the cumulative distribution function F, where $F(x) = P(X \leqslant x)$. (*C 1981*)

6 The continuous random variable X is distributed with probability density function

$$f(x) = \tfrac{1}{2}x, \qquad 0 < x < 1,$$
$$f(x) = \tfrac{1}{6}(4-x), \qquad 1 \leqslant x \leqslant 4.$$

(i) Find the cumulative distribution function of X. (ii) Determine the mean of the random variable Y defined by

$$Y = X^2 \quad \text{for} \quad X < 1, \qquad Y = 1 \quad \text{for} \quad X \geqslant 1.$$

(iii) If $Z = (X+1)^{-1}$ has probability density function g, show that

$$g(z) = (1-z)/(2z^3) \quad \text{for} \quad \tfrac{1}{2} < z < 1,$$

and find an expression for $g(z)$ for all other values of z for which $g(z)$ is non-zero. (*WJEC 1981S*)

7 The maximum length to which a string of natural length a metres can be stretched before it snaps is $a(1+X^2)$ metres, where X is a continuous random variable whose probability density function is

$$f(x) = 4x, \qquad 0{\cdot}25 \leqslant x \leqslant 0{\cdot}75.$$

(i) Calculate the probability that a string can be stretched to $1\frac{1}{2}$ times its natural length without snapping. (ii) Find the value of $E[X^2]$ and hence find μ, the mean maximum stretched length of strings of natural length 1 metre. (iii) Find the probability density function of $Y = 1+X^2$, the maximum stretched length of a string of natural length 1 metre, and use it to verify the value of μ you obtained in (ii). (*WJEC 1982*)

8 The focal length of an adjustable lens system is a random variable F which is uniformly distributed over the interval $(a, 3a/2)$. An object placed at a distance $2a$ from the lens forms an image at a distance V from the lens where $1/2a + 1/V = 1/F$. Write down the probability density function of F and obtain the probability density function and the distribution function of V. Show that the mean of V is $2a(4\ln 2 - 1)$. (*C 1981*)

9 A is a fixed point on a circle with centre O and radius r, and P is a point chosen at random on the circle, so that the angle at O in the triangle OAP is uniformly distributed between 0 and π. Show that the probability density function of the length X of the chord AP is $2/\{\pi(4r^2 - x^2)^{1/2}\}$ for x between 0 and $2r$, and zero outside this range. Calculate the probability that the chord is longer than the radius. Find also the median value of X. Q is a fixed point on the circle and AQ $= k$. Find in terms of k and r, the probability that AP < AQ. (*JMB 1979*)

10 A continuous random variable X takes values in the interval $1 \leqslant x \leqslant 3$. The probability density function of X is given by $f(x) = k/x^2$. (i) Determine the value of k. (ii) Find $E[X]$ and $V[X]$. (iii) Find $P(X \geqslant 5/3)$. (iv) Calculate the lower and upper quartile values of X. (*C 1981*)

11 OA and OB are two perpendicular straight lines each of unit length. Squares are to be constructed using each of the following two methods:

Method 1 A point P is chosen at random on OB, so that the length X of OP is uniformly distributed over the interval (0, 1). A square is then drawn with AP as one of its sides.
Method 2 A straight line is drawn in a random direction from A to cut OB at Q, so that Z, the angle OAQ in radians, is uniformly distributed over the interval $(0, \frac{1}{4}\pi)$. A square is then drawn with AQ as one of its sides.

Assuming that each method is to be repeated a very large number of times, determine which of them will produce squares (i) having the larger area, on average; (ii) having the smaller variation in their areas. (*WJEC 1980S*)

12 Books on the top shelf at a library are directly accessible only to a person having a reachable height of at least 250 cm. It may be assumed that the reachable heights of adult male readers at the library are normally distributed with mean 264 cm and standard deviation 8 cm, and that those of adult female readers are normally distributed with mean 254 cm and standard deviation 5 cm. (i) Find, correct to three significant figures, the proportion of adult male readers and the proportion of adult female readers who are able to reach books on the top shelf. (ii) Given that 40% of all adult readers at the library are male, find the proportion, correct to three significant figures, of all adult readers who are able to reach books on the top shelf. (iii) The library decides to lower the top shelf so that 95% of all adult female readers will be able to reach books there. Find the corresponding percentage, correct to the nearest integer, of all adult readers who will then be able to reach books on the top shelf. *(JMB 1982)*

13 The operational lifetimes, in hours, of certain electronic components are normally distributed with mean μ and standard deviation 200. (i) Find the value of μ if 5% of the components will operate for less than 1200 hours. (ii) Suppose that $\mu = 1512$ and that a good component is one having a life time in excess of 1600 hours. Find the proportion of items that are good.

If the items are sold in batches of 100, (iii) name the distribution of the number of good components per batch, and find the mean and the variance of the proportion of good components per batch; (iv) find an approximate value for the probability that a batch will contain at least 40 good components. *(JMB 1980)*

14 The heights of two-year seedlings of *Tammia sinensis* from a certain nursery have a normal distribution with mean 30 cm and standard deviation 6 cm. The seedlings are graded according to height: Size P, over 38 cm; Size Q, between 24 cm and 38 cm; Size R, under 24 cm.

Seedlings of Size P are sold for £25 per hundred; Size Q, £20 per hundred; Size R, £10 per hundred. (i) Find the proportion of the seedlings in each size. (ii) Find the height exceeded by two seedlings in a hundred, on average. (iii) Find the expected selling price per 1000 seedlings. (iv) A man buys 1000 seedlings selected at random from the nursery but rejecting any of Size R. How much would he expect to pay for his seedlings? *(C 1981)*

15 A filling machine, which has two settings (coarse and fine) when filling 50 kg bags of fertiliser, produces fillings whose weights are normally distributed. On the coarse setting, the standard deviation of the filling is 0·5 kg and the cost per fill is 5 p. On the fine setting, the standard deviation of the filling is 0·25 kg and the cost per fill is 10 p. If the mean weight of fillings has to be adjusted so that only 1% of the fillings are under weight, find the more economical setting if the price of the fertiliser is 10 p per kg. Should the setting be changed if the price of the fertiliser falls to 9 p per kg? *(L 1980)*

16 State under what circumstances it would be appropriate to use, as an approximation to the binomial distribution, (i) the Poisson distribution (ii) the normal distribution.

A random sample of size 200 is taken from a large batch of screws containing a proportion p which are defective. The batch is accepted if the number of defective screws found in the sample is less than or equal to 5. The probability of the batch being accepted is denoted by P_A. Write down an expression for P_A in terms of p and state the values of P_A when $p = 0$ and $p = 1$. Use approximating distributions to obtain values for P_A when $p = 0{\cdot}01$, $p = 0{\cdot}02$. Sketch the graph of P_A against p. Use an approximating distribution to obtain the probability that there are 18 or fewer defective screws in a random sample of size 1000 when $p = 0{\cdot}016$. (*JMB 1981*)

17 Adult men in a certain country have heights which are normally distributed with a mean of 1·81 m and a standard deviation of 0·05 m.
(i) Estimate the number of men in a random sample of 100 men whose heights, when measured to the nearest 0·01 m, exceed 1·90 m. (ii) Find the probability that a man selected at random will have a height, when measured to the nearest 0·01 m, less than 1·72 m. (iii) Find the height which is exceeded by 90% of the men. (*L 1980*)

18 The prices of houses on an estate agent's books are approximately normally distributed with a mean price of £18,000. Given that 90% of the houses are priced at less than £30,000, find the standard deviation of the house prices and the percentage of the houses with a price of less than £10,000. Find the mean price and the standard deviation of the prices when the price of each house is increased by (i) £2,000, (ii) 10%. (*L 1981*)

19 Mass-produced right circular cylindrical pipes have internal diameters that are normally distributed with a mean of 10 cm and a standard deviation of 0·04 cm. (i) Find the probability that a randomly chosen pipe will have an internal diameter greater than 10·3 cm. (ii) Find the expected number of pipes in a random sample of 100 pipes that have internal diameters in the range from 9·7 cm to 10·3 cm. (iii) Find the expected value of the internal cross-sectional area of a randomly chosen pipe; give your answer correct to three significant figures. (*WJEC 1980*)

20 The number of characters that are mistyped by a copytypist in any assignment has a Poisson distribution, the average number of mistyped characters per page being 0·8. In an assignment of 80 pages calculate, to three decimal places, (i) the probability that the first page will contain exactly two mistyped characters, (ii) the probability that the first mistyped character will appear on the third page, (iii) an approximate value for the probability that the total number of mistyped characters in the 80 pages will be at most 50. (*WJEC 1982*)

21 A machine fills and seals bags of dried fruit which are supposed to weigh 1 kg each. To check production, a large random sample of bags was taken and their contents weighed. It was found from these that the mean weight was 1·03 kg and the standard deviation of the weights was 0·011 kg. Assuming that the weights are normally distributed, estimate the percentage of underweight bags which the machine produces. The manager decides that if the machine produces more than 4% of underweight bags he must stop production. Given that the standard deviation remains constant, find the least value to which the mean weight may be lowered whilst still keeping the machine in production. Hence find the average weight of dried fruit which could be saved per 100 bags by lowering the mean in this way, while still maintaining production (*L 1982*)

22 The probability density function $f(t)$ of the length of life, T hours, of a certain colour television tube is given by

$$f(t) = ke^{-kt}, \qquad t > 0,$$

k being a positive constant. Show that the mean and standard deviation of this distribution are each equal to $1/k$. Find the probability that a tube will last for t hours more, given that it has already lasted for t_0 hours without failing. A certain television shop has three similar models working in the window. Find the probability that exactly one will fail in the first t_0 hours, another will fail in the next t_0 hours, and the third will last for more than $2t_0$ hours. (*L 1980*)

23 A person frequently makes telephone calls to destinations for which each call is charged at the rate of 15 p per minute or part of a minute. The cost of such a call is X p, and its duration, T minutes, has the exponential probability density function

$$\mathrm{f}(t) = \alpha e^{-\alpha t}, \qquad t > 0.$$

Show that

$$P(X = 15r) = e^{-r\alpha}(e^{\alpha} - 1), \qquad r = 1, 2, 3 \ldots,$$

and that the mean cost per call in pence is $15/(1 - e^{-\alpha})$.

When a caller telephones a particular company, there is a probability of $\frac{1}{2}$ that he will be asked to hold the line. When he is asked to hold the line and he decides to do so, the total time taken for the call has the above exponential distribution with $\alpha = 1/6$; when he is not asked to hold the line the total time for the call has the above exponential distribution with $\alpha = \frac{1}{2}$. Calculate the expected cost if he rings the company and is asked to hold the line and he (i) holds and completes the call, (ii) rings off and then rings later, completing the second call whether he is asked to hold or not. Assume that a wasted call costs 15 p and take $e^{-1/2} = 0{\cdot}6065$, $e^{-1/6} = 0{\cdot}8465$.

(*JMB 1981*)

4 Joint Distributions and Independent Random Variables

4.1 Joint distribution of two discrete random variables

Let X denote a discrete random variable having range space $R_X = \{x_1, x_2, \ldots, x_m\}$, and let Y denote another discrete random variable having range space $R_Y = \{y_1, y_2, \ldots, y_n\}$. We shall consider situations where X and Y both relate to one random experiment and where they relate to two distinct random experiments.

For the simultaneous consideration of X and Y, we introduce the notion of the two-dimensional random variable (X, Y) having range space R_{XY}, defined to be the set of all possible values of (X, Y). With R_X and R_Y as defined above,

$$R_{XY} = \{(x_i, y_j): i = 1, 2, \ldots, m; j = 1, 2, \ldots, n\}.$$

The *probability distribution of* (X, Y), or equivalently the *joint probability distribution of* X *and* Y, is then a description of how the one unit of probability is shared among the elements of R_{XY}. This requires the specification of the values of $\mathrm{P}\{(X = x_i) \cap (Y = y_j)\}$ for all (x_i, y_j). It is often convenient to display such a joint distribution in the form of a two-way table as shown in the following example.

EXAMPLE 1 *Let X denote the number of heads obtained in three tosses of a fair coin, and let Y denote the number of heads obtained in the first two of these tosses. Find the joint distribution of X and Y.*

Here,

$$R_X = \{0, 1, 2, 3\}, \quad \text{and} \quad R_Y = \{0, 1, 2\}$$

so that

$$R_{XY} = \{(0,0), (0, 1), (0, 2), (1, 0), (1, 1), (1, 2), (2, 0), (2, 1), (2, 2), (3, 0), (3, 1), (3, 2)\}.$$

We now need to evaluate the probabilities of the elements of R_{XY}.

Since X cannot be less than Y and cannot exceed $Y + 1$, the only possible outcomes (x, y) are those such that $y \leqslant x \leqslant y+1$. Any element of R_{XY} not satisfying these conditions will have probability zero. Consequently, we need only evaluate the probabilities of the outcomes (0, 0), (1, 0), (1, 1), (2, 1), (2, 2), (3, 2).

$$
\begin{aligned}
\mathrm{P}\{(0,0)\} &= \mathrm{P}\{(X=0)\cap(Y=0)\} = \mathrm{P}\text{ (no head tossed)} = 1/8,\\
\mathrm{P}\{(1,0)\} &= \mathrm{P}\{(X=1)\cap(Y=0)\} = \mathrm{P}\{(\mathrm{t},\mathrm{t},\mathrm{h})\} = 1/8,\\
\mathrm{P}\{(1,1)\} &= \mathrm{P}\{(X=1)\cap(Y=1)\} = \mathrm{P}\{\mathrm{h},\mathrm{t},\mathrm{t})\cup(\mathrm{t},\mathrm{h},\mathrm{t})\} = \tfrac{1}{4},\\
\mathrm{P}\{(2,1)\} &= \mathrm{P}\{(X=2)\cap(Y=1)\} = \mathrm{P}\{(\mathrm{h},\mathrm{t},\mathrm{h})\cup(\mathrm{t},\mathrm{h},\mathrm{h})\} = \tfrac{1}{4},\\
\mathrm{P}\{(2,2)\} &= \mathrm{P}\{(X=2)\cap(Y=2)\} = \mathrm{P}\{(\mathrm{h},\mathrm{h},\mathrm{t})\} = 1/8,\\
\mathrm{P}\{(3,2)\} &= \mathrm{P}\{(X=3)\cap(Y=2)\} = \mathrm{P}\{(\mathrm{h},\mathrm{h},\mathrm{h})\} = 1/8.
\end{aligned}
$$

Observe that these probabilities sum to unity, as they should. The joint distribution of X and Y can now be displayed as in the two-way table, Table 4.1.

Table 4.1 Joint distribution of X and Y

		x 0	1	2	3	$\mathrm{P}(Y=y)$
	0	$\frac{1}{8}$	$\frac{1}{8}$	0	0	$\frac{1}{4}$
y	1	0	$\frac{1}{4}$	$\frac{1}{4}$	0	$\frac{1}{2}$
	2	0	0	$\frac{1}{8}$	$\frac{1}{8}$	$\frac{1}{4}$
$\mathrm{P}(X=x)$		$\frac{1}{8}$	$\frac{3}{8}$	$\frac{3}{8}$	$\frac{1}{8}$	1

Observe that the sum of the probabilities in any column is the probability that X takes the value x at the head of the column. Hence, the top and bottom rows of Table 4.1 display the probability distribution of X, which was derived directly in Example 1, §2.2. Similarly, the first and last columns of Table 4.1 give the probability distribution of Y. For this reason, individual distributions which are deduced from a joint distribution are often referred to as the *marginal distributions*, but this description is superfluous since any random variable will have a unique distribution.

In addition to providing the individual distributions, a joint distribution also enables us to deduce the distribution of any function of the two random variables, as illustrated in the following example.

EXAMPLE 2 *With X and Y as defined in Example 1, find the distributions of (i) $U = X-Y$, and (ii) $V = XY$. Hence derive the expected values of U and V and compare them with the values of* $\mathrm{E}[X]-\mathrm{E}[Y]$ *and* $\mathrm{E}[X]\mathrm{E}[Y]$, *respectively.*

Tables 4.2a and b show the values of U and V, respectively, corresponding to the various possible values of (x, y), and for convenience, the associated probabilities are given in parentheses.

Table 4.2a Values of U

		x			
		0	1	2	3
y	0	$0(\frac{1}{8})$	$1(\frac{1}{8})$	$2(0)$	$3(0)$
	1	$-1(0)$	$0(\frac{1}{4})$	$1(\frac{1}{4})$	$2(0)$
	2	$-2(0)$	$-1(0)$	$0(\frac{1}{8})$	$1(\frac{1}{8})$

Table 4.2b Values of V

		x			
		0	1	2	3
y	0	$0(\frac{1}{8})$	$0(\frac{1}{8})$	$0(0)$	$0(0)$
	1	$0(0)$	$1(\frac{1}{4})$	$2(\frac{1}{4})$	$3(0)$
	2	$0(0)$	$2(0)$	$4(\frac{1}{8})$	$6(\frac{1}{8})$

The distributions of U and V are then as shown in Tables 4.3a and b, respectively.

Table 4.3a Distribution of U

u	0	1
$P(U = u)$	$\frac{1}{2}$	$\frac{1}{2}$

Table 4.3b Distribution of V

v	0	1	2	4	6
$P(V = v)$	$\frac{1}{4}$	$\frac{1}{4}$	$\frac{1}{4}$	$\frac{1}{8}$	$\frac{1}{8}$

From Tables 4.3a and b we find

$$E[U] = 0 \times \tfrac{1}{2} + 1 \times \tfrac{1}{2} = \tfrac{1}{2}$$

$$E[V] = 0 \times \tfrac{1}{4} + 1 \times \tfrac{1}{4} + 2 \times \tfrac{1}{4} + 4 \times \tfrac{1}{8} + 6 \times \tfrac{1}{8} = 2.$$

From the distributions of X and Y, as displayed in the margins of Table 4.1, we have

$$E[X] = 0 \times \tfrac{1}{8} + 1 \times \tfrac{3}{8} + 2 \times \tfrac{3}{8} + 2 \times \tfrac{1}{8} = 1\tfrac{1}{2},$$

$$E[Y] = 0 \times \tfrac{1}{4} + 1 \times \tfrac{1}{2} + 2 \times \tfrac{1}{4} = 1.$$

Hence,

$$E[X] - E[Y] = 1\tfrac{1}{2} - 1 = \tfrac{1}{2} = E[U],$$

$$E[X]E[Y] = 1\tfrac{1}{2} \times 1 = 1\tfrac{1}{2} \neq E[V].$$

EXERCISE 4.1

1 The discrete random variables X and Y have the joint distribution given in the following table. (i) Find the mean and the variance of X. (ii) Find the distribution of $Z = Y - X$, and hence evaluate $\mathrm{E}[Z]$ and $\mathrm{V}[Z]$. (iii) Evaluate $\mathrm{P}(X > Y)$ (continued in Exercise 4.2 question 1).

		x = 1	x = 2
y	1	$2c$	c
	2	$2c$	$4c$
	3	$2c$	c

2 Three balls are drawn at random without replacement from a bag which contains three white balls, two blue balls, and one red ball. Let X denote the number of white balls drawn, and let Y denote the number of blue balls drawn. (i) Display the joint distribution of X and Y in a two-way table. (ii) Deduce the individual distributions of X, Y, and Z, where Z is the number of red balls drawn (continued in Exercise 4.2 question 3).

3 A perfectly balanced tetrahedral die has its faces numbered 1, 2, 3 and 4, respectively. When this die is thrown onto a table, the score obtained is the number on the face in contact with the table. In three throws of the die, let X denote the lowest and Y the highest of the three scores. (i) Display the joint distribution of X and Y in a table. (ii) Evaluate the expected values of X, $X+Y$, and XY (continued in Exercise 4.2 question 2).

4 Alec and Bill play a game in which three fair dice are thrown simultaneously by Alec. For each die showing a score of 6, Alec pays 3 p into a 'kitty', and for each die showing a score of 3 or less, Bill pays 1 p into the 'kitty'. Let X and Y, respectively, denote the amounts paid into the 'kitty' by Alec and Bill as a result of one throw of the dice. Exhibit the joint distribution of X and Y in a table. Show that the game is fair in the sense that X and Y have equal expected values. Show also that the variance of X is five times that of Y.

5 A discrete random variable X takes the values 0 and 1 only, the respective probabilities of these values being p and $1-p$, where $0 < p < 1$. Find $\mathrm{E}[X]$ and $\mathrm{V}[X]$ in terms of p.

A second discrete random variable Y also takes the values 0 and 1 only. Find the joint probability distribution of X and Y given that $\mathrm{P}(Y=1|X=1) = \mathrm{P}(Y=0|X=0) = p$ and $\mathrm{P}(Y=1|X=0) = \mathrm{P}(Y=0|X=1) = 1-p$. Show that $\mathrm{E}[X+Y] = \mathrm{E}[X]+\mathrm{E}[Y]$, and determine the value of p for which $\mathrm{E}[XY] = \mathrm{E}[X]\mathrm{E}[Y]$.

4.2 Expectation

Let X and Y denote two discrete random variables having the range space $R_{XY} = \{(x_i, y_j)\colon i = 1, 2, \ldots, m;\ j = 1, 2, \ldots, n\}$, and let $P\{(X = x_1) \cap (Y = y_j)\} = p_{ij}$. Then for any function $\mathrm{H}(X, Y)$, we define the *expectation* or *expected value* of $\mathrm{H}(X,Y)$ to be

$$\mathrm{E}[\mathrm{H}(X,Y)] = \sum_{i=1}^{m} \sum_{j=1}^{n} \mathrm{H}(x_i, y_j)p_{ij}, \tag{1}$$

a natural extension to the definition given in §2.3.

Let us apply this definition to evaluate $\mathrm{E}[X-Y]$ and $\mathrm{E}[XY]$ where X and Y are as defined in Example 1, §4.1. Tables 4.2a and b are convenient for this purpose, the entries in the bodies of these tables being the values, and their associated probabilities, of $X-Y$ and XY, respectively. From Table 4.2a we have

$$\begin{aligned}\mathrm{E}[X-Y] = {} & (0)(\tfrac{1}{8}) + (1)(\tfrac{1}{8}) + (2)(0) + (3)(0) \\ & + (-1)(0) + (0)(\tfrac{1}{4}) + (1)(\tfrac{1}{4}) + (2)(0) \\ & + (-2)(0) + (-1)(0) + (0)(\tfrac{1}{8}) + (1)(\tfrac{1}{8}) \\ = {} & \tfrac{1}{2},\end{aligned}$$

exactly as obtained in Example 2, §4.1. Similarly, from Table 4.2b, we have $\mathrm{E}[XY] = 2$, agreeing with the value obtained in Example 2, §4.1.

For the particular case when $\mathrm{H}(X,Y) = X$, the above definition reduces to that given in §2.3.

If $\mathrm{H}(X,Y) = \mathrm{H}_1(X,Y) + \mathrm{H}_2(X,Y)$, then from (1) above,

$$\begin{aligned}\mathrm{E}[\mathrm{H}(X,Y)] &= \sum_{i=1}^{m} \sum_{j=1}^{n} \{\mathrm{H}_1(x_i, y_j) + \mathrm{H}_2(x_i, y_j)\} p_{ij} \\ &= \sum_{i=1}^{m} \sum_{j=1}^{n} \mathrm{H}_1(x_i, y_j)p_{ij} + \sum_{i=1}^{m} \sum_{j=1}^{n} \mathrm{H}_2(x_i, y_j)p_{ij} \\ &= \mathrm{E}[\mathrm{H}_1(X,Y)] + \mathrm{E}[\mathrm{H}_2(X,Y)].\end{aligned} \tag{2}$$

The following examples illustrate the use of (2).

$$\begin{aligned}\mathrm{E}[3X^3 + 2Y^2] &= \mathrm{E}[3X^3] + \mathrm{E}[2Y^2], \\ \mathrm{E}[2XY + X^{1/2}] &= \mathrm{E}[2XY] + \mathrm{E}[X^{1/2}], \\ \mathrm{E}[XY(X^2 - Y^2)] &= \mathrm{E}[X^3Y - XY^3] = \mathrm{E}[X^3Y] - \mathrm{E}[XY^3].\end{aligned}$$

A particular form of (2) which is important is that when $\mathrm{H}(X, Y) = aX + bY$, where a and b are constants. In this case, (2) becomes

$$\begin{aligned}\mathrm{E}[aX + bY] &= \mathrm{E}[aX] + \mathrm{E}[bY] \\ &= a\mathrm{E}[X] + b\mathrm{E}[Y],\end{aligned} \tag{3}$$

on using the properties of E[ ] established in §2.3.1. In particular,

$$\mathrm{E}[X \pm Y] = \mathrm{E}[X] \pm \mathrm{E}[Y]. \tag{4}$$

We demonstrated this equality for $\mathrm{E}[X-Y]$ in Example 2, §4.1.

EXAMPLE 1 *A fair die is tossed six times. Let X denote the number of times a 6 is* *tossed, and let Y denote the number of times an even score is tossed. The pay-out in pence after the die has been tossed six times is given by $Z = 10X - 3Y$. Find the expected pay-out.*

From (3) above the expected pay-out in pence is

$$E[Z] = E[10X - 3Y] = 10E[X] - 3E[Y].$$

Since in any toss of a fair die the probability of a 6 is $\frac{1}{6}$, and the probability of an even score is $\frac{1}{2}$, and the tosses may be assumed to be independent, it follows that

$$X \sim B(n = 6, p = \tfrac{1}{6}) \quad \text{and} \quad Y \sim B(n = 6, p = \tfrac{1}{2}).$$

From (4) of §2.6,

$$E[X] = 6(\tfrac{1}{6}) = 1, \quad \text{and} \quad E[Y] = 6(\tfrac{1}{2}) = 3.$$

Hence, the expected pay-out in pence is

$$E[Z] = 10(1) - 3(3) = 1.$$

EXERCISE 4.2

1 With X and Y having the joint distribution given in Exercise 4.1 question 1, use the definition of expectation given in this section to evaluate $E[Y - X]$ and $V[Y - X]$. Compare your answers with those you obtained for $E[Z]$ and $V[Z]$ in Exercise 4.1 question 1 (ii).

2 With X and Y as defined in Exercise 4.1 question 3, use the definition of expectation given in this section to evaluate $E[X+Y]$ and $E[XY]$, checking your answers with those you obtained in Exercise 4.1 question 3 (ii).

3 In Exercise 4.1 question 2, suppose that each red ball drawn scores 3 points, each blue ball drawn scores 2 points, and each white ball drawn scores 1 point. Find the expected total score from the three balls drawn.

4 The following table shows the joint distribution of two discrete random variables X and Y.

		x 1	2	3	4
y	0	0	0	0	p
	1	0	p^2	p^2	0
	2	p	p^2	p^2	0
	3	0	0	0	p

Find (i) the value of p, (ii) the expected values of $5Y-3X$, X^2-Y^2 and Y/X.

4.3 Independence of two discrete random variables

Two discrete random variables X and Y having range space

$$R_{XY} = \{(x_i, y_j): i = 1, 2, \ldots, m; j = 1, 2, \ldots, n\}$$

are said to be *independent* if and only if

$$\mathrm{P}\{(X = x_i) \cap (Y = y_j)\} = \mathrm{P}(X = x_i)\mathrm{P}(Y = y_j) \qquad (1)$$

for *every* (x_i, y_j) in R_{XY}.

In accordance with the definition of the independence of two events given in §1.9, (1) above states that X and Y are independent only if the events $A_i = (X = x_i)$ and $B_j = (Y = y_j)$ are independent for every $i = 1, 2, \ldots, m$ and $j = 1, 2, \ldots, n$.

EXAMPLE 1 *Determine whether or not the random variables X and Y defined in Example* 1, §4.1 *are independent.*

Referring to Table 4.1 we see that

$$\mathrm{P}\{(X = 0) \cap (Y = 0)\} = \tfrac{1}{8},\ \mathrm{P}(X = 0) = \tfrac{1}{8},\ \text{and}\ \mathrm{P}(Y = 0) = \tfrac{1}{4}.$$

Since $\mathrm{P}(X = 0)\mathrm{P}(Y = 0) = 1/(32) \neq \mathrm{P}(X = 0) \cap (Y = 0)\}$, it follows that X and Y are not independent.

EXAMPLE 2 *X and Y are discrete random variables having the joint distribution displayed in Table* 4.4. *Verify that* (i) *X and Y are independent,* (ii) $\mathrm{E}[X^2Y] = \mathrm{E}[X^2]\mathrm{E}[Y]$, (iii) $\mathrm{V}[Y-2X] = \mathrm{V}[Y]+4\mathrm{V}[X]$.

Table 4.4 Distribution of X and Y

		x = 0	x = 1	x = 2
y	0	p	$2p$	$3p$
	1	$2p$	$4p$	$6p$
	2	$3p$	$6p$	$9p$
	3	$4p$	$8p$	$12p$

Since the total probability must be unity, summing the entries in the body of the table gives

$$60p = 1, \quad \text{or} \quad p = 1/(60).$$

(i) With $p = 1/(60)$ and using the marginal totals from Table 4.4, the distributions of X and Y are as shown in Tables 4.5a and b, respectively.

Table 4.5a Distribution of X

x	0	1	2
$\mathrm{P}(X = x)$	$\frac{1}{6}$	$\frac{1}{3}$	$\frac{1}{2}$

Table 4.5b Distribution of Y

y	0	1	2	3
$\mathrm{P}(Y = y)$	$\frac{1}{10}$	$\frac{1}{5}$	$\frac{3}{10}$	$\frac{2}{5}$

From these tables we find that

$$\mathrm{P}(X = 0)\mathrm{P}(Y = 0) = \tfrac{1}{6} \times \tfrac{1}{10} = \tfrac{1}{60} = \mathrm{P}\{(X = 0) \cap (Y = 0)\},$$
$$\mathrm{P}(X = 1)\mathrm{P}(Y = 0) = \tfrac{1}{3} \times \tfrac{1}{10} = \tfrac{1}{30} = \mathrm{P}\{(X = 1) \cap (Y = 0)\},$$

and proceeding similarly for the remaining 10 possibilities we find that

$$\mathrm{P}\{(X = x_i) \cap (Y = y_j)\} = \mathrm{P}(X = x_i)\mathrm{P}(Y = y_j) \text{ for every } (x_i, y_j).$$

Hence, X and Y are independent.
(ii) From (1) of §4.2 and Table 4.4, on ignoring zero values of x^2y, we find

$$\begin{aligned}\mathrm{E}[X^2Y] &= (4p+24p)+(12p+72p)+(24p+144p)\\ &= 280p = 280/60 = 4\tfrac{2}{3}.\end{aligned}$$

From Tables 4.5a and b,

$$\mathrm{E}[X^2] = 0\times\tfrac{1}{6}+1^2\times\tfrac{1}{3}+2^2\times\tfrac{1}{2} = 2\tfrac{1}{3}.$$
$$\mathrm{E}[Y] = 0\times\tfrac{1}{10}+1\times\tfrac{1}{5}+2\times\tfrac{3}{10}+3\times\tfrac{2}{5} = 2.$$

Hence

$$\mathrm{E}[X^2]\mathrm{E}[Y] = 2\tfrac{1}{3}\times 2 = 4\tfrac{2}{3} = \mathrm{E}[X^2Y].$$

(iii) Let $Z = Y-2X$. To find the variance of Z we shall first find its distribution. The values of Z corresponding to the various combinations of values of X and Y are shown in Table 4.6, and the distribution of Z is shown in Table 4.7.

Table 4.6 Values of $Z = Y-2X$

		x 0	1	2
y	0	0	−2	−4
	1	1	−1	−3
	2	2	0	−2
	3	3	1	−1

Table 4.7 Distribution of Z

z	−4	−3	−2	−1	0	1	2	3
$\mathrm{P}(Z = z)$	1/20	1/10	11/60	4/15	7/60	1/6	1/20	1/15

From Table 4.7 we find,

$$\begin{aligned}\mathrm{E}[Z] &= -4\times\tfrac{1}{20}+-3\times\tfrac{1}{10}+-2\times\tfrac{11}{60}+-1\times\tfrac{4}{15}\\ &\quad +1\times\tfrac{1}{6}+2\times\tfrac{1}{20}+3\times\tfrac{1}{15} = -\tfrac{2}{3},\\ \mathrm{E}[Z^2] &= 16\times\tfrac{1}{20}+9\times\tfrac{1}{10}+4\times\tfrac{11}{60}+1\times\tfrac{4}{15}+1\times\tfrac{1}{6}\\ &\quad +4\times\tfrac{1}{20}+9\times\tfrac{1}{15} = 3\tfrac{2}{3},\end{aligned}$$

and therefore,

$$\mathrm{V}[Z] = 3\tfrac{2}{3}-(-\tfrac{2}{3})^2 = 29/9.$$

Since $\mathrm{E}[Y] = 2$, we shall use the formula $\mathrm{V}[Y] = \mathrm{E}[(Y-2)^2]$ for evaluating $\mathrm{V}[Y]$. Using Table 4.5b we have

$$\mathrm{V}[Y] = \mathrm{E}[(Y-2)^2] = 4\times\tfrac{1}{10}+1\times\tfrac{1}{5}+0+1\times\tfrac{2}{5} = 1.$$

From Table 4.5a,

$$E[X] = 1 \times \tfrac{1}{3} + 2 \times \tfrac{1}{2} = 1\tfrac{1}{3}.$$

In (ii) we established that $E[X^2] = 2\tfrac{1}{3}$; hence,

$$V[X] = 2\tfrac{1}{3} - (1\tfrac{1}{3})^2 = 5/9.$$

It follows that

$$V[Y] + 4V[X] = 1 + 4 \times \tfrac{5}{9} = 29/9 = V[Z].$$

EXERCISE 4.3

1 The two random variables X and Y have the joint distribution shown in the following table.

		x = 0	1	2
y	0	p	p^2	p^2
	1	$2p^2$	p^2	p^2
	2	$2p^2$	$p-p^2$	p^2
	3	p	p^2	p^2

(i) Determine the value of p. (ii) Determine whether or not X and Y are independent. (iii) Find the distribution of $Z = X+Y$ and use it to verify that $E[X+Y] = E[X]+E[Y]$.

2 A committee of 10 members consists of three married couples, two spinsters and two bachelors. Two members of this committee are chosen at random to attend a national conference. Let X denote the number of females chosen and let Y denote the number of married persons chosen. (i) Construct a table to exhibit the joint distribution of X and Y. (ii) By first finding the distribution of $Z = XY$, or otherwise, show that $E[XY] = E[X][Y]$. (iii) Determine whether or not X and Y are independent.

3 X and Y are *independent* random variables having the distributions shown in the following tables:

x	0	1	2
$P(X = x)$	$\frac{1}{6}$	$\frac{3}{4}$	$\frac{1}{12}$

y	0	1	2	3
$P(Y = y)$	$\frac{1}{5}$	$\frac{2}{5}$	$\frac{3}{10}$	$\frac{1}{10}$

(i) Find the mean and the variance of each of X and Y.
(ii) Display the joint distribution of X and Y in a two-way table. Hence determine the distribution of $Z = 2Y - X$, and find the mean and the variance of this distribution
(iii) Use your answers in (i) and (ii) to verify that

$$E[2Y - X] = 2E[Y] - E[X] \quad \text{and that} \quad V[2Y - X] = 4V[Y] + V[X].$$

4.4 Special case of independent random variables

It frequently happens that we are interested in discrete random variables X and Y, where X is defined with respect to one random experiment (e.g. X = the number of heads obtained in three tosses of a coin), and Y is defined with respect to another random experiment which is independent of the first one (e.g. Y = the number of boys in a family of three children). Since any event defined with respect to the first random experiment will be independent of any event defined with respect to the second one, it follows that the event $(X = x_i)$ will be independent of the event $(Y = y_j)$ for all possible x_i and y_j. In accordance with the definition given in §4.3 such random variables X and Y will be independent.

EXAMPLE 1 *Alan tosses two fair coins simultaneously, and, at the same time, Bill tosses three fair coins simultaneously. Calculate the probability that Alan will toss more heads than Bill.*

Let X denote the number of heads tossed by Alan, and let Y denote the number of heads tossed by Bill. Then

$$X \sim \mathrm{B}(n = 2, p = \tfrac{1}{2}) \quad \text{and} \quad Y \sim \mathrm{B}(n = 3, p = \tfrac{1}{2}).$$

Since the random experiments performed by Alan and Bill are independent, X and Y are independent.

We need to evaluate $\mathrm{P}(X > Y)$. Since

$$R_X = \{0, 1, 2\} \quad \text{and} \quad R_Y = \{0, 1, 2, 3\},$$

the event $(X > Y)$ is equivalent to

$$\{(X = 2) \cap (Y = 0)\} \cup \{(X = 2) \cap (Y = 1)\} \cup \{(X = 1) \cap (Y = 0)\},$$

and therefore,

$$\mathrm{P}(X > Y) = \mathrm{P}\{(X = 2) \cap (Y = 0)\} + \mathrm{P}\{(X = 2) \cap (Y = 1)\} + \mathrm{P}\{(X = 1) \cap (Y = 0)\}.$$

Since X and Y are independent we have

$$\mathrm{P}(X > Y) = \mathrm{P}(X = 2)\mathrm{P}(Y = 0) + \mathrm{P}(X = 2)\mathrm{P}(Y = 1) + \mathrm{P}(X = 1)\mathrm{P}(Y = 0)$$

$$= \tfrac{1}{4} \times \tfrac{1}{8} + \tfrac{1}{4} \times \tfrac{3}{8} + \tfrac{1}{2} \times \tfrac{1}{8} = 6/32 = 3/16.$$

A discussion of the joint distribution of two continuous random variables is beyond the mathematical level of this text. However, in the special case where X and Y are continuous random variables defined with respect to two *independent* random experiments, it is intuitively plausible to assume that X and Y are independent in the sense that any event in terms of X only will be independent of any event in terms of Y only. This would also apply if one of X, Y is discrete and the other is continuous.

EXAMPLE 2 *A manufacturer produces rods of two types, A and B. Rods of type*

A have lengths in cm that are uniformly distributed over the interval (10, 15), *while rods of type B have lengths that are normally distributed with mean* 12 *cm and standard deviation* 1 *cm. If one rod of each type is chosen at random, calculate the probability that the longer of the two rods will have a length greater than* 13 *cm.*

Let X cm denote the length of the chosen type A rod, then $X \sim U(10, 15)$. Let Ycm denote the length of the chosen type B rod; then $Y \sim N(12, 1)$. Since choosing a rod of type A and choosing a rod of type B are independent experiments, X and Y are independent.

Let Z denote the length of the longer of the two chosen rods, so that Z is the larger of X and Y; we need to evaluate $P(Z > 13)$.

The event $(Z > 13)$ is equivalent to at least one of X and Y being greater than 13, the complement of which is that neither X nor Y is greater than 13. Hence,

$$\begin{aligned} P(Z > 13) = 1 - P(Z \leqslant 13) &= 1 - P\{(X \leqslant 13) \cap (Y \leqslant 13)\} \\ &= 1 - P(X \leqslant 13)P(Y \leqslant 13), \end{aligned}$$

since X and Y are independent. Now,

$$P(X \leqslant 13) = \frac{13-10}{15-10} = 0{\cdot}6,$$

and

$$P(Y \leqslant 13) = \Phi\left\{\frac{13-12}{1}\right\} = \Phi(1) = 0{\cdot}8413.$$

Hence,

$$P(Z > 13) = 1 - 0{\cdot}6 \times 0{\cdot}8413 = 0{\cdot}495$$

to three decimal places.

EXERCISE 4.4

1 A fair cubical die is thrown twice. Calculate the probability that the score on the second throw will be at least twice that on the first throw.

2 Two balls are drawn at random without replacement from a box which contains five red and five white balls, and then three balls are drawn at random without replacement from another box which contains four red and six white balls. Calculate the probability that (i) the two balls drawn from the first box will include more red balls than the three drawn from the second box, (ii) a total of four red balls will be drawn.

3 X and Y are independent continuous random variables having probability density functions f and g, where

$$\begin{aligned} f(x) &= 3x^2, \quad 0 < x < 1, \\ g(y) &= 2(1-y), \quad 0 < y < 1. \end{aligned}$$

(i) Find the probability that the larger of a randomly observed value of X and a randomly observed value of Y will be greater than $\frac{1}{2}$.

(ii) Find the probability that the smaller of a randomly observed value of X and a randomly observed value of Y will be less than $\frac{1}{2}$.

4.5 Some properties of independent random variables

Let X and Y denote independent discrete random variables having range space

$$R_{XY} = \{(x_i, y_j): i = 1, 2, \ldots, m; j = 1, 2, \ldots, n\},$$

so that

$$\mathrm{P}\{(X = x_i) \cap (Y = y_j)\} = \mathrm{P}(X = x_i)\mathrm{P}(Y = y_j)$$

for every (x_i, y_j) in R_{XY}.

Consider the expectation of the product $\mathrm{H}_1(X)\mathrm{H}_2(Y)$ of a function of X *only* with a function of Y *only*. Using the independence of X and Y in (1) of §4.2,

$$\begin{aligned} \mathrm{E}[\mathrm{H}_1(X)\mathrm{H}_2(Y)] &= \sum_{i=1}^{m} \sum_{j=1}^{n} \mathrm{H}_1(x_i)\mathrm{H}_2(y_j)\mathrm{P}(X = x_i)\mathrm{P}(Y = y_j), \\ &= \left\{\sum_i \mathrm{H}_1(x_i)\mathrm{P}(X = x_i)\right\} . \left\{\sum_j \mathrm{H}_2(y_j)\mathrm{P}(Y = y_j)\right\} \\ &= \mathrm{E}[\mathrm{H}_1(X)]\mathrm{E}[\mathrm{H}_2(Y)]. \end{aligned} \quad (1)$$

Thus, when X and Y are independent, *the expected value of the product of a function of X only and a function of Y only is equal to the product of the expected values of the two functions.* We shall assume that this result is also true when X and Y are continuous.

For example, for any independent random variables X and Y, we have

$$\mathrm{E}[X^2Y] = \mathrm{E}[X^2]\mathrm{E}[Y],$$

a result we demonstrated to be true for X and Y as defined in Example 2, §4.3.

A particularly important special case of (1) is

$$\mathrm{E}[XY] = \mathrm{E}[X]\mathrm{E}[Y] \quad (2)$$

for any two independent random variables X and Y.

It is important that (2) is not misinterpreted as implying that X and Y are independent just because (2) is satisfied; a counter-example follows.

EXAMPLE 1 *The random variables X and Y have the joint distribution shown in Table 4.8. Verify that (i) X and Y are not independent, (ii)* $\mathrm{E}[XY] = \mathrm{E}[X]\mathrm{E}[Y]$.

Table 4.8 Joint distribution of X and Y

		x 0	1	2	$P(Y = y)$
y	0	p	$6p$	$3p$	$10p$
	1	$4p$	$12p$	$9p$	$25p$
	2	p	$6p$	$3p$	$10p$
$P(X = x)$		$6p$	$24p$	$15p$	$45p$

Since the entries in the body of the table must sum to unity, $p = 1/45$.
(i) From the table we find

$$P(X = 0)P(Y = 0) = 10p \times 6p = 60p^2 = 4/135,$$

whereas $P\{(X = 0) \cap (Y = 0)\} = p = 1/45$. Since these are unequal, X and Y are not independent.
(ii) Again from Table 4.8 we find

$$E[XY] = (12p + 18p) + (12p + 12p) = 54p = 1{\cdot}2,$$
$$E[X] = 24p + 30p = 54p = 1{\cdot}2,$$
$$E[Y] = 25p + 20p = 45p = 1,$$

from which it follows that $E[XY] = E[X]E[Y]$, even though X and Y are not independent.

EXAMPLE 2 *Rectangular blocks having square cross-sections are such that the lengths in cm of the sides of the cross-sections are uniformly distributed over the interval* (1, 3), *and independently, their heights in cm are uniformly distributed over the interval* (6, 10). *Find the mean and the standard deviation of the volumes of the blocks, giving each answer correct to two decimal places.*

Let X cm denote the length of a side of the cross-section of a block, and let Y cm denote the height of the block. Then

$$X \sim U(1, 3) \quad \text{and} \quad Y \sim U(6, 10),$$

and X and Y are independent.
The volume of the block in cm^3 is given by

$$Z = X^2Y,$$

and using (1), above, the mean volume of the blocks is

$$E[Z] = E[X^2Y] = E[X^2]E[Y].$$

Since X has probability density function f given by

$$f(x) = \tfrac{1}{2}, \qquad 1 < x < 3,$$
$$E[X^2] = \tfrac{1}{2}\int_1^3 x^2 dx = 13/3,$$

and since Y has probability density function g given by

$$g(y) = \tfrac{1}{4}, \qquad 6 < y < 10,$$

$$E[Y] = \tfrac{1}{4}\int_{6}^{10} y\,dy = 8.$$

Hence, the mean volume of the blocks is

$$\frac{13}{3} \times 8 = \frac{104}{3} = 34{\cdot}67 \text{ cm}^3$$

correct to two decimal places.

To find V[Z], we first find E[Z^2] as follows. From (1) since X and Y are independent, we have

$$E[Z^2] = E[X^4Y^2] = E[X^4]E[Y^2].$$

But

$$E[X^4] = \tfrac{1}{2}\int_{1}^{3} x^4 dx = 121/5,$$

and

$$E[Y^2] = \tfrac{1}{4}\int_{6}^{10} y^2 dy = 196/3,$$

from which it follows that

$$E[Z^2] = \frac{125}{5} \times \frac{196}{3} = 23\,716/15,$$

and therefore,

$$V[Z] = E[Z^2] - \{E[Z]\}^2 = 17\,068/45.$$

Hence, the standard deviation of the volumes of the blocks is

$$SD[Z] = \sqrt{(17\,068/45)} = 19{\cdot}48 \text{ cm}^3,$$

correct to two decimal places.

EXERCISE 4.5A

1 A person draws a card at random from a pack of five cards which are numbered from 1 to 5, respectively, and then draws a card at random from another pack which consists of four cards numbered from 1 to 4, respectively. Find the mean and the variance of the product of the two numbers on the chosen cards, and calculate the probability that the actual product obtained will be greater than the expected value of the product.

2 X and Y are independent random variables with $X \sim U(0, 2)$ and $Y \sim U(1, 5)$. A rectangle is constructed with its adjacent sides having lengths X and Y, respectively. Find the mean and the variance of the area of the rectangle.

3 If X and Y are independent random variables such that $E[X] = 3$, $V[X] = 1$, $E[Y] = 1$, and $V[Y] = 4$, evaluate (i) $E[X(X - Y)]$, (ii) $V[XY]$.

4 The current, Z amperes, that will flow through a circuit when the voltage

across the circuit is X volts and the resistance in the circuit is Y ohms is given by $Z = X/Y$. Suppose that X and Y are independent random variables having probability density functions f and g given by

$$f(x) = 6x(1-x), \qquad 0 \leqslant x \leqslant 1,$$
$$g(y) = 3y^2, \qquad 0 \leqslant y \leqslant 1.$$

Determine the mean and the variance of the current (note that $E[Z] \neq E[X]/E[Y]$).

4.5.1 Variance of a linear combination of two independent random variables

Let $Z = aX + bY$, where a and b are constants and X and Y are random variables. From (3) of §4.2, the mean of Z is

$$\mu_Z \equiv E[aX + bY] = a\mu_X + b\mu_Y, \tag{3}$$

where $\mu_X = E[X]$ and $\mu_Y = E[Y]$. Since

$$Z = aX + bY \quad \text{and} \quad \mu_Z = a\mu_X + b\mu_Y,$$
$$Z - \mu_Z = a(X - \mu_X) + b(Y - \mu_Y),$$

and therefore,

$$\begin{aligned} V[Z] &\equiv E[(Z-\mu_Z)^2] \\ &= a^2 E[(X-\mu_X)^2] + b^2 E[(Y-\mu_Y)^2] \\ &\quad + 2abE[(X-\mu_X)(Y-\mu_Y)]. \end{aligned}$$

Assuming further that X and Y are independent, it follows from (1) that

$$E[(X-\mu_X)(Y-\mu_Y)] = E[(X-\mu_X)]\,E[Y-\mu_Y] = 0,$$

since $E[X-\mu_X] = E[X] - \mu_X = 0$.

Hence, when X and Y are independent, for any constants a and b,

$$V[aX + bY] = a^2 V[X] + b^2 V[Y]. \tag{4}$$

In particular,

$$V[X \pm Y] = V[X] + V[Y]. \tag{5}$$

EXAMPLE 3 *If $X \sim B\,(n = 25, p = 0{\cdot}2)$ and, independently, $Y \sim Po\,(\alpha = 10)$, find the mean and the variance of* (i) $U = Y - X$, (ii) $W = 3X + 2Y$, (iii) $Z = X - \frac{1}{2}Y$.

From §2.6 and §2.7, respectively,

$$E[X] = 25 \times 0{\cdot}2 = 5, \qquad V[X] = 5 \times 0{\cdot}8 = 4,$$
$$E[Y] = V[Y] = 10.$$

(i) From (3) above, the mean of $U = Y - X$ is

$$E[U] = E[Y - X] = E[Y] - E[X] = 10 - 5 = 5,$$

and from (5) the variance of U is

$$V[U] = V[Y-X] = V[Y]+V[X] = 10+4 = 14.$$

(ii) From (3) the mean of $W = 3X+2Y$ is

$$E[W] = E[3X+2Y] = 3E[X]+2E[Y] = 15+20 = 35,$$

and from (4) the variance of W is

$$V[W] = V[3X+2Y] = 9V[X]+4V[Y] = 36+40 = 76.$$

(iii) From (3) and (4) we have

$$E[Z] = E[X-\tfrac{1}{2}Y] = E[X]-\tfrac{1}{2}E[Y] = 5-5 = 0,$$

$$V[Z] = V[X-\tfrac{1}{2}Y] = V[X]+\tfrac{1}{4}V[Y] = 4+2{\cdot}5 = 6{\cdot}5.$$

EXERCISE 4.5B

1 Each of the longer sides of a rectangle has length X cm, where $X \sim U(5, 9)$, and each of the shorter sides has length Y cm, where $Y \sim U(0, 1)$. Given that X and Y are independent, find the mean and the variance of the perimeter of the rectangle.

2 Given that X and Y are independent with $X \sim \text{Geo}(p = 0{\cdot}2)$ and $Y \sim \text{Po}(\alpha = 5)$, determine the mean and the variance of (i) $T = X+Y$, (ii) $Z = X-Y$, (iii) $W = 2X-3Y$.

3 A fair die is thrown twice. Let X_1 denote the score on the first throw, and let X_2 denote the score on the second throw. Random variables W and Z are defined by

$$W = 3X_1 - 2X_2, \qquad Z = X_1 + X_2.$$

Find (i) $E[W]$, (ii) $V[W]$, (iii) $E[Z]$, (iv) $V[Z]$, (v) $E[WZ]$.

4.6 Extensions to three or more random variables

The properties of E[ ] and V[ ] given in §4.2, 4.5 and 4.5.1 may be extended to three or more random variables as follows.

(i) Let $X_1, X_2, \ldots, X_n$ be any n random variables. Then, for any constants $c_1, c_2, \ldots, c_n$,

$$E[c_1X_1 + c_2X_2 + \ldots + c_nX_n] = c_1E[X_1] + c_2E[X_2] + \ldots + c_nE[X_n] \qquad (1)$$

(ii) If $X_1, X_2, \ldots, X_n$ are independent random variables, then
(a) for any functions $H_1(X_1), H_2(X_2), \ldots, H_n(X_n)$,

$$E[H_1(X_1)H_2(X_2)\ldots H_n(X_n)] = E[H_1(X_1)]E[H_2(X_2)]\ldots E[H_n(X_n)] \qquad (2)$$

and, in particular,

$$E[X_1 X_2 \dots X_n] = E[X_1]E[X_2] \dots E[X_n]; \qquad (3)$$

(b) for any constants $c_1, c_2, \dots, c_n$

$$V[c_1 X_1 + c_2 X_2 + \dots + c_n X_n] = c_1^2 V[X_1] + c_2^2 V[X_2] + \dots + c_n^2 V[X_n]. \qquad (4)$$

The above results provide much simpler ways of deriving the mean and the variance of a binomial distribution than those used in §2.6.

Mean and variance of a binomial distribution

Consider a sequence of n independent Bernoulli trials in each of which the probability of a success is p. Then, if X denotes the number of successes, we know that $X \sim B(n, p)$.

Now introduce random variables $X_1, X_2, \dots, X_n$, where X_i is defined with respect to the ith trial ($i = 1, 2, \dots, n$) as

$$X_i = 1 \quad \text{if the } i\text{th trial is a success}$$
$$X_i = 0 \quad \text{if the } i\text{th trial is a failure.}$$

Observe that $X = X_1 + X_2 + \dots + X_n$. Hence, from (1), the mean of X is

$$E[X] = E[X_1] + E[X_2] + \dots + E[X_n].$$

Since the trials are independent, so are $X_1, X_2, \dots, X_n$ independent, and therefore, from (4),

$$V[X] = V[X_1] + V[X_2] + \dots + V[X_n].$$

Thus, to find $E[X]$ and $V[X]$ we need to evaluate $E[X_i]$ and $V[X_i]$ for $i = 1, 2, \dots, n$. Now, each X_i has range space $\{0, 1\}$ and

$$P(X_i = 1) = p, \qquad P(X_i = 0) = 1 - p.$$

Hence, for each $i = 1, 2, \dots, n$,

$$E[X_i] = p, \qquad E[X_i^2] = p, \quad \text{and} \quad V[X_i] = p - p^2 = p(1-p).$$

It follows that the mean and the variance of the distribution $B(n, p)$ are

$$E[X] = np \quad \text{and} \quad V[X] = np(1-p).$$

EXAMPLE 1 *The dimensions of a rectangular block are independent random variables X, Y and Z, where X has mean 3 and standard deviation 1, Y has mean 5 and standard deviation 2, and Z has mean 8 and standard deviation 3. Determine the mean and the variance of the volume of a block.*

The volume W of a block of dimensions X, Y, Z is

$$W = XYZ.$$

Since X, Y, and Z are independent, the mean volume is

$$E[W] = E[X]E[Y]E[Z] = 3 \times 5 \times 8 = 120.$$

Also

$$E[W^2] = E[X^2]E[Y^2]E[Z^2],$$

where

$$E[X^2] = V[X] + (E[X])^2 = 1 + 9 = 10,$$
$$E[Y^2] = V[Y] + (E[Y])^2 = 4 + 25 = 29,$$

and

$$E[Z^2] = V[Z] + (E[Z])^2 = 9 + 64 = 73.$$

Hence,

$$E[W^2] = 10 \times 29 \times 73 = 21170$$

and

$$V[W] = E[W^2] - (E[W])^2 = 21170 - 120^2 = 6770.$$

EXERCISE 4.6

1 Manufactured rods have lengths that are distributed with mean 10 cm and standard deviation 0·5 cm. Three of these rods are chosen at random and placed end to end. Find the mean and the variance of their combined length.

2 A person having a cold may stay away from work for 1, 2 or 3 days. Suppose that in a year in a certain industry the numbers of persons having colds and staying away from work for 1, 2 and 3 days, respectively, are independent random variables having Poisson distributions with means 10, 15 and 20, respectively. Find the mean and the variance of the total number of days lost through colds in a year.

3 A group of labourers offers its services for odd jobs. Suppose that the number X of labourers that are assigned to a particular job is equally likely to be any number from 1 to 3, inclusive, and that independently, the total number of man-hours Y required to complete the job is uniformly distributed over the interval (5, 11). A customer is charged £2 per man on a job together with a charge of £Z per man-hour where, independently of X and Y, Z is uniformly distributed over the interval (2, 6). Find the mean and the variance of the total charge per job.

4 Cylindrical tanks with closed flat ends are manufactured from thin metal. The radius and the height of a tank are independent random variables having means μ_R and μ_H, respectively. Given also that the radius has variance σ_R^2, find an expression for the mean surface area of a tank.

5 The probability of a success in each trial of a random experiment is 0·2. Let X_1 denote the number of trials that will be performed for the first success to occur; let X_2 denote the number of *further* trials that will be performed for the next success to occur; and let X_3 denote the number of *further* trials for the third success to occur. Write down the expected values of X_1, X_2 and X_3. Deduce the expected number of trials that will be performed to obtain three successes.

4.7 Additive property of independent Poisson distributions

Let X and Y be independent random variables having Poisson distributions with means μ and λ, respectively. Then, $Z = X + Y$ has a Poisson distribution with mean $\mu + \lambda$.

To prove this result we first observe that since $R_X = R_Y = \{0, 1, 2, 3, \ldots\}$, the range space of Z is $R_Z = \{0, 1, 2, 3, \ldots\}$. We shall now derive an expression for $\mathrm{P}(Z = z)$ for an arbitrary value z in R_Z.

Since $Z = X + Y$, the event $(Z = z)$ is equivalent to

$$\{(X = 0) \cap (Y = z)\} \cup \{(X = 1) \cap (Y = z - 1)\} \cup \ldots \cup \{(X = z) \cap (Y = 0)\},$$

and since X and Y are independent,

$$\mathrm{P}(Z = z) = \mathrm{P}(X = 0)\,\mathrm{P}(Y = z) + \mathrm{P}(X = 1)\,\mathrm{P}(Y = z - 1) + \ldots + \mathrm{P}(X = z)\,\mathrm{P}(Y = 0).$$

But

$$\mathrm{P}(X = x) = \mathrm{e}^{-\mu}\mu^x/x!, \qquad x = 0, 1, 2, \ldots.$$

and

$$\mathrm{P}(Y = y) = \mathrm{e}^{-\mu}\mu^y/y!, \qquad y = 0, 1, 2, \ldots.$$

Hence, for $0 \leqslant r \leqslant z$,

$$\begin{aligned}\mathrm{P}(X = r)\,\mathrm{P}(Y = z - r) &= (\mathrm{e}^{-\mu}\mu^r/r!)\,\mathrm{e}^{-\lambda}\lambda^{z-r}/(z-r)! \\ &= \mathrm{e}^{-(\mu+\lambda)}\,\mu^r\lambda^{z-r}/r!\,(z-r)! \\ &= \mathrm{e}^{-(\mu+\lambda)}\binom{z}{r}\frac{\mu^r\lambda^{z-r}}{z!}.\end{aligned}$$

It follows that

$$\begin{aligned}\mathrm{P}(Z = z) &= \frac{\mathrm{e}^{-(\mu+\lambda)}}{z!}\left\{\lambda^z + \binom{z}{1}\mu\lambda^{z-1} + \binom{z}{2}\mu^2\lambda^{z-2} + \ldots + \mu^z\right\} \\ &= \frac{\mathrm{e}^{-(\mu+\lambda)}}{z!}(\lambda + \mu)^z, \qquad z = 0, 1, 2, \ldots,\end{aligned}$$

from which we see that $Z \sim \mathrm{Po}(\mu + \lambda)$. The result extends to the sum of three or more independent random variables having Poisson distributions. Thus, if $X_1, X_2, \ldots, X_n$ are independent random variables having Poisson distributions with means $\lambda_1, \lambda_2, \ldots, \lambda_n$, then

$$Z = X_1 + X_2 + \ldots + X_n \sim \mathrm{Po}(\lambda_1 + \lambda_2 + \ldots + \lambda_n),$$

a result which is referred to as the *additive property of the Poisson distribution.*

EXAMPLE 1 *The numbers X, Y, of outgoing and incoming calls to a telephone switchboard during a lunch hour are independent random variables with* $X \sim \text{Po}(3)$ and $Y \sim \text{Po}(5)$. *Calculate the probability that during a lunch hour there will be a total of three calls to the switchboard.*

Let Z denote the total number of calls to the switchboard during a lunch hour. Then $Z = X + Y$, and from the additive property given above, $Z \sim \text{Po}(8)$. Hence,

$$\text{P}(Z = 3) = \text{e}^{-8}\, 8^3/3! = 256\text{e}^{-8}/3 \simeq 0{\cdot}0286,$$

exactly as obtained using the less direct method in Example 1 (iii), §2.7.

EXERCISE 4.7

1 The numbers of men, women, and children arriving per hour at a doctor's surgery may be assumed to be independent random variables having Poisson distributions with means 3, 4, and 2, respectively. Find, to three decimal places, the probabilities that in an hour (i) at least three adults will arrive at the surgery, (ii) no more than three patients will arrive at the surgery.

2 Independently for each day, the number of oil tankers arriving at a certain refinery has a Poisson distribution with mean 2.2.
(i) Find, to three decimal places, the probability that over three successive days the total number of tankers that will arrive at the refinery is four or more.
(ii) Find the smallest r for which there is a probability of at least 0·999 that at least one tanker will arrive at the refinery in a period of r successive days.

3 The numbers X and Y of two types of bacterial organisms that may be present in a sample of liquid are independent random variables, each having a Poisson distribution with mean μ.
(i) Given that a sample of the liquid contained a total of four organisms, calculate the probability that there were two organisms of each type.
(ii) Given that a sample contained at least one organism, show that the probability that all the organisms in the sample are of one and the same type is $2/(1+\text{e}^{\mu})$.

4.8 Distribution of a linear combination of independent normal random variables

If $X_1, X_2, \ldots, X_n$ are independent random variables with $X_i \sim N(\mu_i, \sigma_i^2)$, $i = 1, 2, 3, \ldots, n$, then it may be shown that for any constants $c_1, c_2, \ldots, c_n$,

$$Y = c_1 X_1 + c_2 X_2 + \ldots + c_n X_n$$

is also normally distributed. From (1) of §4.6, the mean of this normal distribution is

$$\mu_Y = c_1 \mu_1 + c_2 \mu_2 + \ldots + c_n \mu_n, \tag{1}$$

and from (4) of §4.6, its variance is

$$\sigma_Y^2 = c_1^2 \sigma_1^2 + c_2^2 \sigma_2^2 + \ldots + c_n^2 \sigma_n^2. \tag{2}$$

EXAMPLE 1 *A piece of equipment has to be assembled in three stages. The time X minutes taken to complete the first stage is normally distributed with mean 15·4 and standard deviation 3; the time Y minutes taken to complete the second stage is normally distributed with mean 25·8 and standard deviation 4; and the time Z minutes to complete the third stage is normally distributed with mean 10·3 and standard deviation 2. In addition it is also necessary to allow a time of $2Y$ minutes between completing the second stage and starting the third stage. Given that X, Y and Z are independent, calculate the probabilities that (i) the first two stages will be completed in under 30 minutes, (ii) the equipment will be completely assembled in under 120 minutes.*

(i) The time in minutes taken to complete the first two stages is $T = X + Y$. Since $X \sim N(15{\cdot}4, 3^2), Y \sim N(25{\cdot}8, 4^2)$, and X and Y are independent, it follows from the result given above that $T \sim N(\mu_T, \sigma_T^2)$, where

$$\mu_T = \mu_X + \mu_Y = 15{\cdot}4 + 25{\cdot}8 = 41{\cdot}2,$$

and

$$\sigma_T^2 = \sigma_X^2 + \sigma_Y^2 = 3^2 + 4^2 = 25.$$

Hence,

$$\mathrm{P}(T < 30) = \Phi\left(\frac{30 - 43{\cdot}2}{5}\right) = \Phi(-2{\cdot}24) \simeq 0{\cdot}125.$$

(ii) The time in minutes to complete the assembly of the equipment is $W = X + Y + 2Y + Z = X + 3Y + Z$.
Since X, Y, Z are independent and $Z \sim N(10{\cdot}3, 2^2)$, it follows that $W \sim N(\mu_W, \sigma_W^2)$, where

$$\mu_W = \mu_X + 3\mu_Y + \mu_Z = 15{\cdot}4 + 3 \times 25{\cdot}8 + 10{\cdot}3 = 103{\cdot}1,$$

$$\sigma_W^2 = \sigma_X^2 + 9\sigma_Y^2 + \sigma_Z^2 = 3^2 + 9 \times 4^2 + 2^2 = 157.$$

Hence, the probability that the assembly is completed in under 120 minutes is

$$\mathrm{P}(W < 120) = \Phi\left(\frac{120 - 103{\cdot}1}{\sqrt{157}}\right) \simeq \Phi(1{\cdot}3488) \simeq 0{\cdot}9113.$$

EXAMPLE 2 *Cylindrical rods have diameters that are normally distributed with mean 35·4 mm and standard deviation 0·08 mm. The rods are to be inserted into circular holes whose diameters are normally distributed with mean 35·5 mm and standard deviation 0·01 mm. A satisfactory fit is obtained provided the hole diameter exceeds the rod diameter by between 0·04 mm and 0·05 mm. If a rod is chosen at random and inserted into a hole chosen at random, find the probability that a satisfactory fit will be obtained.*

Let X mm denote the diameter of the chosen rod and let Y mm denote the diameter of chosen hole. Then

$$X \sim N(35{\cdot}4, 0{\cdot}08^2), \qquad Y \sim N(35{\cdot}5, 0{\cdot}01^2),$$

and it is clear that X and Y are independent. For a satisfactory fit it is necessary that $0{\cdot}04 < Y - X < 0{\cdot}05$. From the results given in this section, $Y - X \sim N(\mu, \sigma^2)$, where

$$\mu = \mu_Y - \mu_X = 35{\cdot}5 - 35{\cdot}4 = 0{\cdot}1,$$

and

$$\sigma^2 = \sigma_Y^2 + \sigma_X^2 = 0{\cdot}01^2 + 0{\cdot}08^2 = 0{\cdot}0065.$$

Thus, the probability of a satisfactory fit is

$$\begin{aligned} \mathrm{P}(0{\cdot}04 < Y - X < 0{\cdot}05) &= \Phi\left(\frac{0{\cdot}05 - 0{\cdot}1}{\sqrt{0{\cdot}0065}}\right) - \Phi\left(\frac{0{\cdot}04 - 0{\cdot}1}{\sqrt{0{\cdot}0065}}\right) \\ &\simeq \Phi\,(-0{\cdot}6202) - \Phi\,(-0{\cdot}7442) \\ &\simeq 0{\cdot}2675 - 0{\cdot}2283 \simeq 0{\cdot}0392. \end{aligned}$$

EXERCISE 4.8

1 The weight of fruit delivered into a can is normally distributed with mean 250 g and standard deviation 1·2 g. The weight of an empty can is normally distributed with mean 25 g and standard deviation 0·5 g. Calculate (i) the mean and the standard deviation of the weight of a filled can, (ii) the probability that a filled can will weigh more than 278 g.

2 A salesman is due to visit a certain town. Suppose that the time in hours that he will spend in the town is normally distributed with mean 5 and standard deviation 1·6. Independently of the time that he spends in the town, the times in hours that he will take to travel to the town and to return home are independent and each has a normal distribution with mean 1·2 and standard deviation 0·4. Find the probabilities that (i) his total time away from home will be less than 9 hours, (ii) the time he spends in the town will be more than twice his total travelling time.

3 Hollow steel bases for wooden posts have rectangular cross-sections whose lengths and breadths are independent random variables, the lengths being normally distributed with mean 10 cm and standard deviation 0·4 cm, and the breadths being normally distributed with mean 6 cm and standard deviation 0·2 cm. The wooden posts have rectangular cross-sections whose lengths and breadths are independent normally distributed random variables, the lengths having mean 9·9 cm and standard deviation 0·3 cm, and the breadths having mean 5·9 cm and standard deviation 0·15 cm. Find the probability that a randomly chosen post will go into a randomly chosen steel base.

4 Orange-flavoured sweets have weights which are normally distributed with mean 8 g and standard deviation 0·2 g. (i) Find the probability that the weight of the sweets in a packet containing 16 sweets will exceed 130 g. (ii) Show that a packet should contain at least 26 sweets if there is to be a probability of at least 0·99 that the weight of the sweets in the packet will exceed 200 g. (iii) The weights of lemon-flavoured sweets are normally distributed with mean 9 g and standard deviation 0·3 g. A packet of 10 sweets consist of four orange-flavoured ones and six lemon-flavoured ones. Calculate the probability that the weight of the sweets in the packet exceeds 88 g.

5 The weights of male and female students at a college may be assumed to be normally distributed, the males' weights having mean 69 kg and standard deviation 10 kg, and the females' weights having mean 56 kg and standard deviation 8 kg. If one male and one female student are chosen at random, calculate the probabilities that (i) the sum of their weights exceeds 130 kg; (ii) the female is heavier than the male; (iii) the female's weight is at least $\frac{3}{4}$ of the male's weight.

REVIEW PROBLEMS ON CHAPTER 4

1 A boy is to have three attempts at performing a certain task. The probability that he will succeed on his first attempt is $\frac{1}{2}$, while on each subsequent attempt the probability that he will succeed is $\frac{3}{4}$ if his preceding attempt was successful, and $\frac{1}{2}$ if his preceding attempt was not successful. Let X denote the number of successes by the boy in his three attempts, and let Y denote the number of the attempt on which he is first successful; define Y to be zero if the boy fails on all three attempts. (i) Display the joint probability distribution of X and Y in a two-way table. (ii) Having completed his three attempts, the student is awarded a score of 2 if $X > Y$, a score of 1 if $X = Y$, and a score of 0 if $X < Y$. Find the mean and the standard deviation of the boy's score. *(WJEC 1982)*

2 The joint probability function of two discrete random variables X and Y is given by

$$P(X = r, Y = s) = c|r+s| \quad \text{for} \quad r = -1, 0, 1 \text{ and } s = -2, -1, 0, 1, 2,$$

$$P(X = r, Y = s) = 0, \text{ otherwise.}$$

(i) Show that (a) $c = 0{\cdot}5$, (b) $V[Y] = 2 + V[X]$. (ii) Evaluate $V[Y - X]$. *(WJEC 1980)*

3 Four balls are to be drawn at random without replacement from a bag containing ten balls, of which two are red, one is blue, and seven are white. Show that the probability that all four balls will be white is equal to 1/6.

Let X and Y, respectively, denote the numbers of red and blue balls that will be drawn. Display the joint probability distribution of X and Y in a two-way table. Use entries from your table to show that X and Y are not independent.

Find the probability distribution of $Z = X + Y$, and evaluate its mean and variance.

If, instead of as above, the four balls were to be drawn with replacement, identify the distribution of $Z = X + Y$ by name and write down the values of its mean and variance. *(WJEC 1981)*

4 The following table gives the joint probability distribution of two discrete random variables X and Y. You may assume that $0 < \alpha < 1$ and $0 < \beta < 1$.

		x 0	1	2
y	1	α	β	α
	2	β	0	β
	3	α	β	α

(i) Show that $\alpha + \beta = \frac{1}{4}$.

(ii) Find $E[X]$ and $E[Y]$ and show that $E[XY] = E[X]E[Y]$.
(iii) Determine whether or not X and Y are independent.
(iv) Find the variance of $Z = X + Y$ in terms of α. (*WJEC 1978*)

5 When two dice are thrown there are 36 points in the sample space. The variables X and Y are defined as 'the greater score (or the common score when the scores are equal)' and as 'the remainder when the greater score is divided by the smaller score', respectively. The joint distribution of X and Y is shown in the following table (divide each entry by 36).

		y = 0	1	2	
x	1	1			1
	2	3			3
	3	3	2		5
	4	5	2		7
	5	3	4	2	9
	6	7	2	2	11
		22	10	4	36

Verify the entries 7, 2, 2 and 11 in the line $x = 6$. Evaluate $P(Y = 0 | X = 5)$ and $P(Y = 0 | X = 2)$. Explain why it must be concluded that X and Y are not independent. Calculate the expected values $E[X]$ and $E[X | Y = 2]$. (*L 1977*)

6 The number of goals X scored by football team A in home matches against team B has a Poisson distribution with mean 2. Verify that

$$rP(X = r) = 2P(X = r-1), \qquad r = 1, 2, \ldots.$$

The number of goals scored by team B in away matches against A has a Poisson distribution with mean 1. Write down the relationship connecting $P(Y = r)$ and $P(Y = r-1)$ for $r \geqslant 1$. Assuming that X and Y are independent, find the probabilities, correct to two decimal places, that in a match between A and B on A's home ground

(i) neither A nor B scores,
(ii) A and B score an equal non-zero number of goals,
(iii) A scores more goals than B. (*JMB 1981*)

7 Two types of flaw, A and B, may occur in a manufactured cloth. The numbers of flaws of type A and of type B occurring per metre length of the cloth are independent random variables having Poisson distributions with means 0·5 and 1, respectively.

(i) Find the probabilities, to three significant figures, that a length of 1 metre of the cloth will have
(a) two or fewer flaws of type A,
(b) no flaw of either type.
(ii) Show that the probability of a length of 1 metre of the cloth containing 1 flaw only is *exactly* three times that of it containing 1 flaw of each type.

(iii) Removing a type A flaw from the cloth costs 8 p and removing a type B flaw costs 2 p. Find the mean and the standard deviation of the cost of removing flaws per 1 metre length of the cloth. (*WJEC 1981*)

8 At the 'hot drinks' counter in a cafeteria both tea and coffee are sold. The number of cups of coffee sold per minute may be assumed to be a Poisson variable with mean 1·5, and the number of cups of tea sold per minute may be assumed to be an independent Poisson variable with mean 0·5.
(i) Calculate the probability that in a given one-minute period exactly one cup of coffee and one cup of tea are sold.
(ii) Calculate the probability that in a given three-minute period fewer than five drinks altogether are sold.
(iii) In a given one-minute period exactly three drinks are sold. Calculate the probability that these are all cups of coffee. (*C 1981*)

9 The numbers of emissions per minute from two sources of radioactivity are independent random variables X_1 and X_2 having Poisson distributions with means 4 and 6, respectively.
(i) Calculate the probability that in any minute the total number of emissions from the two sources is equal to 2.
(ii) Write down an expression for the probability that in any minute the value of X_2 is exactly twice the value of X_1.
(iii) Determine the mean and the variance of $Z = 3X_1 - 2X_2$. (*L 1979*)

10 The number X of air bubbles in a mass-produced lens is a discrete random variable such that

$$P(X = r) = \tfrac{1}{3} - (r/15), \qquad r = 0, 1, 2, 3, 4.$$

A lens which has two or more air bubbles is rejected as being unsuitable. Evaluate the probabilities that (i) a randomly chosen lens will be rejected, (ii) a lens chosen at random from lenses that have been rejected will have exactly two air bubbles.

A lens having one or no air bubble is then tested to determine its dispersion index. Such a lens is passed only if it has *either* no air bubble and a dispersion index less than 4, *or* one air bubble and a dispersion index less than 3·5. It may be assumed that, independently of the number of air bubbles, the dispersion indices of the lenses are normally distributed with mean 3·6 and standard deviation 0·5.
(iii) Find the proportion of all lenses that are passed, giving your answer correct to three decimal places.
(iv) A lens is chosen at random from those that were passed. Find the probability that it has no air bubble, giving your answer correct to three decimal places.
(v) A random sample of 20 lenses is chosen from those lenses that are passed. Find, correct to two decimal places, the mean and the variance of the proportion of lenses in the sample that have no air bubble. (*JMB 1981*)

11 A random variable X is the number of heads obtained when a coin is tossed eight times. The random variable Y has a Poisson distribution whose mean is 7. Calculate the mean and variance of the random variable Z where $Z = 3X - Y$. Find approximately the value of $P(Z > 15)$. (*L 1979*)

12 The lifetimes of electric light bulbs of brands A and B are independent and normally distributed. For brand A bulbs the mean and the standard deviation of the life times are 1010 hours and 5 hours, respectively, while for

brand B bulbs the corresponding values are 1020 hours and 10 hours, respectively.
(i) Calculate the probability that a brand A bulb will have a lifetime in excess of 1020 hours. (ii) Calculate the probability that a brand A bulb will have a longer life time than a brand B bulb.

A box contains eight bulbs of brand A and 2 bulbs of brand B. (iii) If one bulb is drawn at random from the box, calculate the probability that its lifetime will exceed 1020 hours. (iv) Calculate the probability that the mean of the lifetimes of the 10 bulbs in the box will exceed 1010 hours.
(*WJEC 1982*)

13 The daily consumption of electricity per house in an estate with 200 similar houses has a normal distribution with mean 80 units and standard deviation 20 units. The daily consumption of electricity in each house is independent of the consumption in the other houses. (i) Find the probability that a house selected at random uses not less than 40 units and not more than 110 units on one day. (ii) Find the probability that, on a given day, not more than 20 houses have a consumption in excess of 110 units. (iii) Find the total daily consumption for the whole estate, which is exceeded on only 5% of the days.
(*C 1981*)

14 An extensive survey showed that the proportion of males and females who eat cereal for breakfast are $\frac{1}{4}$ and $\frac{1}{3}$, respectively. (i) In a random sample of 192 males, find an approximate value for the probability that at least 50 eat cereal for breakfast. (ii) In a random sample of 64 males and 108 females find an approximate value for the probability that no more than 47 of them eat cereal for breakfast. (iii) A random sample of $4n$ males and $3n$ females is to be drawn. Find the value of n for there to be a probability of approximately 0·05 that the sample will include at least 10 more females than males who eat cereal for breakfast.
(*WJEC 1981*)

15 The tensile strengths, measured in newtons (N), of a large number of ropes of equal lengths are independently and normally distributed such that 5% are under 706 N and 5% are over 1294 N. Four such ropes are randomly selected and joined end-to-end to form a single rope; the strength of the combined rope is equal to the strength of the weakest of the four selected ropes. Derive the probabilities that this combined rope will not break under tensions of 1000 N and 900 N, respectively.

A further four ropes are randomly selected and attached between two rings, the strengths of the arrangement being the sum of the strengths of the four separate ropes. Derive the probabilities that this arrangement will break under tensions of 4000 N and 4200 N, respectively.

Find the smallest number of ropes that should be selected if the probability that at least one of them has a strength greater than 1000 N is to exceed 0·99.
(*JMB 1981*)

16 A man travels to work by train and bus. His train is due to arrive at 08.45 and the bus he hopes to catch is due to leave the station at 08.48. The time of arrival of the train has a normal distribution with mean at 08.44 and standard deviation 2 minutes: the departure time of the bus is independently normally distributed with mean at 08.48 and standard deviation 1 minute. Calculate, giving your answers correct to two significant figures in (i) and (ii), and to one significant figure in (iii), the probabilities that (i) the train is late, (ii) the bus departs before the train arrives (iii) in a period of five days there are at least three days on which the bus departs before the train arrives. (*C 1981*)

17 In testing the length of life of electric light bulbs of a particular type, it was found that 12·3 % of the bulbs tested failed within 800 hours and that 28·1 % were still operating 1100 hours after the start of the test. Assuming that the distribution of the length of life is normal, calculate, to the nearest hour in each case, the mean μ and the standard deviation σ of the distribution.

A light fitting takes a single bulb of this type. A packet of three bulbs is bought, to be used one after the other in this fitting. State the mean and the variance of the total life of the three bulbs in the packet in terms of μ and σ and calculate, to two decimal places, the probability that the total life is more than 3300 hours.

Calculate the probability that all three bulbs have lives in excess of 1100 hours, so that again the total life is more than 3300 hours. Explain why this answer should be different from the previous one. (*JMB 1980*)

18 A reel of telephone wire holds a length, X, of wire which is a normal variable with mean 250 m. If $99\frac{1}{2}$ % of reels hold more than 236 m of wire, find the variance of X correct to the nearest 0.01 m^2. Find the probability that a randomly selected reel holds a length of wire greater than 260 m.

If ten reels are selected at random find (i) the probability that the total length of wire on them is more than 2480 m, (ii) the probability that not more than one of them holds less than 236 m of wire. (*C 1980*)

19 Mass-produced right circular cylindrical pipes have internal diameters that are normally distributed with a mean of 10 cm and a standard deviation of 0·4 cm, while mass-produced pistons have diameters that are normally distributed with a mean of 9·9 cm and a standard deviation of 0·3 cm. Find the probability that a randomly selected piston will have a diameter less than the internal diameter of a randomly selected pipe. (*WJEC 1980*)

20 A transport company finds that the amount of fuel that its lorries use during a week may be taken as a normal variable with mean 5000 litres and standard deviation 400 litres. (i) Calculate the probability that in a particular week less than 6000 litres will be used. (ii) The probability that more than L litres will be used in any week is 0·75. Find L. (iii) Calculate the probability that in a particular four-week period more than 21,000 litres will be used, assuming that fuel consumption in any week is independent of that in other weeks. (iv) A working year consists of 50 weeks. Calculate limits between which the company can state with probability 0·95 that a year's fuel consumption will lie. (*C 1982*)

5 Sampling Distributions

5.1 Introduction

In Chapters 2 and 3 we considered random variables whose probability distributions were known, and we calculated the probabilities of various events and determined the values of some summary measures. However, in Statistics, a fundamental problem area, generally known as *statistical inference*, is one in which the probability distribution of the random variable of interest is not completely known, and a sample of observed values of the random variable is to be used to make inferences about the probability distribution. Formal introductions to some standard inference problems will be given in later chapters, but the following two types of examples illustrate situations where inferences are appropriate.

TYPE A EXAMPLES: ESTIMATING A DISTRIBUTION MEAN

A new approach has been proposed for teaching mathematics in primary schools and is to be assessed according to performance on a standard test. Suppose that the new approach will be regarded as more effective than the current approach if, in the standard test, the average mark attained by children following the new approach is higher than that attained by children following the current approach.

Let X denote the mark that will be attained in the test by a child following the new approach. Then X is a random variable whose probability distribution is not known. For the purpose of deciding whether or not the new approach is more effective than the current approach, we would like to know the value of the mean $\mu = \mathrm{E}[X]$ of the distribution of X, so as to compare it with the known mean mark for children who have followed the current approach.

In order to obtain information on $\mathrm{E}[X]$, it is decided to use the new approach on a class of n children. Suppose that the marks attained in the standard test by these n children were $x_1, x_2, \ldots, x_n$. It is then intuitively reasonable to take the average of these marks, namely $\bar{x} = (\Sigma x_i)/n$, as an estimate of $\mathrm{E}[X]$.

Similar problems arise in many other areas of investigation. For example, (i) in horticultural experimentation, the random variable X may be the yield of a tomato plant grown according to some new fertiliser programme; (ii) in medical research, X may be the time taken for a new treatment to completely cure some ailment; and (iii) in the manufacturing industry, X may be the quality of a product (such as the lifetime of a television tube) under some modification of the process conditions.

TYPE B EXAMPLES: ESTIMATING A PROBABILITY

Let θ denote the success rate for some new medical treatment. To obtain information on θ it is decided to administer the treatment to n patients. Let X denote the number of these patients that will be cured by the treatment. Then, under reasonable assumptions, we may say that X has the binomial distribution $B(n, \theta)$. But the value of θ is unknown. Suppose that the observed value of X was x; that is, exactly x of the n patients were cured by the treatment. Then, intuition suggests the sample success rate $p = x/n$ as a suitable estimate of θ.

Other examples of this type include those where θ may be (i) the proportion of electors who will vote for a particular party in a forthcoming election; (ii) the germination rate of seeds sown under pre-specified conditions; and (iii) the probability that a mass-produced item will be defective.

In each of the above examples a sample is being used to estimate some characteristic of a probability distribution, namely the mean in Examples A and the probability parameter of a binomial distribution in Examples B.

Any quantity which is calculated from sample values for the purpose of estimating a characteristic of a probability distribution is called a *statistic*. In the above examples our intuition suggested a suitable statistic to use in each case, but our intuition is less helpful in assessing how good it is by providing some indication of the possible discrepancy between the estimate and the true value of the quantity being estimated. For such an assessment it is necessary to take into account the fact that different samples generally lead to different estimates. In this chapter we shall study some properties of particular statistics by looking at all the possible samples (of a given size) that may arise. These properties will then be used in later chapters to establish some important results that are relevant to making inferences.

5.2 Sampling without replacement from a finite population

Let X denote some numerical characteristic of an object which is to be drawn at random from a collection of N objects. For example, (i) the collection may be all sixth form pupils at a school and X the height of a randomly chosen pupil; (ii) the collection may be a batch of electric light bulbs and X the lifetime of a bulb chosen at random from the batch. The probability distribution of X will be determined uniquely by the X-values of the N objects in the collection.

A collection of objects is frequently referred to as a *population* (an extension of its use to describe a collection of people), and the probability distribution of a random variable associated with the objects in the collection is referred to as the *population distribution of X*.

Any subcollection of n ($< N$) objects from a given collection of N objects is called a *sample of size n from the population*, and the X-values of the n objects in the sample are collectively called a *sample of size n from the population distribution of X.*

Suppose that the population distribution of X is unknown and that a sample of size n is to be taken with a view to estimating some characteristic of the population distribution. For example, the characteristic may be the mean or the variance of X, or the probability that X has a specific value. Such an estimate will be obtained by taking a certain combination of the observed X-values of the n objects in the sample. Let T denote the *verbal description* of the particular combination of the sample values that we decide to take. Then T is a random variable, a *statistic* as defined earlier, whose probability distribution will depend upon the distribution of X. After the sample X-values become available, we can compute the value of T, which we shall denote by t (in keeping with our earlier convention for a random variable and a value it may take). The value t will then be our estimate of the quantity of interest. We shall refer to T as the *estimator* of the quantity of interest. Thus, an estimator T is a random variable and the estimate t is a realised value of T.

Since only n objects are to be chosen from the N in the collection, the particular sample of n objects that will be chosen may be any one of the $\binom{N}{n}$ possible samples, for each of which there will be a T-value. If the objects are chosen at random, then each possible sample and its associated T-value will have probability $1/\binom{N}{n}$ of occurring. By generating all the possible samples of size n and evaluating the T-value for each sample we can deduce the probability distribution of the statistic T. In this context, the probability distribution of a statistic T is aptly referred to as the *sampling distribution of T.* These ideas are illustrated in the following example.

EXAMPLE 1 *The five flats in a building are occupied by families A, B, C, D and E. Each of families A and B has no child, each of families C and D has one child, and family E has two children. Three of the families are to be chosen at random without replacement. Determine the sampling distribution of* (i) *the mean number of children per family in the three chosen families;* (ii) *the proportion of the three chosen families that have no child.*

Let X denote the number of children in a randomly chosen family. From the given information on the family sizes the population distribution of X is as displayed in Table 5.1.

Table 5.1 Population distribution of X

x	0	1	2
$P(X = x)$	$\frac{2}{5}$	$\frac{2}{5}$	$\frac{1}{5}$

The total number of possible samples of size 3 drawn without replacement from a population of size 5 is $\binom{5}{3} = 10$; these are listed in the first column of Table 5.2. The second column in that table gives the X-values for each sample, while the third and fourth columns show the values of the sample mean, $\bar{X}$, of the number of children per family in the sample, and the sample proportion, Y, of the sampled families having no child.

Table 5.2 Sample values of $\bar{X}$ and Y

Sample	X-values	$\bar{X}$	Y
{A, B, C}	{0, 0, 1}	1/3	2/3
{A, B, D}	{0, 0, 1}	1/3	2/3
{A, B, E}	{0, 0, 2}	2/3	2/3
{A, C, D}	{0, 1, 1}	2/3	1/3
{A, C, E}	{0, 1, 2}	1	1/3
{A, D, E}	{0, 1, 2}	1	1/3
{B, C, D}	{0, 1, 1}	2/3	1/3
{B, C, E}	{0, 1, 2}	1	1/3
{B, D, E}	{0, 1, 2}	1	1/3
{C, D, E}	{1, 1, 2}	4/3	0

Since each sample has probability 1/10 of being the chosen one, the sampling distributions of $\bar{X}$ and Y are as shown in Tables 5.3 and 5.4, respectively.

Table 5.3 Sampling distribution of $\bar{X}$

$\bar{x}$	$\frac{1}{3}$	$\frac{2}{3}$	1	$\frac{4}{3}$
$P(\bar{X} = \bar{x})$	$\frac{2}{10}$	$\frac{3}{10}$	$\frac{4}{10}$	$\frac{1}{10}$

Table 5.4 Sampling distribution of Y

y	0	$\frac{1}{3}$	$\frac{2}{3}$
$P(Y = y)$	$\frac{1}{10}$	$\frac{6}{10}$	$\frac{3}{10}$

In Example A of §5·1 we suggested that it was intutively reasonable to use the statistic $\bar{X}$ as an estimator of the population mean μ. Since the population distribution of X is known here we can use Table 5.3 to assess the qualities of $\bar{X}$ as an estimator of μ. From Table 5.1, the population mean μ is given by

$$\mu = E[X] = 0 \times \frac{2}{5} + 1 \times \frac{2}{5} + 2 \times \frac{1}{5} = \frac{4}{5}.$$

It is apparent from Table 5.3 that X will never equal μ in this example. However, the mean of the sampling distribution of $\bar{X}$ is given by

$$\mathrm{E}[\bar{X}] = \frac{1}{3} \times \frac{2}{10} + \frac{2}{3} \times \frac{3}{10} + 1 \times \frac{4}{10} + \frac{4}{3} \times \frac{1}{10} = \frac{4}{5},$$

which is precisely the value of μ. Thus, the average value of $\bar{X}$ (averaged over all 10 possible samples) is equal to μ. This property, namely $\mathrm{E}[\bar{X}] = \mu$, is true generally for a sample of any size drawn at random without replacement from a finite population. In particular, it is true in the more realistic generalisation of our example to one in which a sample of n families is chosen from all the families in a large town, and the sample mean is used to estimate the population mean. The fact that $\mathrm{E}[\bar{X}] = \mu$ is one reason why $\bar{X}$ is an appropriate statistic for estimating μ.

Knowing that $\bar{X}$ gives the true value of μ 'on average' does not in itself offer much confidence that the observed value $\bar{x}$ for a randomly chosen sample is close to the value of μ. Since $\mathrm{E}[\bar{X}] = \mu$, an appropriate measure of the closeness of $\bar{X}$ to μ is the standard deviation of the sampling distribution of $\bar{X}$. This is because the smaller this standard deviation the more densely concentrated is the distribution of $\bar{X}$ around μ, and consequently the more likely it will be that $\bar{X}$ will have a value close to μ. For this reason, the standard deviation of the sampling distribution of a statistic is often referred to as the *standard error* (SE) of that statistic. Let us now evaluate the standard error of our $\bar{X}$. From Table 5.3,

$$\mathrm{E}[\bar{X}^2] = \frac{1}{9} \times \frac{2}{10} + \frac{4}{9} \times \frac{3}{10} + 1 \times \frac{4}{10} + \frac{16}{9} \times \frac{1}{10} = \frac{11}{15}.$$

Since $\mathrm{E}[\bar{X}] = 4/5$, it follows that the variance of $\bar{X}$ is

$$\mathrm{V}[\bar{X}] = \frac{11}{15} - \left(\frac{4}{5}\right)^2 = \frac{7}{75},$$

and therefore, the standard error of $\bar{X}$ is given by

$$\mathrm{SE}[\bar{X}] = \sqrt{(7/75)} \simeq 0{\cdot}3055.$$

If in our example Z is another statistic such that $\mathrm{E}[Z] = \mu$, then we would prefer Z to $\bar{X}$ only if $\mathrm{SE}[Z] < \mathrm{SE}[\bar{X}]$, since then Z would be more likely than $\bar{X}$ to give a value close to μ.

Suppose now that, instead of taking a sample of three families in our example, we opted to take a sample of two families or a sample of four families. It may be shown (see Exercise 5.2 question 1) that in each of these cases the sample mean number of children per family has an average value equal to the population mean $\mu(= 4/5)$, and that the standard errors of these sample means are $\sqrt{(21/100)} \simeq 0{\cdot}4583$ and $\sqrt{(7/200)} \simeq 0{\cdot}1871$, respectively. It follows that the standard errors of the sample means for samples of 2, 3, and 4 families from our population of five families are approximately equal to 0·4583, 0·3055 and 0·1871, respectively. As we might have guessed, the larger the sample the smaller will be the standard error of the sample mean.

Now consider Y as an estimator of the proportion θ of the five families in our example that have no children. From the given information on the family sizes, the proportion of families having no children is $\theta = 2/5$. From Table 5.4, it is clear that no sample of three children will yield a sample proportion y which is exactly equal to θ. Proceeding as we did for $\bar{X}$, the mean of the sampling distribution of Y, as displayed in Table 5.4, is

$$\mathrm{E}[Y] = 0 \times \frac{1}{10} + \frac{1}{3} \times \frac{6}{10} + \frac{2}{3} \times \frac{3}{10} = \frac{2}{5},$$

which is precisely the value of θ. Thus, the average value of Y over all possible samples of size three is equal to θ, and again, this result is generally true when estimating a proportion. From Table 5.4 we also find

$$\mathrm{E}[Y^2] = 0 \times \frac{1}{10} + \frac{1}{9} \times \frac{6}{10} + \frac{4}{9} \times \frac{3}{10} = \frac{1}{5},$$

and therefore, the standard error of Y is

$$\mathrm{SE}[Y] = \sqrt{\left\{\frac{1}{5} - \left(\frac{2}{5}\right)^2\right\}} = \frac{1}{5}.$$

Again, it may be verified that the larger the sample size the smaller will be the standard error of Y.

EXERCISE 5.2

1 For the five families in Example 1, §5.2, determine the sampling distribution of $\bar{X}_2$ and $\bar{X}_4$, where $\bar{X}_2$ is the mean number of children in a randomly selected sample of two families, and $\bar{X}_4$ is the mean number of children in a randomly selected sample of four families. Verify that $\mathrm{E}[\bar{X}_2] = \mathrm{E}[\bar{X}_4] = 4/5$, $\mathrm{SE}[\bar{X}_2] = \sqrt{0{\cdot}21}$, and $\mathrm{SE}[\bar{X}_4] = \sqrt{0{\cdot}035}$.

2 A building contractor has contracts on five different sites. He employs two labourers on each of two of the sites, three on each of two of the other sites, and six on the remaining site. Calculate (i) μ, the mean number of labourers per site, (ii) ξ, the median number of labourers per site. (The median of a set of numbers is the middle number when the numbers are ordered from the smallest to the largest.)

Three of the five sites are chosen at random without replacement. Let $\bar{X}$ and M denote the mean and the median, respectively, of the number of labourers in the sampled sites.

(iii) Find the sampling distributions of $\bar{X}$ and M.

(iv) Show that $\mathrm{E}[\bar{X}] = \mu$ and evaluate $\mathrm{SE}[\bar{X}]$.

(v) Show that $\mathrm{E}[M] \neq \xi$.

3 The five cards in a pack are numbered 1, 2, 3, 4 and 5, respectively. Let X denote the number on a randomly drawn card from the pack. Write down the probability distribution of X, and determine its mean μ and its variance σ^2.

List the various possible pairs of numbers that may be obtained when two of the five cards are chosen at random without replacement. For each possible pair $\{X_1, X_2\}$ of numbers calculate the value of

$$S^2 = (X_1 - \bar{X})^2 + (X_2 - \bar{X})^2,$$

where $\bar{X} = \frac{1}{2}(X_1 + X_2)$. Hence display the sampling distribution of S^2 in a table. Determine whether or not $\mathrm{E}[S^2]$ is equal to σ^2.

4 Repeat question 3 above for the case when the two cards are chosen at random *with replacement*.

5.3 Random samples

The terms 'sample' and 'population' introduced in the preceding section are also used in situations when there is no collection of objects as such. For instance, continually throwing a die will generate an infinite sequence of scores, each of which will be one of the numbers 1, 2, 3, 4, 5, 6. This infinite sequence is a collection of numbers which is also defined to be a *population.* The score X in any one throw will be a discrete random variable having range space $\{1, 2, 3, 4, 5, 6\}$ and, assuming the die to be fair, its probability distribution is given by

$$\mathrm{P}(X = x) = \tfrac{1}{6}, \qquad x = 1, 2, 3, 4, 5, 6.$$

We may refer to this distribution as being the *population distribution of X.* The scores obtained in a finite number n of throws of the die may then be referred to as a sample of n observations of X.

Generalising the above, let X denote a random variable associated with a particular random experiment. Suppose that n independent trials of the random experiment are performed under identical conditions. Denote the outcomes of these n trials by $X_1, X_2, \ldots, X_n$. Then $X_1, X_2, \ldots, X_n$ are independent random variables (since the trials are independent) and each X_i has the same probability distribution as X (since the trials are performed under identical conditions). Under the conditions just described we refer to $X_1, X_2, \ldots, X_n$ as being a *random sample of n observations of X* or as a *sample of n independent observations of X.* Sampling *with* replacement from a finite population is a special case where the above conditions are satisfied. However, this is not so when sampling *without* replacement from a finite population since the conditions vary from one trial to another because the population being sampled is depleted by one value after each trial. In the remaining parts of this chapter we shall assume that the conditions for a random sample are satisfied, and we shall derive some general properties of the sampling distribution of the mean and of the proportion of successes in a specified number of independent Bernoulli trials.

5.4 Distribution of a sample mean

Consider a random variable X whose distribution has mean $\mu = \mathrm{E}[X]$ and variance $\sigma^2 = \mathrm{V}[X]$. Let $X_1, X_2, \ldots, X_n$ denote a random sample of n observations of X and let $\bar{X} = \Sigma X_i/n$ denote the sample mean. Then

$$\mathrm{E}[\bar{X}] = \mu, \quad \text{and} \quad \mathrm{V}[\bar{X}] = \sigma^2/n. \tag{1}$$

To prove (1) we shall make use of the results derived in §4.6. Since $\bar{X} = (X_1 + X_2 + \ldots + X_n)/n$, it follows from (1) of §4.6 that

$$\mathrm{E}[\bar{X}] = \frac{1}{n}\mathrm{E}[X_1] + \frac{1}{n}\mathrm{E}[X_2] + \ldots + \frac{1}{n}\mathrm{E}[X_n].$$

But each X_i has the same distribution as X, so that in particular, $E[X_i] = E[X] = \mu$ for $i = 1, 2, \ldots, n$. Hence

$$E[\bar{X}] = \frac{1}{n} \times n\mu = \mu.$$

Since $X_1, X_2, \ldots, X_n$ are independent and $V[X_i] = V[X] = \sigma^2$ for each i, it follows from (4) of §4.6 that

$$V[\bar{X}] = V\left[\frac{X_1}{n} + \frac{X_2}{n} + \ldots + \frac{X_n}{n}\right]$$
$$= \frac{1}{n^2} \times n\sigma^2 = \frac{\sigma^2}{n}$$

The results given in (1) are very general in that they are valid whatever be the distribution of X, provided only that the sample arises from independent trials under identical conditions.

EXAMPLE 1 *Suppose (unrealistically) that three families are chosen at random with replacement from the five families in Example* 1, §5.2. *Let us now find the sampling distribution of the mean number of children per family in the sample, and then use it to demonstrate the results given in* (1).

Let X denote the number of children in one randomly chosen family. Since two of the families have no children, two have one child, and one has two children, the population distribution of X is as displayed in Table 5.5.

Table 5.5 Population distribution of X

x	0	1	2
$P(X = x)$	$\frac{2}{5}$	$\frac{2}{5}$	$\frac{1}{5}$

From Table 5.5 we find that the population mean is

$$\mu = E[X] = \frac{2}{5} + \frac{2}{5} = \frac{4}{5},$$

and the population variance is

$$\sigma^2 = E[X^2] - \mu^2 = \frac{2}{5} + \frac{4}{5} - \left(\frac{4}{5}\right)^2 = \frac{14}{25}.$$

Let X_1, X_2, X_3, respectively, denote the numbers of children in the first, second, and third families sampled. Since the sampling is with replacement, each of X_1, X_2, X_3 may have any one of the values 0, 1, 2, and the total number of triples possible for (X_1, X_2, X_3) will be $3^3 = 27$, but note well that these are not equally probable. A complete listing of the 27 triples is not necessary since the same combination of three numbers may appear several times among the triples. For example, if the numbers of children in the families in the order in which they are drawn were (1, 2, 2), then this same combination will also appear in two other triples, namely (2, 1, 2) and (2, 2, 1). Since the sampling is at random with replacement, each of these triples will have probability

$$\{P(X = 2)\}^2\{P(X = 1)\} = \left(\frac{1}{5}\right)^2\left(\frac{2}{5}\right) = \frac{2}{125}.$$

Similarly, the three numbers 0, 1, 2 will appear in the six different ordered triples (0, 1, 2), (0, 2, 1), (1, 0, 2), (1, 2, 0), (2, 0, 1), and (2, 1, 0), each of these triples having probability

$$P(X = 0)P(X = 1)P(X = 2) = \frac{4}{125}.$$

Table 5.6 gives a complete listing of all the possible combinations of three numbers that may be obtained, the number of triples associated with each combination, the probability of each such triple, and the value of $\bar{X}$ corresponding to each combination.

Table 5.6 Sample values of $\bar{X}$

Unordered sample	Number of triples	Probability of triple	Total probability	$\bar{X}$
{0, 0, 0}	1	$(2/5)^3 = 8/125$	8/125	0
{0, 0, 1}	3	$(2/5)^2(2/5) = 8/125$	24/125	1/3
{0, 0, 2}	3	$(2/5)^2(1/5) = 4/125$	12/125	2/3
{0, 1, 1}	3	$(2/5)(2/5)^2 = 8/125$	24/125	2/3
{0, 1, 2}	6	$(2/5)(2/5)(1/5) = 4/125$	24/125	1
{0, 2, 2}	3	$(2/5)(1/5)^2 = 2/125$	6/125	4/3
{1, 1, 1}	1	$(2/5)^3 = 8/125$	8/125	1
{1, 1, 2}	3	$(2/5)^2(1/5) = 4/125$	12/125	4/3
{1, 2, 2}	3	$(2/5)(1/5)^2 = 2/125$	6/125	5/3
{2, 2, 2}	1	$(1/5)^3 = 1/125$	1/125	2
Total	27	—	1	—

Observe that the total number of triples is $27 = 3^3$, and that the sum of all the probabilities is unity. Summing the probabilities corresponding to each distinct value of $\bar{X}$ gives the sampling distribution of $\bar{X}$, which is displayed in Table 5.7.

Table 5.7 Sampling distribution of $\bar{X}$

$\bar{x}$	0	1/3	2/3	1	4/3	5/3	2
$P(\bar{X} = \bar{x})$	8/125	24/125	36/125	32/125	18/125	6/125	1/125

Hence,

$$E[\bar{X}] = (24 + 72 + 96 + 72 + 30 + 6)/375 = 4/5 = \mu,$$

and

$$\mathrm{V}[\bar{X}] = \mathrm{E}[\bar{X}]^2 - \mu^2 = (930/1125) - (4/5)^2$$
$$= 14/75 = \sigma^2/3,$$

in agreement with the results stated in (1) on noting that $n = 3$ here.

In Example 1, §5.2 we showed that when a sample of three families was chosen without replacement, the standard error of the mean number of children per sampled family was $\sqrt{(7/75)}$ as compared with the value $\sqrt{(14/75)}$ obtained here for sampling with replacement. Thus, whereas each of sampling without replacement and sampling with replacement provides an estimate of μ which is correct 'on average', the former is to be preferred because it yields an estimate with a smaller standard error. This is intuitively obvious on noting that when sampling without replacement no family can appear more than once in the sample, and should therefore be more informative than when sampling with replacement.

EXAMPLE 2 *Determine the mean and the standard error of the mean $\bar{X}$ of a random sample of* 11 *observations of the random variable X whose probability density function f is given by*

$$\mathrm{f}(x) = x + \tfrac{1}{2}, \qquad 0 \leqslant x \leqslant 1.$$

In Examples 1 and 5 of §3.4 we showed that the mean and the variance of the distribution of X were, respectively,

$$\mathrm{E}[X] = 7/12, \qquad \mathrm{V}[X] = 11/144.$$

Thus, using (1) above, if $\bar{X}$ is the mean of a random sample of $n = 11$ observations of X, the sampling distribution of $\bar{X}$ is such that

$$\mathrm{E}[\bar{X}] = \mathrm{E}[X] = 7/12,$$

and

$$\mathrm{V}[\bar{X}] = \mathrm{V}[X]/11 = 1/144.$$

It follows that $\bar{X}$ has mean 7/12 and standard error $\sqrt{(1/144)} = 1/12$.

EXERCISE 5.4A

1 In the situation described in Exercise 5.2 question 2 suppose that three sites are sampled at random with replacement. Derive the sampling distribution of $\bar{X}$, the mean number of labourers employed per site in the sample, and use it to verify the results given in (1) of this section. Compare your answers with those you obtained in Exercise 5.2 question 2 and comment.

2 A fair cubical die has three of its faces numbered 1, two other faces numbered 2, and the remaining faces numbered 3. When the die is thrown, the score X is defined to be the number showing on the uppermost face of the die. Write down the probability distribution of X and evaluate its mean and variance.
(i) Let $\bar{X}_3$ denote the mean of the scores in three throws of the die. Derive the sampling distribution of $\bar{X}_3$ and hence verify the results in (1) of this section.
(ii) Let $\bar{X}_5$ denote the mean of the scores in five throws of the die. Calculate the mean and the standard error of $\bar{X}_5$.

3 The mass X g of inedibles per kg of a particular joint of meat is distributed with probability density function f, where

$$f(x) = 3(100-x)^2/10^6, \qquad 0 < x < 100.$$

Determine the mean and the variance of X.

Find the mean and the variance of the mean mass of inedibles in a random sample of four joints each of mass 1 kg.

4 Find the mean and the standard deviation of the mean of a random sample of four observations from the exponential distribution

$$f(x) = \tfrac{1}{2}e^{-\frac{1}{2}x}, \qquad x > 0.$$

5.4.1 Distribution of the mean of a random sample from a normal distribution

Consider a random variable X which is normally distributed with mean μ and variance σ^2. Let $X_1, X_2, \ldots, X_n$ denote a random sample of n observations of X, having mean

$$\bar{X} = (X_1 + X_2 + \ldots + X_n)/n.$$

Since $X_1, X_2, \ldots, X_n$ are independent and each has the same distribution as X, namely $N(\mu, \sigma^2)$, it follows from the results quoted in §4.8 that $\bar{X} \sim N(\mu, \sigma^2/n)$; that is, $\bar{X}$ is also normally distributed with mean and variance

$$E[\bar{X}] = \mu, \qquad V[\bar{X}] = \sigma^2/n,$$

respectively. The mean and variance of $\bar{X}$ agree with those derived in §5.4; the additional result here is that $\bar{X}$ is also normally distributed.

EXAMPLE 3 *A machine produces cylindrical rods whose diameters are normally distributed with mean* 1 *cm and standard deviation* 0·01 *cm. If four of these rods are selected at random, calculate the probability that the mean of their diameters will exceed* 0·99 *cm.*

Let $\bar{X}$ denote the mean of the diameters in cm of the four selected rods. Since $X \sim N(1, 0{\cdot}01^2)$, it follows from the results stated above that $E[\bar{X}] = 1$, $V[\bar{X}] = 0{\cdot}01^2/4 = 0{\cdot}005^2$, and $\bar{X} \sim N(1, 0{\cdot}005^2)$. Hence

$$Z = (\bar{X} - 1)/0{\cdot}005 \sim N(0, 1)$$

and therefore,

$$P(\bar{X} > 0{\cdot}99) = P\left(Z > \frac{0{\cdot}99 - 1}{0{\cdot}005}\right) = P(Z > -2) = 0{\cdot}97725$$

EXERCISE 5.4B

1 The operational lifetimes in hours of manufactured light bulbs are normally distributed with mean 1060 and standard deviation 20.

(i) Calculate the probability that the average of the lifetimes of a random sample of 25 bulbs will be greater than 1050 hours.

(ii) Find the smallest n for which there is a probability of at least 0·8 that the average of the life times of a random sample of n bulbs will be greater than 1055 hours.

2 When a certain instrument is used to measure a length it is known that the error made is normally distributed with mean zero and standard deviation 0·5 mm. In 10 independent applications of the instrument, calculate the probability that the average error will be numerically less than 0·05 mm.

3 The wages paid to the weekly-paid staff of a business concern are normally distributed with mean £46.80 and standard deviation £4.
(i) Calculate the probability that the average of the wages of a random sample of 9 weekly-paid staff is within £3 of the population mean (£46.80).
(ii) How large a random sample should be taken if there is to be a probability of approximately 0·9 that the sample mean wage will be within £1 of the population mean?

4 In a certain examination with a very large entry, the percentage marks obtained by male candidates were normally distributed with mean 56 and standard deviation 16. Let $\bar{X}$ denote the mean of the marks obtained by a randomly chosen sample of four of the male candidates. Calculate the probability that $\bar{X}$ exceeds 70, and find the value of c if the probability is 0·95 that $\bar{X}$ is within c marks of the overall mean mark of 56.

In the same examination, the percentage marks obtained by the female candidates were normally distributed with mean 61 and standard deviation 20. Let $\bar{Y}$ denote the mean mark obtained by a randomly chosen sample of 5 of the female candidates.

What is the sampling distribution of (i) Y, (ii) $W = \bar{Y} - \bar{X}$? Calculate the probability that $\bar{Y}$ exceeds $\bar{X}$.

5.4.2 The Central Limit Theorem

Let $\bar{X}$ denote the mean of a random sample of n observations of a random variable X. Recall from §5.4 that knowing only that X has mean μ and variance σ^2, the sampling distribution of $\bar{X}$ has mean μ and variance σ^2/n. This information alone is not sufficient to enable us to make probablistic statements about the value of $\bar{X}$. In the particular case when it is known that X is normally distributed, then $\bar{X}$ is also normally distributed (§5.4.1) and we are then able to make probabilistic statements about the value of $\bar{X}$.

Using mathematics beyond the level of this text, it may be shown that, whatever be the distribution of X, as the sample size n is increased, the sampling distribution of $\bar{X}$ approaches that of a normal distribution with mean $E[X]$ and variance $(V[X]/n)$. This result is known as the *Central Limit Theorem* for a sample mean. The practical value of the theorem is that, for a large sample size n, the sampling distribution of $\bar{X}$ may be approximated by the normal distribution $N(\mu, \sigma^2/n)$, where μ and σ^2 are the mean and variance of X. It is not possible to stipulate a precise value for the minimum n for which the approximation may be regarded as a good one. Empirical studies suggest that a sample size of 40 or more is a reasonably good guideline for most population distributions that are likely to be met in practice. However, the approximation can be quite good for much smaller sample sizes, especially when the population distribution is fairly symmetrical.

To demonstrate this theorem, consider sampling with replacement from the five families of Example 1. In Fig. 5.1 we show a diagrammatic representation of the population distribution of X as displayed in Table 5.5, while in Figs. 5.2 and 5.3, respectively, we show diagrammatic representations of the sampling distribution of $\bar{X}_3$ as displayed in Table 5.7, and that of $\bar{X}_5$, the mean of a random sample of five observations of X. These diagrams clearly illustrate that as the sample size is increased from 1 to 3 and then from 3 to 5, the sampling distribution of $\bar{X}_n$ has a smaller spread and becomes increasingly like the bell-shaped normal distribution. These trends would be even more pronounced for sample sizes much larger than those considered here.

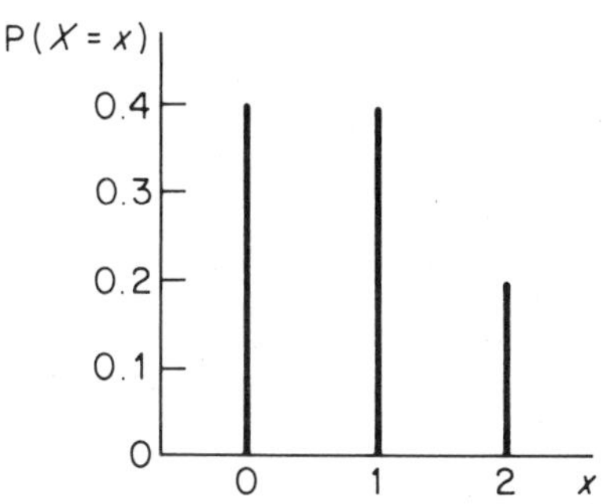

Fig. 5.1 Distribution of X

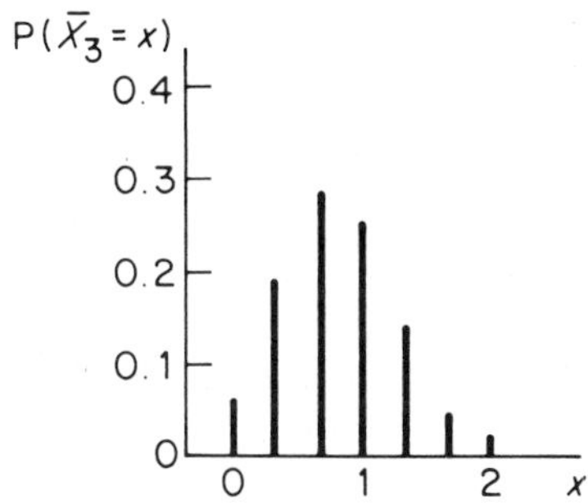

Fig. 5.2 Distribution of $\bar{X}_3$

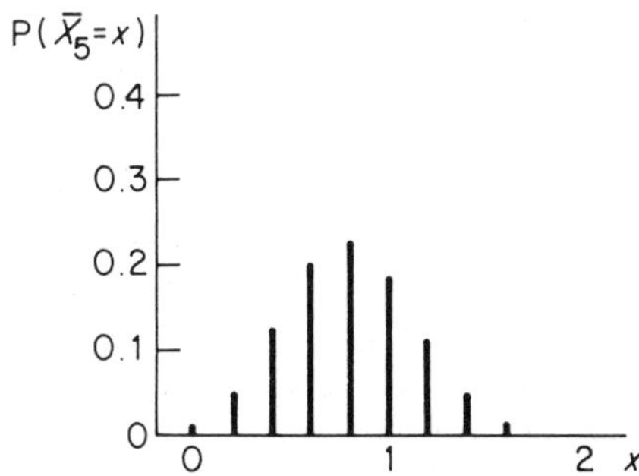

Fig. 5.3 Distribution of $\bar{X}_5$

A more convicing demonstration of the Central Limit Theorem can be achieved on a computer programmed to simulate randomly observed values from a specified probability distribution. Alternatively, it may be demonstrated collectively by a class of pupils, each pupil throwing a fair die (for example) several times and evaluating the mean scores $\bar{X}_n$ for successive groups of n scores thrown (for appropriately chosen values of n), and finally pooling the results to produce a histogram for the observed sampling distribution for each n.

The Central Limit Theorem also justifies our use of the normal approximation to the binomial distribution described in §3.9.1, on noting how we interpreted a binomially distributed random variable in §4.6 as being the sum of independent Bernoulli random variables.

EXAMPLE 4 *A random sample of 50 observations is to be taken of the random variable X whose probability density function* f *is given by*

$$f(x) = x + \tfrac{1}{2}, \qquad 0 < x < 1.$$

Denoting the sample mean by $\bar{X}$, determine the mean and the variance of $\bar{X}$. Find an approximate value for the probability that $\bar{X}$ will be less than $\tfrac{1}{2}$.

From Examples 1 and 5 of §3.4, the mean and the variance of X are, respectively,

$$E[X] = 7/12, \qquad V[X] = 11/144.$$

Using (1) in §5.4 with $n = 50$, the mean and the variance of $\bar{X}$ are

$$E[\bar{X}] = E[X] = 7/12, \qquad V[\bar{X}] = V[X]/50 = 11/7200.$$

Now assume that a sample of size 50 is large enough to justify approximating the sampling distribution of $\bar{X}$ by a normal distribution having mean $E[\bar{X}]$ and variance $V[\bar{X}]$. Then,

$$Z = \frac{\bar{X} - (7/12)}{\sqrt{(11/7200)}}$$

is approximately distributed as $N(0, 1)$. Hence,

$$P(\bar{X} < \tfrac{1}{2}) \simeq P\left\{Z < \frac{\tfrac{1}{2} - (7/12)}{\sqrt{(11/7200)}}\right\} = P(Z < -2{\cdot}13) = 0{\cdot}0166.$$

EXERCISE 5.4C

1 The distance travelled in a week by a motorist is a continuous random variable having mean 890 km and standard deviation 80 km. Find an approximate value for the probability that over a complete year of 52 weeks the average distance travelled per week will be more than 900 km.

2 A certain type of fuse has a lifetime X with is exponentially distributed with mean 1500 hours. Find an approximate value for the probability that a random sample of 40 such fuses will have an average lifetime in the range from 1500 hours to 1550 hours.

3 When a number is rounded off to its nearest integer value, the rounding-off error X may be regarded as a continuous random variable which is uniformly distributed over the interval $(-\tfrac{1}{2}, \tfrac{1}{2})$. Let $\bar{X}$ denote the mean error when n numbers are rounded off to their nearest integer values. Assuming that the individual errors are independent, write down the mean and the variance of $\bar{X}$.

Assuming that n is very large, show that the probability that $\bar{X}$ will be numerically less than $1/(2\sqrt{n})$ is approximately 0·9. Find the largest n for which there is a probability of at most 0·6 that $\bar{X}$ will be numerically less than 0·04.

4 Determine the mean and the variance of the average of the scores obtained in 30 throws of a fair die. Hence find an approximate value for the probability that the average score will be 4 or more.

5.5 Distribution of a sample proportion

Let θ denote the probability of a success in each trial of a Bernoulli experiment, and let X denote the number of successes in n independent trials. Then, the sample proportion of successes is $P = X/n$.

Since $X \sim \mathrm{B}(n, \theta)$,

$$\mathrm{E}[X] = n\theta, \qquad \mathrm{V}[X] = n\theta(1-\theta).$$

Using the properties of expectation and variance established earlier, it follows that

$$\mathrm{E}[P] = (\mathrm{E}[X])/n = \theta, \qquad \mathrm{V}[P] = (\mathrm{V}[X])/n^2 = \{\theta(1-\theta)\}/n, \quad (1)$$

so that the sampling distribution of P has mean θ and standard deviation $\{\theta(1-\theta)/n\}^{1/2}$.

These results are valid more generally than they may at first appear. For instance, suppose X is a quality measurement of a mass produced item and that an item is satisfactory only if X exceeds some known value c. Then the proportion of satisfactory items produced is $\theta = P(X > c)$. If in a random sample of n items the proportion that are satisfactory is P, then the sampling distribution of P will have the properties given by (1) above. As another example, let θ denote the proportion of objects in a finite collection of objects that have a particular attribute. Then, if in a random sample of n objects drawn *with replacement* from the collection the proportion of objects having the attribute is P, the sampling distribution of this P will also have the properties given by (1) above; this is demonstrated in the example that follows.

EXAMPLE 1 *With reference to Example* 1 *of* §5.4, *consider the sampling distribution of the proportion P of families having no child in a random sample of* 3 *families chosen with replacement.*

Recall from Example 1, §5.4 that the proportion θ of the families having no child is 2/5. Hence, according to (1) with $n = 3$, the sampling distribution of P is such that $\mathrm{E}[P] = \theta = 2/5$ and $\mathrm{V}[P] = \frac{1}{3}\theta(1-\theta) = 2/25$. Let us now verify these results by deriving the sampling distribution of P in this case.

From Table 5.6, the values of P and their respective probabilities, corresponding to all possible samples of size 3, are as shown in Table 5.8. The sampling distribution of P is then as shown in Table 5.9.

Table 5.8 Sample values of P

Unordered sample	Probability	Value of P
{0, 0, 0}	8/125	1
{0, 0, 1}	24/125	$\frac{2}{3}$
{0, 0, 2}	12/125	$\frac{2}{3}$
{0, 1, 1}	24/125	$\frac{1}{3}$
{0, 1, 2}	24/125	$\frac{1}{3}$
{0, 2, 2}	6/125	$\frac{1}{3}$
{1, 1, 1}	8/125	0
{1, 1, 2}	12/125	0
{1, 2, 2}	6/125	0
{2, 2, 2}	1/125	0

Table 5.9 Sampling distribution of P

p	0	$\frac{1}{3}$	$\frac{2}{3}$	1
$P(P = p)$	27/125	54/125	36/125	8/125

From Table 5.9

$$E[P] = (0 + 54 + 72 + 8)/375 = 2/5,$$

which agrees with value obtained above using (1). Also

$$E[P^2] = (54 + 144 + 72)/1125 = 6/25,$$

and therefore

$$V[P] = (6/125) - (2/25)^2 = 2/25,$$

again in agreement with the result obtained from (1).

In Example 1, §5.2 we derived the sampling distribution of the proportion of families having no child in a sample of 3 families drawn at random *without replacement*. This sampling distribution is displayed in Table 5.4. We showed (at the end of §5.2) that its mean was 2/5, exactly as above, and that its variance was 1/25, which is exactly one half of the variance given above for sampling with replacement. Thus, as we found in §5.4 when estimating the mean of a random variable associated with objects in a collection, it is preferable to use sampling without replacement to estimate the proportion of objects in a collection that have a particular attribute.

EXERCISE 5.5

1 A fair cubical die has three of its faces numbered 1, two other faces numbered 2, and the remaining face numbered 3. (Compare Exercise 5.4A question 2). The die is to be thrown five times. Let P_3 denote the proportion of the first three throws that give a score of 2, and let P_5 denote the proportion of all five throws that give a score of 2.
(i) Derive the sampling distribution of P_3 and use it to verify the results given in (1) of this section.
(ii) Calculate the mean and the variance of P_5.

2 The mass X g of inedibles per kg of a particular joint of meat is distributed with probability density function f, where

$$f(x) = 3(100-x)^2/10^6, \qquad 0 < x < 100.$$

(Compare Exercise 5.4A question 3). Suppose that a joint of mass 1 kg is regarded as substandard if its inedible content exceeds 75 kg. For a random sample of 10 joints of the meat, each of mass 1 kg, find the mean and the variance of the proportion of joints that will be substandard.

REVIEW PROBLEMS ON CHAPTER 5

1 The number of days that each of five employees (A, B, C, D, E) in an office was absent from work during a year is shown in the following table.

Employee	A	B	C	D	E
No. of days absent	10	6	0	4	0

(i) Calculate the mean μ and the variance σ^2 of the numbers of days these employees were absent from work during the year.
(ii) Three of these employees are selected at random *without replacement.* Let $\bar{X}$ denote the mean number of days absent for the chosen three employees.
(a) Determine the sampling distribution of $\bar{X}$ and display it in a table.
(b) Determine whether or not $E[\bar{X}] = \mu$.
(c) Find the variance of $\bar{X}$ and verify that it is equal to one-half of the variance of the sample mean if the three employees are chosen *with replacement.* (*WJEC 1979*)

2 One number is to be drawn at random from the set $\{1, 2, 3, 4\}$. Denoting the drawn number by X, calculate the mean μ and the variance σ^2 of X.

Three numbers are to be drawn at random *with replacement* from the above set. Let $\bar{X}$ denote the mean and M the median of the three numbers drawn.
(i) Write down the values of the mean and the variance of $\bar{X}$.
(ii) Show that $P(M=4)=5/32$, and calculate the values of $P(M=r)$ for $r = 1, 2, 3$. Hence verify that $E[M] = \mu$, and calculate $V[M]$. (*JMB 1980*)

3 A cubical die has two of its faces numbered 1, two numbered 2, and the remaining two faces numbered 3. Find the mean μ and the variance σ^2 of the score obtained when the die is thrown once.

If the die is thrown three times, derive the sampling distribution of (i) the mean, (ii) the median, of the three scores. Verify that each of these sampling distributions has mean equal to μ and determine which of the sample mean and the sample median has the smaller standard error.

4 For the die in question 3 above, let X_1, X_2, and X_3 denote the respective scores in three throws of the die. Derive the sampling distributions of
(i) $Y = \max(X_1, X_2, X_3) =$ the largest of the three scores,
(ii) $Z = \frac{1}{2}[(X_1-\bar{X})^2+(X_2-\bar{X})^2+(X_3-\bar{X})^2]$,
where $\bar{X}$ is the mean of the three scores. Verify that $\mathrm{E}[Z] = \sigma^2$.

5 A random experiment has the three possible outcomes 0, 1, 2, occurring with probabilities p, $1-2p$, and p, respectively, where $0 < p < \frac{1}{2}$. In three independent trials of the experiment show that the probability of at least two zeros occurring is $p^2(3-2p)$.

Let M denote the median of the outcomes of the three independent trials. Derive the sampling distribution of M and hence show that the variance of M is less than the variance of the mean of the three outcomes only if $6p^2-9p+1>0$. *(WJEC 1974S)*

6 Let $\bar{X}$ denote the mean of a random sample of four observations from a normal distribution having mean μ and standard deviation σ. Find the probability that $\bar{X}$ will take a value in the interval from $\mu-\sigma$ to $\mu+\sigma$. *(JMB 1981)*

7 In a certain geographical region the heights of girls and boys in the age range 16 to 18 years can be regarded as having normal distributions as follows.

Girls: mean 162·5 cm, standard deviation 4·0 cm,
Boys: mean 173·5 cm, standard deviation 4·8 cm.

Mean values of samples of sizes 64 and 36, drawn from the given normal populations of heights of girls and boys, respectively, are denoted by $\bar{X}_G$ and $\bar{X}_B$, respectively. State, or calculate, the means and the variances of the sampling distributions of the means $\bar{X}_G$ and $\bar{X}_B$, and of the sampling distribution of differences $\bar{X}_B - \bar{X}_G$.

Deduce the probability that in a sixth form containing 64 girls and 36 boys the mean height of the boys will be at least 12 cm more than that of the girls. *(JMB 1979)*

8 Let $\bar{X}$ denote the mean of a random sample of 80 observations of the random variable X whose probability density function f is given by

$$\mathrm{f}(x) = \tfrac{3}{4}x(2-x), \qquad 0 < x < 2.$$

Using an appropriate approximation to the sampling distribution of $\bar{X}$, calculate the probabilities that $\bar{X}$ will be (i) less than 1, (ii) less than 0·95. *(JMB 1980)*

9 A random sample of 100 observations is to be drawn from a normally distributed population. Let P denote the proportion of the observations in the sample which will have values within one standard deviation of the mean of the population. Calculate the mean and the variance of P, giving your answers correct to three significant figures. *(JMB 1978)*

10 With reference to question 1, let P_1 denote the proportion of three employees selected at random *without replacement* who had not been absent at all during the year, and let P_2 denote the corresponding proportion when three employees are selected *with* replacement.

(i) Derive the sampling distribution of P_1 and evaluate $E[P_1]$ and $V[P_1]$.

(ii) Write down the values of $E[P_2]$ and $V[P_2]$.

(iii) Express $V[P_2]$ as a percentage of $V[P_1]$.

6 Estimation

6.1 Introduction

In many practical situations little or nothing may be known about a population distribution that is of interest. Some examples of such situations were given in §5.1. In order to obtain some information about such a distribution, experiments are conducted to yield a sample of observations and the results obtained are then used to make inferences. Sometimes, the inferences to be made will consist of estimating the values of some particular characteristic features of the population distribution, such as its mean, or its quartiles, or its variance. The examples given in §5.1 were concerned with the estimation of a population mean and of a population proportion.

Situations also arise where the functional form of a population distribution is known but involves some unknown quantity or quantities, referred to as *parameters* of the distribution. For example, let X denote the number of successes that are obtained in n independent Bernoulli trials, in each of which the probability of a success is θ whose value is unknown. Then we know that the distribution of X is $\mathrm{B}(n, \theta)$, and having carried out the specified number n of trials, the observed value X/n may be used to estimate the value of θ; some examples were given in §5.1. As another example, there may exist evidence to indicate that a population has a normal distribution, but the parameters μ and σ^2 of the distribution are not known, in which case sample values from the distribution may be used to provide estimates of μ and σ^2.

In the present chapter we shall discuss how sample values may be used to estimate an unknown parameter by (i) quoting a single value (called a *point estimate*), and (ii) quoting a range of values (an *interval estimate*).

6.2 Point estimation of a parameter

Let θ denote an unknown parameter of the population distribution of a random variable X. To obtain information about θ, suppose n independent experiments are to be conducted to yield a random sample of n observations of X. The problem now is that of deciding on how to combine the n sample values to produce an estimate of the value of θ. As mentioned in §5.2, any combination (or function) of sample values is called a *statistic*.

Denote the sample observations that will be obtained from the n experiments by $X_1, X_2, \ldots, X_n$, and suppose that the statistic we choose for estimating θ is $T \equiv T(X_1, X_2, \ldots, X_n)$. For example, as indicated in §5.1, if $\theta \equiv \mu$, the population mean, then an intuitively sensible choice of statistic is the sample mean $\bar{X} = (X_1 + X_2 + \ldots + X_n)/n$.

The statistic $T \equiv T(X_1, X_2, \ldots, X_n)$ we choose is referred to as a *point estimator* of θ. Having conducted the n experiments, suppose that the actual observed values of $X_1, X_2, \ldots, X_n$ are $x_1, x_2, \ldots, x_n$, respectively. For these observed values, the statistic T will have the value $t = T(x_1, x_2, \ldots, x_n)$ and we take t to be our point estimate of θ. Note that t will be a randomly observed value from the sampling distribution of T.

Choosing an appropriate statistic T in any given situation can be a very challenging problem, but in many (although not all) cases, intuition leads to a sensible choice. But what is a sensible choice? What sort of properties should T have for it to be regarded as being a good estimator of a parameter θ? Some answers to these questions can be obtained from a study of the sampling distribution of T. In this text, we shall restrict consideration to one particular property of an estimator, namely *unbiasedness*, which is generally regarded as being desirable. (In a more advanced textbook, consideration would be given to other desirable properties of an estimator.)

Unbiasedness

Let θ denote an unknown parameter of a population distribution, and let $X_1, X_2, \ldots, X_n$ denote a random sample of n observations from the distribution. A statistic $T \equiv T(X_1, X_2, \ldots, X_n)$ is said to be an *unbiased estimator* of θ if and only if the sampling distribution of T is such that

$$\mathrm{E}[T] = \theta, \tag{1}$$

whatever be the value of θ.

A statistic T not satisfying (1) is said to be a *biased estimator* of θ. It follows from (1) that an unbiased estimator T of θ is such that its average value over all the possible samples of size n that could materialise is equal to θ.

If T is an unbiased estimator of θ and the observed sample values are $x_1, x_2, \ldots, x_n$, then the calculated value $t = T(x_1, x_2, \ldots, x_n)$ will be referred to as an *unbiased estimate* of θ.

6.2.1 Point estimation of a population mean

Consider a population distribution whose mean μ is unknown and is to be estimated from a sample of observations. As indicated in §5.1, intuition suggests choosing the sample mean as the statistic for providing an estimate of μ. Let $\bar{X}$ denote the mean of a random sample of n observations from the distribution. From §5.4, we know that

$$\mathrm{E}[\bar{X}] = \mu,$$

so that *a sample mean is always an unbiased estimator of the population mean.* Thus, in this case, intuition has led to a choice of estimator which is unbiased.

However, as illustrated by the following example, intuition can lead to an estimator which is biased.

EXAMPLE 1 *A random sample of n observations from a population distribution whose mean μ is unknown and whose standard deviation is known to be 1, is to be used to estimate the value of μ^2. Show that $\bar{X}^2$, where $\bar{X}$ is the sample mean, is a biased estimator of μ^2. Suggest an unbiased estimator of μ^2.*

Having established above that $\bar{X}$ is an unbiased estimator of μ, intuition suggests that we should take $\bar{X}^2$ as an estimator of μ^2. We now show that $\bar{X}^2$ is, in fact, a biased estimator of μ^2.

From §5.4, the sampling distribution of $\bar{X}$ is such that

$$\mathrm{E}[\bar{X}] = \mu \quad \text{and} \quad \mathrm{V}[\bar{X}] = \frac{\sigma^2}{n} = \frac{1}{n}.$$

Now, for any random variable Y,

$$\mathrm{V}[Y] = \mathrm{E}[Y^2] - \{\mathrm{E}[Y]\}^2,$$

and, therefore,

$$\mathrm{V}[\bar{X}] = \mathrm{E}[\bar{X}^2] - \{\mathrm{E}[\bar{X}]\}^2.$$

Hence,

$$\mathrm{E}[\bar{X}^2] = \mathrm{V}[\bar{X}] + \{\mathrm{E}[\bar{X}]\}^2 = \frac{1}{n} + \mu^2,$$

which is seen to be greater than μ^2. Thus, $\bar{X}^2$ is a biased estimator of μ^2.

Transforming the $1/n$ on the right-hand side of the above equation to the left-hand side of the equation gives

$$\mathrm{E}[\bar{X}^2] - \frac{1}{n} = \mu^2.$$

Since $1/n$ is a constant this equation may be rewritten as

$$\mathrm{E}\left[\bar{X}^2 - \frac{1}{n}\right] = \mu^2,$$

from which it follows that the statistic

$$T \equiv \bar{X}^2 - \frac{1}{n}$$

has the property $\mathrm{E}[T] = \mu^2$ and, consequently, T is an unbiased estimator of μ^2.

Returning now to the estimation of μ (as opposed to μ^2 as in the above example), let $X_1, X_2, \ldots, X_n$ denote a random sample of n observations of a random variable X whose mean μ is to be estimated. From the definition of a random sample given in §5.3, we know that each X_i has the same distribution as X. Hence, in particular, we have

$$\mathrm{E}[X_i] = \mu, \qquad i = 1, 2, \ldots, n.$$

Thus, any one of the sample observations could be used as an unbiased estimator of μ. Furthermore, if $\bar{X}_{(r)}$ is the mean of any r ($\leqslant n$) of the sample observations, then $\mathrm{E}[\bar{X}_{(r)}] = \mu$, so that $\bar{X}_{(r)}$ is also an unbiased estimator of μ. We thus have a wide choice of unbiased estimators of the population mean μ. Which should we choose? We could argue that $\bar{X}_{(n)} \equiv \bar{X}$ is the best choice because it is the only one of the estimators considered that depends on *all* n observations and it seems reasonable to suppose that every observation contributes some information about the value of μ. Another argument in favour of $\bar{X}$ is as follows. Denoting the population variance by σ^2, we have

$$\mathrm{V}[X_i] = \sigma^2, \qquad \mathrm{V}[\bar{X}_{(r)}] = \frac{\sigma^2}{r}, \qquad \mathrm{V}[\bar{X}] = \frac{\sigma^2}{n},$$

from which we see that $\bar{X}$ has the smallest variance, implying that the sampling distribution of $\bar{X}$ is the one most densely concentrated around μ. Hence, $\bar{X}$ is more likely than any one of the other estimators to have a value close to μ. In fact, it may be shown that of all possible linear combinations of $X_1, X_2, \ldots, X_n$ that are unbiased estimators of μ, the one of least variance is $\bar{X} = (X_1 + X_2 + \ldots + X_n)/n$. (For a proof when $n = 2$, see Exercise 6.2A question 2.)

As mentioned in §5.2, the standard deviation of the sampling distribution of any statistic T is more aptly referred to as the *standard error of T*, which we abbreviate as SE[T]. *Whenever we have a choice of unbiased estimators of a population parameter θ we should always choose the one having the least standard error, since that is the one which is the most likely to give an estimate close to θ.*

In particular, for a random sample of n observations from a population distribution having mean μ and variance σ^2, the best unbiased estimator of μ is the sample mean $\bar{X}$, whose standard error is

$$\mathrm{SE}[\bar{X}] = \frac{\sigma}{\sqrt{n}}.$$

Observe that SE[$\bar{X}$] decreases as the sample size increases, so that the larger the sample size the more likely it will be that $\bar{X}$ has a value close to μ. This is consistent with the general maxim that 'the greater the effort, the better the reward'.

EXERCISE 6.2A

1 Let X_1, X_2, X_3 denote a random sample of three observations from a population distribution having mean μ and variance σ^2. Consider the three

statistics

$$T_1 = X_1 + X_2 - X_3, \quad T_2 = \frac{1}{4}(2X_1 + X_2 + X_3), \quad T_3 = \frac{1}{3}(X_1 + X_2 + X_3).$$

Show that each of T_1, T_2, T_3 is an unbiased estimator of μ, and verify that T_3 is the one of least variance. (Hint: Use the results of §4.6.)

2 A statistic of the form $T = aX_1 + bX_2$, where a, b are constants, and X_1, X_2 are independent observations of a random variable X, is to be used to estimate $\mu \equiv \mathrm{E}[X]$. Find a relation connecting a and b for T to be an unbiased estimator of μ. Write down an expression for the variance of T in terms of a, b and $\sigma^2 = \mathrm{V}[X]$. Hence find the values of a and b for which T will be an unbiased estimator of μ having the smallest possible variance.

3 Let $\bar{X}$ denote the mean of a random sample of n observations from the uniform distribution $U(0, \theta)$, where θ is unknown. Find the value of the constant c for $T = c\bar{X}$ to be an unbiased estimator of θ.

4 Steel bearings manufactured to have a nominal diameter of μ mm are known to have diameters which are normally distributed with mean μ mm and standard deviation 0·03 mm. A random sample of 9 bearings had diameters (in mm)

5·01, 5·03, 4·96, 4·91, 4·96, 5·06, 5·02, 4·94, 4·93.

(i) Calculate an unbiased estimate of μ and write down the value of the standard error of your estimator.
(ii) Calculate the probability that another random sample of 9 bearings will have a mean diameter within 0·01 mm of the true value of μ. (Hint: Use the result given in §5.4.1.)

6.2.2 Point estimation of a probability

Consider the estimation of the probability θ of success in a Bernoulli trial (some examples were given in §5.1). Suppose that n independent trials are to be conducted for this purpose. Denoting by X the number of successes that will be obtained in the n trials, we know that $X \sim \mathrm{B}(n, \theta)$. The proportion P of successes that will be obtained in the n trials is given by

$$P = \frac{X}{n},$$

and as indicated in §5.1, P would appear to be a sensible choice of estimator of θ. We showed in §5.5 that

$$\mathrm{E}[P] = \theta \tag{1}$$

and

$$\mathrm{V}[P] = \frac{\theta(1-\theta)}{n}. \tag{2}$$

It follows directly from (1) that P is an unbiased estimator of θ, so that here again our intuition has led to an estimator which is unbiased. From

(2), the standard error of P is

$$\mathrm{SE}[P] = \sqrt{\left\{\frac{\theta(1-\theta)}{n}\right\}}. \tag{3}$$

As was the case for $\bar{X}$ when estimating μ, we see that the larger the value of n the smaller the standard error of P, and, consequently, the more likely that P will have a value close to θ.

Since $\mathrm{SE}[P]$ involves the unknown quantity θ, its value cannot be determined even after the observed value p of P becomes available. (Contrast this with $\mathrm{SE}[\bar{X}] = \sigma/\sqrt{n}$, which, when σ^2 is known, can be evaluated given only the size of the sample.) However, we can obtain an upper limit on the value of $\mathrm{SE}[P]$. We have

$$\theta(1-\theta) = \theta - \theta^2 = \frac{1}{4} - \left(\frac{1}{2} - \theta\right)^2,$$

from which it follows that the maximum value of $\theta(1-\theta)$ is $\frac{1}{4}$, occurring when $\theta = \frac{1}{2}$. Hence, for any θ,

$$\mathrm{SE}[P] \leqslant \sqrt{\left(\frac{1}{4n}\right)}. \tag{4}$$

One way of estimating $\mathrm{SE}[P]$ is to replace θ in (3) by the observed value $p = x/n$, the resulting estimate being

$$\mathrm{ESE}[P] = \sqrt{\left\{\frac{p(1-p)}{n}\right\}}, \tag{5}$$

where we have written ESE for 'estimated standard error'. We shall have occasion to use (5) even though it is a biased estimate, the proof of which is beyond the level of this text.

As mentioned in §5.5, if θ denotes the proportion of objects in a finite collection of objects that have a particular attribute, and P denotes the proportion of objects in a random sample of n objects that have the attribute, then (3) above will be valid only if the objects are sampled *with* replacement. However, (3) will still be approximately true when sampling without replacement provided the size N of the collection is very large relative to n. This is because a very large N implies that the proportion of objects in the collection having the particular attribute will be approximately the same for each draw.

EXAMPLE 2 *In order to predict the proportion of all votes that will be cast for a particular candidate in a forthcoming election, a random sample of* 100 *voters was canvassed and it was found that* 38 *of them stated that they intended to vote for the candidate. Calculate an unbiased estimate of the proportion of votes that will be cast for the candidate, and calculate an estimate of its standard error.*

Since it is reasonable to assume that the total number of voters is very large, we can use the results of this section.

The observed proportion of the voters who stated that they will vote for the candidate is

$$p = \frac{38}{100} = 0{\cdot}38,$$

which, from (1), is an unbiased estimate of the proportion θ of all votes that will be cast for the candidate. (Of course, we are assuming that the sampled voters responded truthfully and that none will vote differently on polling day.)

From (3), with $n = 100$, the standard error of our estimate is

$$\text{SE}[P] = \sqrt{\left\{\frac{\theta(1-\theta)}{100}\right\}}. \tag{6}$$

Replacing θ by $p = 0{\cdot}38$, an estimate of this standard error is

$$\text{ESE}[P] = \sqrt{\left\{\frac{0{\cdot}38 \times 0{\cdot}62}{100}\right\}} \simeq 0{\cdot}0485.$$

In terms of percentages our estimate of the percentage of votes for the particular candidate is 38% with an estimated standard error of approximately 4·9%: From (4), the standard error of our estimate is certainly less than $100/\sqrt{400} = 5\%$.

It is of interest to observe that the standard error of P does not depend on the total number N of voters, provided N is very large. This refutes the claim often made against a sample poll that the sample size was too small a proportion of the total electorate to provide a reliable prediction.

EXERCISE 6.2B

1 Fifty tosses of a damaged coin resulted in 30 heads and 20 tails. Calculate an unbiased estimate of the probability of obtaining a head in a single toss of this coin. Also calculate an estimate of the standard error of your estimator and the maximum possible value of this standard error.

2 A random sample of 100 mass-produced items was found to contain two defectives. Estimate the proportion of such items that are defective. Calculate an estimate of the standard error of your estimator and obtain an upper bound for the value of this standard error.

3 In a random sample of 200 customers at a supermarket it was found that 120 of them spent more than £5 at the supermarket. Estimate the proportion of all the customers at the supermarket that spend more than £5 there, and obtain an upper limit for the standard error of your estimator.

6.2.3 Point estimation of a population variance

Now consider estimating the unknown variance of a population. In this section we shall assume that the population mean is also unknown (for the case when the population mean is actually known see Exercise 6.2C question 1).

Let $X_1, X_2, \ldots, X_n$ denote a random sample of n observations of a random variable X having unknown mean μ and unknown variance σ^2.

What statistic should we choose for estimating σ^2? Intuitively, we might choose the sample variance V defined to be

$$V = \frac{1}{n} \sum_{i=1}^{n} (X_i - \bar{X})^2, \tag{1}$$

where $\bar{X}$ is the sample mean. To determine whether or not V is an unbiased estimator of σ^2 we need to evaluate $\mathrm{E}[V]$. Before doing so, we shall first expand the summation term in (1) as follows:

$$\begin{aligned} \sum_{i=1}^{n} (X_i - \bar{X})^2 &\equiv \sum_{i=1}^{n} (X_i^2 - 2\bar{X} X_i + \bar{X}^2) \\ &= \sum_{i=1}^{n} X_i^2 - 2\bar{X} \sum_{i=1}^{n} X_i + n\bar{X}^2 \\ &= \sum_{i=1}^{n} X_i^2 - n\bar{X}^2, \end{aligned} \tag{2}$$

since $\sum_{i=1}^{n} X_i = n\bar{X}$. Using properties of expectation,

$$\mathrm{E}\left[\sum_{i=1}^{n} (X_i - \bar{X})^2\right] = \sum_{i=1}^{n} \mathrm{E}[X_i^2] - n\mathrm{E}[\bar{X}^2].$$

But, since X_i has the same distribution as X,

$$\mathrm{E}[X_i^2] \equiv \mathrm{V}[X_i] + \{\mathrm{E}[X_i]\}^2 = \sigma^2 + \mu^2, \qquad i = 1, 2, \ldots, n,$$

and, on using the sampling distribution properties of $\bar{X}$ given in §5.4,

$$\mathrm{E}[\bar{X}^2] \equiv \mathrm{V}[\bar{X}] + \{\mathrm{E}[\bar{X}]\}^2 = \frac{\sigma^2}{n} + \mu^2.$$

Hence,

$$\begin{aligned} \mathrm{E}[V] &= \frac{1}{n} \mathrm{E}\left[\sum_{i=1}^{n} (X_i - \bar{X})^2\right] \\ &= \frac{1}{n} \sum_{i=1}^{n} \mathrm{E}[X_i^2] - \mathrm{E}[\bar{X}^2] \\ &= \frac{1}{n} n(\sigma^2 + \mu^2) - \left(\frac{\sigma^2}{n} + \mu^2\right) \\ &= \left(1 - \frac{1}{n}\right) \sigma^2. \end{aligned} \tag{3}$$

It follows that V is a biased estimator of σ^2, underestimating σ^2 on average. The larger the value of n the smaller will be the bias.

Multiplying throughout (3) by $n/(n-1)$, we have

$$\mathrm{E}\left[\frac{n}{n-1}V\right]=\sigma^2,$$

from which it follows that

$$S^2 \equiv \frac{n}{n-1}V = \frac{1}{n-1}\sum_{i=1}^{n}(X_i-\bar{X})^2 \tag{4}$$

is an unbiased estimator of σ^2 (this result was demonstrated for $n = 2$ in Exercise 5.2 question 4). So as to minimise possible confusion, we shall refer to S^2 as the *sample unbiased estimator* of σ^2, thus distinguishing it from the sample variance V defined by (1).

Given the observed values $x_1, x_2, \ldots, x_n$, the corresponding unbiased estimate of σ^2 is

$$s^2 = \frac{1}{n-1}\sum_{i=1}^{n}(x_i-\bar{x})^2. \tag{5}$$

Calculating the value of the sum in (5) can often be simplified using the alternative equivalent expression given by the right-hand side of

$$\sum_{i=1}^{n}(x_i-\bar{x})^2 = \sum_{i=1}^{n}x_i^2 - n\bar{x}^2, \tag{6}$$

which follows from (2) on replacing X_i and $\bar{X}$ by x_i and $\bar{x}$, respectively.

EXAMPLE 3 *Ten independent weighings of an object on a chemical balance gave the following readings in mg:*

2·36, 2·43, 2·31, 2·38, 2·41, 2·39, 2·42, 2·39, 2·41, 2·37.

Calculate an unbiased estimate of the variance of readings from repeated weighings on the chemical balance.

Denoting the observations by $x_1, x_2, \ldots, x_{10}$ we have

$$\sum_{i=1}^{10}x_i = 23{\cdot}87, \qquad \bar{x} = 2{\cdot}387,$$

and

$$\sum_{i=1}^{10}x_i^2 = 56{\cdot}9887.$$

Hence, the required unbiased estimate is

$$s^2 = \frac{1}{9}\left\{\sum_{i=1}^{10}x_i^2 - 10\bar{x}^2\right\} = 0{\cdot}001223,$$

to four significant figures.

EXAMPLE 4 *The continuous random variable X has probability density function* f *defined by*

$$f(x) = 2x/\theta^2, \qquad 0 < x < \theta.$$

A random sample of five observations of X had the values 0·6, 1·5, 0·8, 1·1, 1·3, *respectively. Calculate unbiased estimates of* (*i*) θ, (*ii*) θ^2.

(i) The mean value of X is

$$E[X] = \frac{2}{\theta^2}\int_0^\theta x^2\,dx = \frac{2}{3}\theta.$$

The sample mean is

$$\bar{x} = \frac{0{\cdot}6 + 1{\cdot}5 + 0{\cdot}8 + 1{\cdot}1 + 1{\cdot}3}{5} = 1{\cdot}06,$$

which we know to be an unbiased estimate of $E[X] = \frac{2}{3}\theta$. Hence, an unbiased estimate of $\theta = \frac{3}{2}E[X]$ is

$$\frac{3}{2}\bar{x} = 1{\cdot}59.$$

(ii) $E[X^2] = \dfrac{2}{\theta^2}\displaystyle\int_0^\theta x^3\,dx = \dfrac{1}{2}\theta^2.$

Therefore,

$$V[X] = \frac{1}{2}\theta^2 - \left(\frac{2}{3}\theta\right)^2 = \frac{1}{18}\theta^2.$$

The sample unbiased estimate of $V[X] = \frac{1}{18}\theta^2$ is

$$s^2 = \frac{1}{4}\left\{\sum_{i=1}^{5} x_i^2 - 5\bar{x}^2\right\} = \frac{1}{4}\{6{\cdot}15 - 5(1{\cdot}06)^2\} = 0{\cdot}133.$$

Hence, an unbiased estimate of $\theta^2 = 18V[X]$ is

$$18s^2 = 2{\cdot}394.$$

EXERCISE 6.2C

1 If $X_1, X_2, \ldots, X_n$ denote n independent observations of a random variable X whose mean is known to be μ_0 and whose variance σ^2 is unknown, show that

$$T \equiv \frac{1}{n}\sum_{i=1}^{n}(X_i - \mu_0)^2$$

is an unbiased estimator of σ^2.

2 A random sample of 10 observations from a Poisson distribution having unknown mean λ were such that the sum of the observations was 33 and the sum of their squares was 144. Calculate two unbiased estimates of λ.

3 The operational life times, in hours, of a random sample of five electric bulbs of a particular brand and type were found to be 1641, 1519, 1621, 1586 and

1563, respectively. Calculate an unbiased estimate of the variance of the lifetimes of such bulbs.

4 A random sample of 20 observations of a random variable X had values $x_1, x_2, \ldots, x_{20}$ such that $\Sigma x_i = 38{\cdot}6$ and $\Sigma x_i^2 = 96{\cdot}88$. Calculate unbiased estimates of the mean and the variance of X.

Suppose that X has a uniform distribution over the interval $(0, \theta)$, where θ is unknown. Deduce unbiased estimates of (i) θ, (ii) θ^2.

5 Given that $X_1, X_2, \ldots, X_n$ are independent observations of a random variable X whose variance σ^2 is unknown, find the value of the constant c for

$$T = c\sum_{i=1}^{n-1}(X_{i+1} - X_i)^2$$

to be an unbiased estimator of σ^2.

6 An unbiased estimator is required of $\phi = 4\lambda + \lambda^2$, where λ is the mean of a Poisson distribution. Given that $X_1, X_2, \ldots, X_n$ is a random sample of n observations from the Poisson distribution, and that $\bar{X} = \left(\sum_{i=1}^{n} X_i\right)/n$, show that $T = 3\bar{X} + \frac{1}{n}\sum_{i=1}^{n} X_i^2$ is an unbiased estimator of ϕ.

6.2.4 Some further examples of unbiased estimators

In this section we give two further examples to illustrate the use of the concept of unbiasedness.

EXAMPLE 5 *A continuous random variable X is uniformly distributed over the interval $(a - c, a + c)$. Determine the expected values of X and X^2.*

An instrument for measuring the length of a line is such that the recorded value for a line of length a cm is equally likely to be any value in the interval $(a - c, a + c)$, where c $(< a)$ is a known positive constant. The instrument is used to obtain two independent observations, X_1 and X_2, of the length of a side of a square. Consider the following two methods for estimating the area A of the square:

Method 1 *Estimate A by $T_1 = X_1X_2$,*

Method 2 *Estimate A by $T_2 = \frac{1}{4}(X_1 + X_2)^2$.*

Show that Method 1 is the only one of these two methods that will give an unbiased estimate of the area of the square, and determine the standard error of this estimator in terms of a and c. *(WJEC 1972)*

Since $X \sim U(a - c, a + c)$ its probability density function f is such that

$$\mathrm{f}(x) = \frac{1}{2c}, \qquad a - c < x < a + c.$$

Hence,

$$\mathrm{E}[X] = \frac{1}{2c}\int_{a-c}^{a+c} x\,\mathrm{d}x = a,$$

and

$$E[X^2] = \frac{1}{2c}\int_{a-c}^{a+c} x^2 dx = \frac{1}{3}(c^2 + 3a^2).$$

Supposing that the square has side of length a cm, its area is $A = a^2$ cm^2. Consider Method 1.

Since X_1 and X_2 are independent,

$$E[T_1] = E[X_1 X_2] = E[X_1]E[X_2].$$

Each of X_1 and X_2 has the same distribution as X, so that, in particular, $E[X_1] = E[X_2] = E[X] = a$. Hence

$$E[T_1] = a^2,$$

which shows that T_1 is an unbiased estimator of A.

Now consider Method 2. Here, the estimator is

$$T_2 = \tfrac{1}{4}(X_1 + X_2)^2 = \tfrac{1}{4}(X_1^2 + 2X_1X_2 + X_2^2).$$

Using properties of expectation and noting that $E[X_1] = E[X_2] = a$ and $E[X_1^2] = E[X_2^2] = E[X^2] = \frac{1}{3}(c^2 + 3a^2)$,

$$\begin{aligned} E[T_2] &= \tfrac{1}{4}\{E[X_1^2] + 2E[X_1]E[X_2] + E[X_2^2]\} \\ &= \tfrac{1}{4}\left\{\frac{1}{3}(c^2 + 3a^2) + 2a^2 + \frac{1}{3}(c^2 + 3a^2)\right\} \\ &= a^2 + \frac{1}{6}c^2 \end{aligned}$$

It follows that T_2 is a biased estimator of A.

To find the standard error of T_1 we shall first determine $V[T_1]$. We have

$$V[T_1] = E[T_1^2] - \{E[T_1]\}^2 = E[T_1^2] - a^4.$$

But, using properties of expectation and noting that X_1, X_2 are independent,

$$E[T_1^2] = E[X_1^2 X_2^2] = E[X_1^2]E[X_2^2] = \frac{1}{9}(c^2 + 3a^2)^2.$$

Hence,

$$V[T] = \frac{1}{9}(c^2 + 3a^2)^2 - a^4 = \frac{1}{9}c^2(c^2 + 6a^2)$$

and

$$SE[T] = \frac{1}{3}c\sqrt{(c^2 + 6a^2)}.$$

EXAMPLE 6 *Let Y denote the largest of three random observations from the distribution $U(0, \theta)$ where θ is an unknown positive constant. Find the expected value of Y in terms of θ, and hence find the constant c so that $T = cY$ is an unbiased estimator of θ. Determine the standard error of T in terms of θ.*

If $\overline{X}$ denotes the mean of the three random observations, state with your reasons, which of $U = 2\overline{X}$ and T you would prefer as an estimator of θ.

If $X \sim U(0, \theta)$, the probability density function f of X is given by

$$\mathrm{f}(x) = \frac{1}{\theta}, \qquad 0 < x < \theta.$$

Denote the three random observations by X_1, X_2, X_3, so that $Y = \max(X_1, X_2, X_3)$. To find $\mathrm{E}[Y]$ it is first necessary to find the distribution of Y. Denoting the cumulative distribution function of Y by G, we have

$$\begin{aligned}\mathrm{G}(y) = \mathrm{P}(Y \leqslant y) &= \mathrm{P}[\max(X_1, X_2, X_3) \leqslant y] \\ &= \mathrm{P}[\text{each of } X_1, X_2, X_3 \leqslant y].\end{aligned}$$

Since X_1, X_2, X_3 are independent and each has the same distribution as X,

$$\mathrm{G}(y) = [\mathrm{P}(X \leqslant y)]^3 = \frac{y^3}{\theta^3}, \qquad 0 < y < \theta.$$

Differentiating, the probability density function of Y is g, where

$$\mathrm{g}(y) = \frac{3y^2}{\theta^3}, \qquad 0 < y < \theta.$$

Thus,

$$\mathrm{E}[Y] = \frac{3}{\theta^3}\int_0^\theta y^3\,\mathrm{d}y = \frac{3}{4}\theta.$$

It follows that $\mathrm{E}[\frac{4}{3}Y] = \theta$, so that $T = \frac{4}{3}Y$ is an unbiased estimator of θ. Using properties of variance

$$\mathrm{V}[T] = \mathrm{V}\left[\frac{4}{3}Y\right] = \frac{16}{9}\mathrm{V}[Y].$$

Since

$$\mathrm{E}[Y^2] = \frac{3}{\theta^3}\int_0^\theta y^4\,\mathrm{d}y = \frac{3}{5}\theta^2,$$

$$\mathrm{V}[Y] = \frac{3}{5}\theta^2 - \left(\frac{3}{4}\theta\right)^2 = \frac{3}{80}\theta^2,$$

and therefore

$$\mathrm{V}[T] = \frac{16}{9} \times \frac{3}{80}\theta^2 = \frac{1}{15}\theta^2.$$

It follows that

$$\mathrm{SE}[T] = \theta/\sqrt{15}.$$

If $\overline{X}$ is the mean of three random observations of X then we know that $\mathrm{E}[\overline{X}] = \mathrm{E}[X] = \frac{1}{2}\theta$ and $\mathrm{V}[\overline{X}] = \frac{1}{3}\mathrm{V}[X] = \frac{1}{36}\theta^2$. Hence, with $U = 2\overline{X}$ we have

$$\mathrm{E}[U] = 2E[\overline{X}] = \theta,$$

and

$$V[U] = 4V[\bar{X}] = \frac{1}{9}\theta^2.$$

It follows that U is also an unbiased estimator having standard error given by

$$SE[U] = \frac{1}{3}\theta.$$

Thus both T and U are unbiased, but since $SE[T] < SE[U]$, T is the preferred estimator since it is the more likely to give an estimate close to θ.

EXERCISE 6.2D

1 It is known that the two mutually exclusive events A and B are equally probable to occur in any trial of a random experiment; denote their common probability by θ. The following two methods have been suggested for estimating θ.
Method 1 Conduct 20 independent trials, record the number R of occasions that A occurs and take $T_1 = R/20$ to be the estimator of θ.
Method 2 Conduct 10 independent trials, record the total number S of occasions that either A or B occur and take $T_2 = S/20$ to be the estimator of θ.
Show that both T_1 and T_2 are unbiased estimators of θ. Determine the variances of T_1 and T_2 and state, with reasons, which estimator you prefer.

2 Let $\bar{X}$ denote the mean of a random sample of n observations from a distribution whose mean is $(\mu + \lambda)$ and whose variance is σ^2, and let $\bar{Y}$ denote the mean of an independent random sample of $2n$ observations from a distribution whose mean is $(2\mu - \lambda)$ and whose variance is $2\sigma^2$. Find the values of a_1, a_2, b_1, b_2, for
(i) $T_1 = a_1\bar{X} + b_1\bar{Y}$ to be an unbiased estimator of μ,
(ii) $T_2 = a_2\bar{X} + b_2\bar{Y}$ to be an unbiased estimator of λ.
Determine the variances of T_1 and T_2 in terms of σ^2 and n.

3 Let Y denote the larger of two randomly observed values of the random variable X whose distribution has probability density function f, where

$$f(x) = 2x/\theta^2, \qquad 0 < x < \theta.$$

Find the probability density function of Y and hence express $E[Y]$ in terms of θ. (i) Deduce an unbiased estimator, T_1, of θ. (ii) Find the constant k so that $T_2 = k\bar{X}$, where $\bar{X}$ is the mean of the two observed values of X, is an unbiased estimator of θ. (iii) Determine which of T_1 and T_2 has the smaller standard error.

4 A certain type of electronic equipment has an operational lifetime of X hours, where X has the exponential distribution whose probability density function f is such that

$$f(x) = \theta^{-1}e^{-x/\theta}, \qquad x > 0.$$

Suppose three of the components have operational lifetimes X_2, X_2 and X_3 hours, respectively. Let Y denote the minimum of X_1, X_2, X_3. Find the constant c so that $T = cY$ is an unbiased estimator of θ, and obtain the variance of T in terms of θ.

5 AT is the tangent at a fixed point A on a circle of radius γ. AP is a chord to the circle which is to be drawn in a random direction from A; that is, the angle PAT may be regarded as a random variable which is uniformly distributed over the interval $(0, \pi)$. Determine, in terms of γ and π, the mean and the variance of the length of the chord AP.

Suppose that γ is unknown and that it is to be estimated from the observed lengths $x_1, x_2, \ldots, x_n$ of n chords which have been independently and randomly drawn through A. Denoting the mean of these observed lengths by $\bar{x}$, find the value of the constant k for $t = k\bar{x}$ to be an unbiased estimate of γ and find the variance of this estimator in terms of γ, π and n.

6 With reference to the result for $E[X^2]$ obtained in Example 4 of §6.2, deduce another unbiased estimator of θ^2.

6.3 Interval estimation of a parameter

In §6.2 an unknown population parameter was estimated by a single value (a point estimate) calculated from a random sample of observations. If the estimator used is unbiased then its standard error is an appropriate measure of its reliability, in the sense that the smaller the standard error the more likely it will yield an estimate close to the true value of the parameter. However, knowing the standard error of an estimator does not by itself provide direct information on how close the estimate is to the true parameter value. This inadequacy has led to the development of an interval estimate of a parameter, the interval being a range of values, which, with a measurable degree of confidence, includes the true parameter value. In this section we show how an estimate and its standard error may be combined to provide an interval estimate.

Let $X_1, X_2, \ldots, X_n$ denote a random sample of n observations from a population whose distribution involves an unknown parameter θ. Further, let $U \equiv U(X_1, X_2, \ldots, X_n)$ denote an unbiased estimator of θ. In this section we shall restrict consideration to the case where the sampling distribution of U is known to be normal, or at least approximately so.

6.3.1 Interval estimation of the mean of a normal distribution whose variance is known

Let $\bar{X}$ denote the mean of a random sample of n observations from the normal distribution $N(\mu, \sigma^2)$, where μ is unknown and σ^2 is known. From §5.4.1, we know that the sampling distribution of $\bar{X}$ is normal with mean $E[\bar{X}] = \mu$ and standard error $SE[\bar{X}] = \sigma/\sqrt{n}$. Hence,

$$Z = \frac{\bar{X} - \mu}{SE[\bar{X}]} \sim N(0, 1). \tag{1}$$

Referring to a table of the cumulative distribution of $N(0, 1)$ we find, for example, that

$$P(Z \geqslant 1{\cdot}96) = P(Z \leqslant -1{\cdot}96) = 0{\cdot}025.$$

Combining these (See Fig. 6.1) we obtain

$$P(-1{\cdot}96 \leqslant Z \leqslant 1{\cdot}96) = 0{\cdot}95. \qquad (2)$$

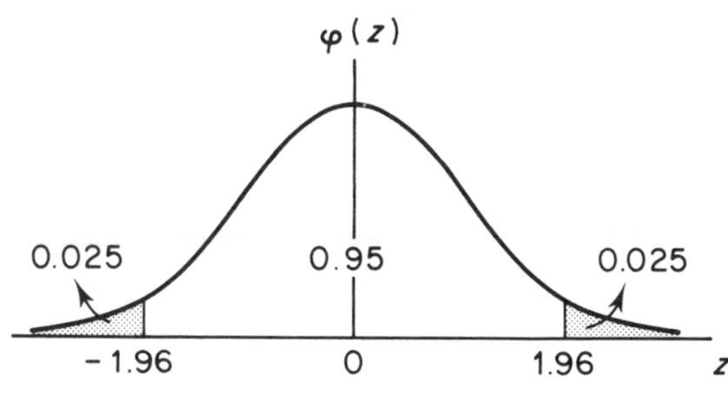

Fig. 6.1

In particular, for Z defined by (1)

$$P\left(-1{\cdot}96 \leqslant \frac{\bar{X}-\mu}{\mathrm{SE}[\bar{X}]} \leqslant 1{\cdot}96\right) = 0{\cdot}95,$$

or, equivalently,

$$P(\bar{X} - 1{\cdot}96\ \mathrm{SE}[\bar{X}] \leqslant \mu \leqslant \bar{X} + 1{\cdot}96\ \mathrm{SE}[\bar{X}]) = 0{\cdot}95. \qquad (3)$$

Reading (3) may suggest that it is a probabilistic statement about μ, but this cannot be so since μ is a constant, not a random variable. The correct interpretation of (3) is that it is a probabilistic statement about the random variable $\bar{X}$. It states that the random interval $(\bar{X} - 1{\cdot}96\ \mathrm{SE}[\bar{X}],\ \bar{X} + 1{\cdot}96\ \mathrm{SE}[\bar{X}])$ has probability 0·95 of including the value μ. This means that of all possible samples of size n from the population distribution $N(\mu, \sigma^2)$, a proportion 0·95 (or 95 %) of them will yield a value $\bar{x}$ of $\bar{X}$ such that the interval $(\bar{x} - 1{\cdot}96\ \mathrm{SE}[\bar{X}], \bar{x} + 1{\cdot}96\ \mathrm{SE}[\bar{X}])$, where $\mathrm{SE}[\bar{X}] = \sigma/\sqrt{n}$, includes the value μ. Equivalently, 5 % of all such intervals will not include the value μ.

For an observed sample mean $\bar{x}$, the interval

$$(\bar{x} - 1{\cdot}96\ \mathrm{SE}[\bar{X}], \qquad \bar{x} + 1{\cdot}96\ \mathrm{SE}[\bar{X}]) \qquad (4)$$

is called a 95 % *confidence interval for* μ, and the endpoints of the interval are called 95 % *confidence limits for* μ. The method used to derive the interval (4) enables us to be 95 % confident that the randomly selected sample that is obtained will be one of those for which the interval (4) does include the value μ.

We can proceed similarly to derive an interval for any specified *confidence level* (95 % above). The confidence level to use in any situation is a matter of choice dependent upon the consequences of any erroneous decisions that may result from assuming that μ does lie in the specified range when in fact it does not. The more serious these consequences the higher should be the chosen confidence level. The most popularly used confidence levels are 90%, 95% and 99%.

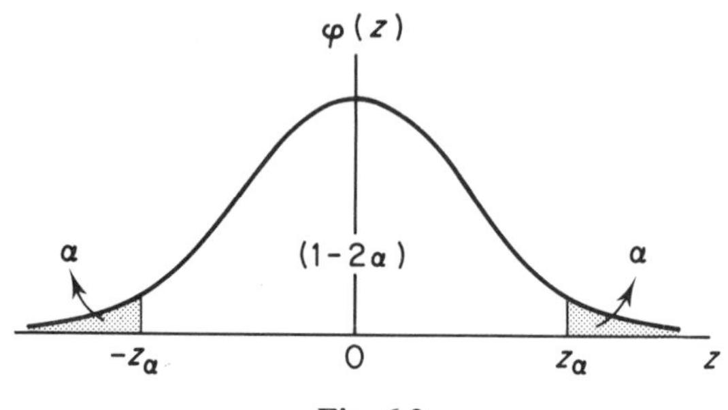

Fig. 6.2

With reference to Fig. 6.2, let z_α denote the value such that $P(Z \geqslant z_\alpha) = \alpha$, for some specified value of α between 0 and 0·5. Then

$$P(-z_\alpha \leqslant Z \leqslant z_\alpha) = 1 - 2\alpha.$$

On replacing Z by $(\bar{X} - \mu)/\text{SE}[\bar{X}]$ and rearranging the inequalities we have

$$P(\bar{X} - z_\alpha \,\text{SE}[\bar{X}] \leqslant \mu \leqslant \bar{X} + z_\alpha \,\text{SE}[\bar{X}]) = 1 - 2\alpha.$$

Hence, $100(1-2\alpha)\%$ confidence limits for μ are

$$\bar{x} \pm z_\alpha \,\text{SE}[\bar{X}], \tag{5}$$

where $\bar{x}$ is the observed sample mean and $\text{SE}[\bar{X}] = \sigma/\sqrt{n}$. Table 6.1 gives the values of z_α, to two decimal places, for selected values of α. Thus, for example, to calculate 90% confidence limits for μ we require $1 - 2\alpha = 0{\cdot}9$, or $\alpha = 0{\cdot}05$, and from Table 6.1 we find that $z_{0\cdot05} = 1{\cdot}64$. Hence, 90% confidence limits for μ are given by

$$\bar{x} \pm 1{\cdot}64 \,\text{SE}[\bar{X}]. \tag{6}$$

Table 6.1 Values of z_α

α	0·005	0·01	0·02	0·025	0·03	0.04	0·05	0·10
z_α	2·58	2·33	2·05	1·96	1·88	1·75	1·64	1·28

EXAMPLE 1 *Repeated weighings of an object on a chemical balance give readings that are known to be normally distributed with mean equal to the true weight of the object and standard deviation* 0·5 *mg*.
(*i*) *Given that* 10 *independent weighings of an object gave a mean reading of* 12.3 *mg, calculate* 98% *confidence limits for the true weight of the object.*

(ii) Determine the smallest number of independent weighings of an object that should be made in order that the 98 % confidence interval for the object's true weight has a width of less than 0·5 mg.

(i) Denote the true weight of the object by μ mg. Then, the sample mean, $\bar{X}$ mg, of the readings from 10 independent weighings of the object will be normally distributed with mean μ and standard error $SE[\bar{X}] = 0{\cdot}5/\sqrt{10}$. For 98 % confidence limits we require $1-2\alpha = 0{\cdot}98$ or $\alpha = 0{\cdot}01$, and from Table 6.1 we find that $z_{0{\cdot}01} = 2{\cdot}33$. Hence, from (5) above with $n = 10$, $\bar{x} = 12{\cdot}3$ and $SE[\bar{X}] = 0{\cdot}5/\sqrt{10}$, the 98 % confidence limits for μ are

$$12{\cdot}3 \pm 2{\cdot}33(0{\cdot}5/\sqrt{10}) = 12{\cdot}3 \pm 0{\cdot}37,$$

that is, 11·93 to 12·67.

(ii) From (5) above the width of the $100(1-2\alpha)$% confidence interval for μ is given by

$$W = 2z_\alpha \, SE[\bar{X}].$$

Suppose n weighings are to be made. Then $SE[\bar{X}] = 0{\cdot}5/\sqrt{n}$, and the width of the 98 % confidence interval for μ will be

$$W = 2(2{\cdot}33)\,(0{\cdot}5/\sqrt{n}).$$

To ensure that $W < 0{\cdot}5$ we require

$$\frac{2(2{\cdot}33)\,(0{\cdot}5)}{\sqrt{n}} < 0{\cdot}5,$$

or

$$n > \left[\frac{2(2{\cdot}33)\,(0{\cdot}5)}{0{\cdot}5}\right]^2 = 4{\cdot}66^2 \simeq 21{\cdot}7.$$

Hence, at least 22 weighings should be made.

Corresponding to any specified confidence level there are a multitude of confidence intervals for μ. For example, we showed in (4) above that the interval $(\bar{x} - 1{\cdot}96\, SE[\bar{X}], \bar{x} + 1{\cdot}96\, SE[\bar{X}])$ is a 95 % confidence interval for μ, and this was derived using the results

$$P(Z \leqslant -1{\cdot}96) = P(Z \geqslant 1{\cdot}96) = 0{\cdot}025,$$

where Z is distributed as $N(0, 1)$ and taking $Z \equiv (\bar{X} - \mu)/SE[\bar{X}]$. Referring to Table 6.1 we find, for example (see Fig. 6.3) that

$$P(Z \leqslant -2{\cdot}33) = 0{\cdot}01 \quad \text{and} \quad P(Z \geqslant 1{\cdot}75) = 0{\cdot}04.$$

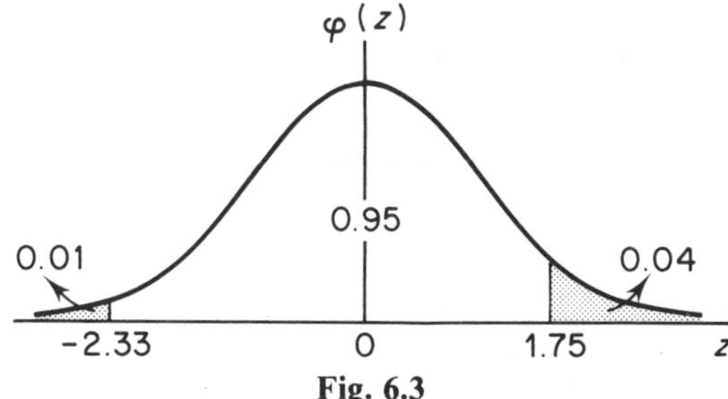

Fig. 6.3

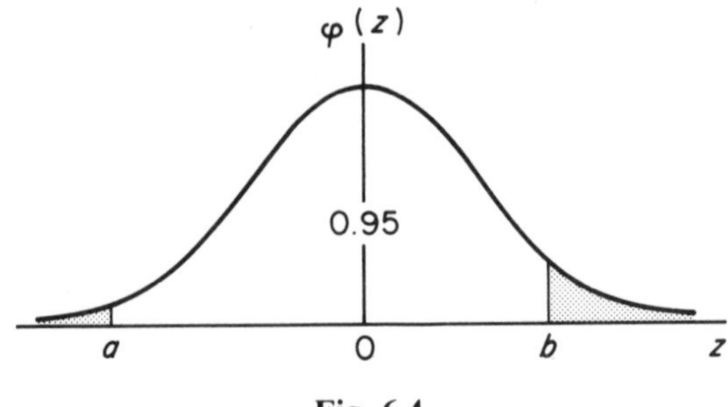

Fig. 6.4

Combining these results we obtain

$$P(-2{\cdot}33 \leqslant Z \leqslant 1{\cdot}75) = 0{\cdot}95.$$

In particular, replacing Z by $(\bar{X}-\mu)/\text{SE}[\bar{X}]$ and rearranging the inequalities we have

$$P(\bar{X}-1{\cdot}75\ \text{SE}[\bar{X}] \leqslant \mu \leqslant \bar{X}+2{\cdot}33\ \text{SE}[\bar{X}]) = 0{\cdot}95.$$

It follows that the interval having the limits

$$\bar{x}-1{\cdot}75\ \text{SE}[\bar{X}] \quad \text{and} \quad \bar{x}+2{\cdot}33\ \text{SE}[\bar{X}] \tag{7}$$

is also a 95% confidence interval for μ.

To generalise, let a and b denote any two values (see Fig. 6.4) such that

$$P(a \leqslant Z \leqslant b) = 0{\cdot}95. \tag{8}$$

Replacing Z by $(\bar{X}-\mu)/\text{SE}[\bar{X}]$ and rearranging the inequalities we have

$$P(\bar{X}-b\ \text{SE}[\bar{X}] < \mu < \bar{X}-a\ \text{SE}[\bar{X}]) = 0{\cdot}95.$$

Thus, for any a and b satisfying (8), the values

$$\bar{x}-b\ \text{SE}[\bar{X}] \quad \text{and} \quad \bar{x}-a\ \text{SE}[\bar{X}]$$

will be 95% confidence limits for μ. For the particular limits $\bar{x} \pm 1{\cdot}96\ \text{SE}[\bar{X}]$ we chose a and b in such a way that each of the shaded tail regions in Fig. 6.4 had an area of 0·025. For this reason, the 95% confidence interval having these limits is called the *central or symmetrical confidence interval for* μ. Similarly, the interval having the limits $\bar{x} \pm z_\alpha$ $\text{SE}[\bar{X}]$ is called the *symmetrical* $100(1-2\alpha)\%$ *confidence interval for* μ.

The symmetrical $100(1-2\alpha)\%$ confidence interval for μ is the preferred one since it is the shortest of all the $100(1-2\alpha)\%$ confidence intervals. To see this refer to Fig. 6.5, in which $a = -z_\alpha$ and $b = z_\alpha$, so that the area under the graph above the interval (a, b) is equal to $1-2\alpha$.

Suppose that $a' > a$ and $b' > b$ are such that the area under the graph above (a', b') is also equal to $1-2\alpha$. Since $\varphi(a) = \varphi(b)$ and the curve $\varphi(z)$ is

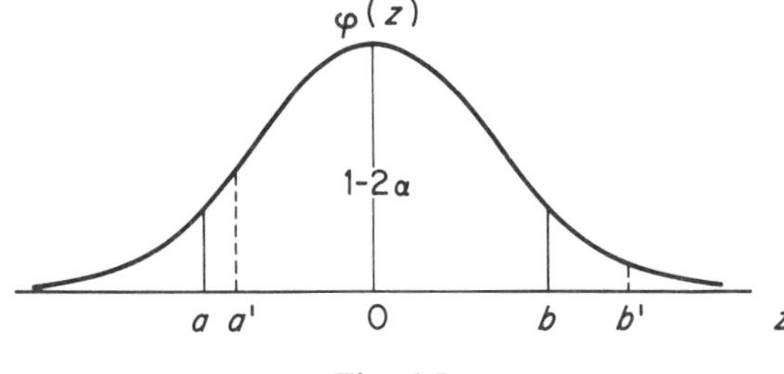

Fig. 6.5

higher to the right of a than it is to the right of b, it follows that $b' - b > a' - a$, and consequently the interval (a', b') is wider than the interval (a, b). A similar argument applies for $a' < a$ and $b' < b$. Hence, the interval $(a, b) = (-z_\alpha, z_\alpha)$ provides the shortest $100(1-2\alpha)\%$ confidence interval for μ.

For example, the width of the symmetrical 95% confidence interval for μ given by (4) is $2 \times 1{\cdot}96\ \text{SE}[\bar{X}] = 3{\cdot}92\ \text{SE}[\bar{X}]$, whereas that of the interval having the limits in (7) is $(2{\cdot}33 + 1{\cdot}75)\ \text{SE}[\bar{X}] = 4{\cdot}08\ \text{SE}[\bar{X}]$.

EXERCISE 6.3A

1 A random sample of 25 labourers had a mean weight of 75·8 kg. Assuming that the weights of labourers are normally distributed with standard deviation 9 kg, find the symmetrical 99% confidence limits for the mean weight of labourers.

2 From the results obtained in a random sample of n observations from a normal distribution having standard deviation 2, an investigator reported that (0·73, 1·71) was the shortest 95% confidence interval for the mean of the distribution. Deduce the value of n and the mean of the sample observations.

3 A random sample of 100 mass-produced washers had a mean thickness of 3·036 mm. Assuming that the thickness of such washers are normally distributed with standard deviation 0·2 mm, calculate the symmetrical 95% confidence interval for the mean thickness of such washers. Does your result support the manufacturer's claim that the washers have a mean thickness of 3 mm?

4 The outcome X of a certain biological experiment is known to be a normally distributed random variable having standard deviation 5. A biologist would like to estimate the distribution mean by a 95% confidence interval of width less than 3. Determine the least number of experiments that the biologist should perform.

5 Let $\bar{X}$ denote the mean of a random sample of 10 observations from a normal distribution whose standard deviation is 1·6. Denoting the distribution mean by μ, find values a and b such that

$$P(\bar{X} - \mu < a) = 0{\cdot}01, \qquad P(\bar{X} - \mu > b) = 0{\cdot}04.$$

Hence deduce a 95% confidence interval for μ and find the amount by which its width exceeds that of the shortest 95% confidence interval for μ.

6.3.2 Interval estimation of the mean of a normal distribution whose variance is unknown

Let $x_1, x_2, \ldots, x_n$ denote a random sample of n values from a normal distribution having mean μ and variance σ^2, where μ and σ^2 are both unknown. From (5) of §6.3.1, the symmetrical $100(1-2\alpha)\%$ confidence limits for μ are

$$\bar{x} \pm z_\alpha \mathrm{SE}[\bar{X}], \tag{1}$$

where $\mathrm{SE}[\bar{X}] = \sigma/\sqrt{n}$, which can be evaluated only when σ is known. For unknown σ, one possible way of proceeding to obtain approximate $100(1-2\alpha)\%$ confidence limits for μ is to replace σ by s, where

$$s^2 = \frac{1}{n-1}\sum_{i=1}^{n}(x_i - \bar{x})^2$$

is the sample unbiased estimate of σ^2, the limits in (1) then becoming

$$\bar{x} \pm z_\alpha s/\sqrt{n}. \tag{2}$$

The actual confidence level of the limits (2) will be close to $100(1-2\alpha)\%$ only if the value of s^2 is close to the value of σ^2, which is a reasonable assumption to make when n is very large. However, when n is not very large, the uncertainty about the value of s^2 relative to that of σ^2 means that the limits given by (2) will actually correspond to a confidence level which is less than $100(1-2\alpha)\%$. For $100(1-2\alpha)\%$ confidence limits, the value z_α in (2) will have to be replaced by some greater value t_α, say. To find the appropriate t_α, let us first recall that the limits given by (1) above were derived using the result that if $\bar{X}$ is the mean of a random sample of n observations from $N(\mu, \sigma^2)$, then the sampling distribution of $\bar{X}$ is such that

$$Z = \frac{\bar{X}-\mu}{\sqrt{(\sigma^2/n)}} \sim N(0, 1).$$

For the case where σ^2 is unknown, consider the statistic

$$T = \frac{\bar{X}-\mu}{\sqrt{(S^2/n)}}, \tag{3}$$

where $S^2 = \dfrac{1}{n-1}\sum(X_i - \bar{X})^2$ is the sample unbiased estimator of σ^2. The sampling distribution of the statistic T was derived by W. S. Gosset, who published his result under the pseudonym 'Student'; the resulting distribution is referred to as *Student's t distribution*, the probability density function of which is given by

$$\mathrm{f}(t) = k\left(1 + \frac{t^2}{n-1}\right)^{-\frac{1}{2}n}, \qquad -\infty < t < \infty, \tag{4}$$

where k is a constant chosen so that the total area under the graph of $f(t)$ is unity. A sketch of $f(t)$ is shown in Fig. 6.6. The shape of $f(t)$ closely resembles that of $\varphi(t)$, the probability density function of $N(0, 1)$, being symmetrical about the origin and tailing off towards zero in a bell-shaped manner either side of the origin. The essential difference is that $\varphi(t)$ is more peaked than $f(t)$ at the origin. It may be shown that, as n increases, the graph of $f(t)$ approaches that of $\varphi(t)$, and that when n is infinite, the two curves become coincident.

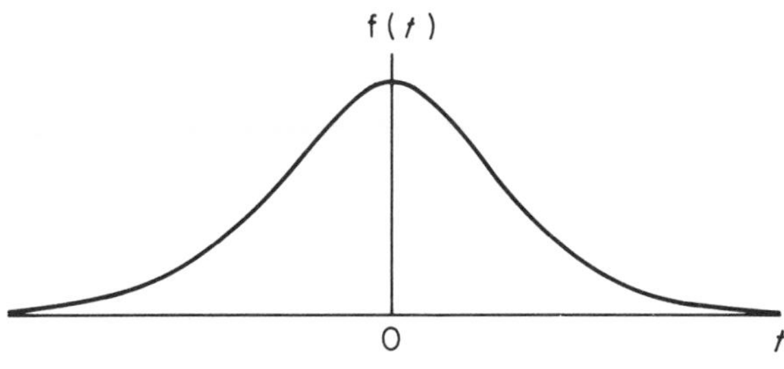

Fig. 6.6

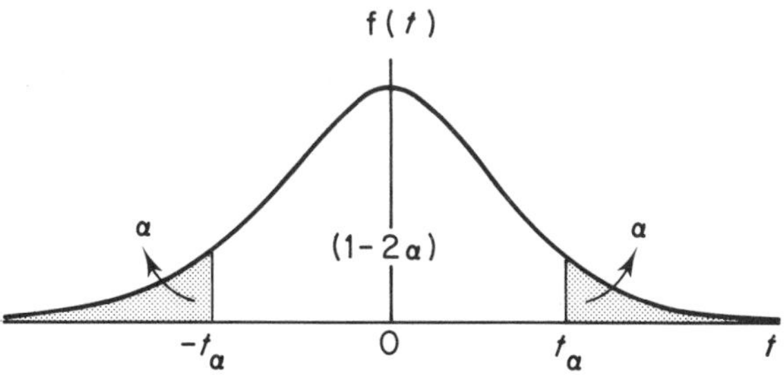

Fig. 6.7

To obtain the symmetrical $100(1-2\alpha)\%$ confidence interval for μ in the present case we can proceed as in §6.3.1 but now using the distribution of T instead of that of Z. With reference to Fig. 6.7, let t_α denote the value such that

$$P(T < -t_\alpha) = P(T > t_\alpha) = \alpha$$

Combining these we have

$$P(-t_\alpha < T < t_\alpha) = 1 - 2\alpha,$$

and, in particular, for T defined by (3),

$$P\left(-t_\alpha < \frac{\bar{X} - \mu}{\sqrt{(S^2/n)}} < t_\alpha\right) = 1 - 2\alpha,$$

or, equivalently,

$$P\left(\bar{X} - t_\alpha\sqrt{\frac{S^2}{n}} < \mu < \bar{X} + t_\alpha\sqrt{\frac{S^2}{n}}\right) = 1 - 2\alpha.$$

Thus, if the sample observed values of $\bar{X}$ and S^2 are $\bar{x}$ and s^2, respectively, it follows that the symmetrical $100(1-2\alpha)\%$ confidence limits for μ are

$$\bar{x} \pm t_\alpha\sqrt{\frac{s^2}{n}} \equiv \bar{x} \pm t_\alpha \text{ESE}[\bar{X}], \tag{5}$$

where $\text{ESE}[\bar{X}] \equiv s/\sqrt{n}$ is our estimate of $\text{SE}[\bar{X}] \equiv \sigma/\sqrt{n}$. To compute the limits given by (5) we will need to know the value of t_α. As was the case for z_α, numerical procedures are necessary to determine t_α. Table 6.2 gives the values of t_α, to two decimal places, for selected values of α and $\nu = n - 1$, where ν is the Greek letter nu (pronounced as 'new'); ν is referred to as the number of degrees of freedom (the explanation for which is beyond the level of this text). The entries in the last row of Table 6.2 ($\nu = \infty$) are precisely the values of z_α as given in Table 6.1. As an example to illustrate the use of Table 6.2, suppose we require the symmetrical 90% confidence limits for the mean μ of a normal distribution using the values in a random sample of 18 observations from the distribution. With $1 - 2\alpha = 0{\cdot}90$ we have $\alpha = 0{\cdot}05$, and in (5) we require the value of $t_\alpha = t_{0\cdot05}$ corresponding to $\nu = 18 - 1 = 17$. Referring to Table 6.2 the required value of t_α is 1·74. Hence, if the sample unbiased estimates of μ and σ^2 are $\bar{x}$ and s^2, respectively, then, from (5), the 90% symmetrical confidence limits for μ are

$$\bar{x} \pm 1{\cdot}74\sqrt{(s^2/18)}$$

EXAMPLE 2 *A random sample of* 10 *women was chosen to take part in an experiment to assess the effectiveness of a weight-reducing diet. The weights in kg of the women before and after following the diet for one month are shown in the following table.*

Woman	1	2	3	4	5	6	7	8	9	10
Before	58·6	61·4	57·8	67·6	55·2	51·0	52·6	61·2	55·4	57·1
After	58·0	60·3	56·9	65·8	55·6	51·8	50·9	59·6	54·5	56.4

Assuming that the weight losses of women following the diet for one month are normally distributed, calculate the symmetrical 95% confidence limits for the mean loss in weight.

The individual weight losses in kg are

$$0{\cdot}6,\ 1{\cdot}1,\ 0{\cdot}9,\ 1{\cdot}8,\ -0{\cdot}4,\ -0{\cdot}8,\ 1{\cdot}7,\ 1{\cdot}6,\ 0{\cdot}9,\ 0{\cdot}7,$$

and we are assuming that these weight losses are normally distributed.

Table 6.2 Values of t_α

$\nu = n-1$	α 0·005	0·01	0·025	0·05	0·10
1	63·66	31·82	12·71	6·31	3·08
2	9·92	6·96	4·30	2·92	1·89
3	5·84	4·54	3·18	2·35	1·64
4	4·60	3·75	2·78	2·13	1·53
5	4·03	3·36	2·57	2·02	1·48
6	3·71	3·14	2·45	1·94	1·44
7	3·50	3·00	2·36	1·89	1·41
8	3·36	2·90	2·31	1·86	1·40
9	3·25	2·82	2·26	1·83	1·38
10	3·17	2·76	2·23	1·81	1·37
11	3·11	2·72	2·20	1·80	1·36
12	3·05	2·68	2·18	1·78	1·36
13	3·01	2·65	2·16	1·77	1·35
14	2·98	2·62	2·14	1·76	1·35
15	2·95	2·60	2·13	1·75	1·34
16	2·92	2·58	2·12	1·75	1·34
17	2·90	2·57	2·11	1·74	1·33
18	2·88	2·55	2·10	1·73	1·33
19	2·86	2·54	2·09	1·73	1·33
20	2·85	2·53	2·09	1·72	1·33
21	2·83	2·52	2·08	1·72	1·32
22	2·82	2·51	2·07	1·72	1·32
23	2·81	2·50	2·07	1·71	1·32
24	2·80	2·49	2·06	1·71	1·32
25	2·79	2·49	2·06	1·71	1·32
26	2·78	2·48	2·06	1·71	1·31
27	2·77	2·47	2·05	1·70	1·31
28	2·76	2·47	2·05	1·70	1·31
29	2·76	2·46	2·05	1·70	1·31
30	2·75	2·46	2.04	1·70	1·31
40	2·70	2·42	2·02	1·68	1·30
60	2·66	2·39	2·00	1·67	1·30
120	2·62	2·36	1·98	1·66	1·29
∞	2.58	2.33	1.96	1.64	1.28

Denoting a weight loss by x, we have

$$n = 10, \qquad \Sigma x = 8{\cdot}1, \qquad \Sigma x^2 = 13{\cdot}17.$$

Hence, the unbiased estimates of the population mean and variance are

$$\bar{x} = \frac{8{\cdot}1}{10} = 0{\cdot}81,$$

and

$$s^2 = \frac{1}{9}\{13{\cdot}17 - 10(0{\cdot}81)^2\} \simeq 0{\cdot}7343.$$

For 95% confidence limits, $\alpha = 0{\cdot}025$ and with $\nu = 10-1 = 9$ we find from Table 6.2 that $t_{0{\cdot}025} = 2{\cdot}26$. Substituting in (5) the required limits are

$$0{\cdot}81 \pm 2{\cdot}26\sqrt{(0{\cdot}7343/10)}$$
$$= 0{\cdot}20 \text{ and } 1{\cdot}42$$

EXERCISE 6.3B

1 For the data given in Example 2, §6·3, calculate the symmetrical 90% confidence limits for the mean loss in weight.

2 A random sample of 15 observations from a normal distribution yielded unbiased estimates of the distribution mean and variance equal to 26·8 and 127·95, respectively. Determine the symmetrical 95% confidence interval for the distribution mean. What would be the effect, if any, on the width of this interval if (i) a higher confidence level than 95% is used, (ii) the given estimates of the distribution mean and variance had been obtained from a random sample of 50 observations?

3 The drained weights, in grammes, of a random sample of 12 cans of strawberries were:

339, 348, 346, 337, 340, 336, 341, 342, 335, 339, 341, 342.

Find the symmetrical 99% confidence limits for the mean drained weight of such cans.

4 The operational lifetimes in hours of a random sample of 15 dry-cell batteries were found to be

730, 758, 724, 741, 754, 745, 751, 753, 732, 778, 729, 786, 719, 772, 701.

Assuming that the operational lifetimes of such batteries are normally distributed, calculate the symmetrical 95% confidence interval for their mean operational lifetime. Does your result support the manufacturer's claim that these batteries have an average operational lifetime of 750 hours?

5 In an investigation of the effectiveness of a particular training schedule for performing a certain task, eight persons were required to perform the task before and after following the training schedule. The times, in minutes, taken by each of the eight persons to complete the task are given in the following table.

Person	A	B	C	D	E	F	G	H
Time before	28	38	29	37	42	30	34	31
Time after	23	35	29	33	43	32	30	28

Assuming that the time differences are normally distributed, calculate a 90% confidence interval for the mean reduction in the time taken to complete the task after following the training schedule.

6.3.3 Interval estimation of the difference between the means of two normal distributions whose variances are known

Consider the estimation of $\mu_1 - \mu_2$, where μ_1 and μ_2 are the means of two normal distributions having known variances σ_1^2 and σ_2^2, respectively. Let $\bar{X}_1$ denote the mean of a random sample of n_1 observations from $N(\mu_1, \sigma_1^2)$ and let $\bar{X}_2$ denote the mean of an *independent* random sample of n_2 observations from $N(\mu_2, \sigma_2^2)$. Then, from §5.4.1 and §4.8 the sampling distribution of $\bar{X}_1 - \bar{X}_2$ is normal with mean

$$\mathrm{E}[\bar{X}_1 - \bar{X}_2] = \mu_1 - \mu_2, \tag{1}$$

and standard error

$$\mathrm{SE}[\bar{X}_1 - \bar{X}_2] = \left(\frac{\sigma_1^2}{n_1} + \frac{\sigma_2^2}{n_2}\right)^{1/2}. \tag{2}$$

In particular,

$$Z = \frac{(\bar{X}_1 - \bar{X}_2) - (\mu_1 - \mu_2)}{\mathrm{SE}[\bar{X}_1 - \bar{X}_2]} \sim N(0, 1). \tag{3}$$

Substituting (3) in

$$\mathrm{P}(-z_\alpha \leqslant Z \leqslant z_\alpha) = 1 - 2\alpha,$$

and rearranging the inequalities then gives

$$\mathrm{P}\{(\bar{X}_1 - \bar{X}_2) - z_\alpha \mathrm{SE}[\bar{X}_1 - \bar{X}_2] \leqslant \mu_1 - \mu_2 \leqslant (\bar{X}_1 - \bar{X}_2) + z_\alpha \mathrm{SE}[\bar{X}_1 - \bar{X}_2]\}$$
$$= 1 - 2\alpha.$$

Hence, if $\bar{x}_1$ and $\bar{x}_2$ are the observed values of $\bar{X}_1$ and $\bar{X}_2$, respectively, the symmetrical $100(1 - 2\alpha)\%$ confidence limits for $\mu_1 - \mu_2$ are

$$(\bar{x}_1 - \bar{x}_2) \pm z_\alpha \mathrm{SE}[\bar{X}_1 - \bar{X}_2], \tag{4}$$

where $\mathrm{SE}[\bar{X}_1 - \bar{X}_2]$ is given by (2) above.

EXAMPLE 3 *The quality of a mass-produced item is measurable on a continuous scale and experience has shown that the qualities are normally distributed with a variance of 4·72. It is also known that any minor modification to the process will affect only the mean quality of the items. A random sample of 25 items produced under one type of minor modification had a mean quality of 26·4, while a random sample of 20 items under another type of minor modification had a mean quality of 25·6. Determine the symmetrical 95% confidence interval for the difference between the mean qualities under the two types of modification. Does the result suggest that one of the modifications will lead to better quality items on the average?*

From the given information, under the first modification we have

$$n_1 = 25, \qquad \bar{x}_1 = 26{\cdot}4, \qquad \sigma_1^2 = 4{\cdot}72,$$

and under the second modification we have

$$n_2 = 20, \qquad \bar{x}_2 = 25{\cdot}6, \qquad \sigma_2^2 = 4{\cdot}72.$$

From (2) above

$$\text{SE}[\bar{X}_1 - \bar{X}_2] = \left(\frac{\sigma_1^2}{n_1} + \frac{\sigma_2^2}{n_2}\right)^{1/2} = \left(\frac{4{\cdot}72}{25} + \frac{4{\cdot}72}{20}\right)^{1/2} = \sqrt{0{\cdot}4248}.$$

For the symmetrical 95% confidence interval we need $1 - 2\alpha = 0{\cdot}95$ or $\alpha = 0{\cdot}025$ and from Table 6.1, we find that $z_{0\cdot025} = 1{\cdot}96$. Hence, from (4), the symmetrical 95% confidence interval for $\mu_1 - \mu_2$ has the limits

$$(26{\cdot}4 - 25{\cdot}6) \pm 1{\cdot}96\sqrt{0{\cdot}4248} = 0{\cdot}8 \pm 1{\cdot}28.$$

The required interval is therefore $(-0{\cdot}48, 2{\cdot}08)$. Since this interval includes the value zero we are admitting the value $\mu_1 - \mu_2 = 0$ within our range of possible values of $\mu_1 - \mu_2$ at the specified 95% level. Consequently we cannot conclude with 95% confidence that the average qualities under the two modifications are different. (It is possible that if larger samples were taken the resulting 95% confidence interval for $\mu_1 - \mu_2$ would have two limits of the same sign, thus providing evidence that there was a difference between the average qualities of items produced under the two modifications.)

EXERCISE 6.3C

1 A random sample of 25 observations from a normal distribution having standard deviation 5 had a mean of 80. A random sample of 36 observations from another normal distribution having standard deviation 3 had a mean of 75. Calculate the symmetrical 99% confidence interval for the difference between the means of the two distributions.

2 Repeated weighings of an object on a chemical balance give readings which are normally distributed with mean equal to the true weight of the object and standard deviation 0·5 mg. Ten weighings of an object A gave a mean reading of 8·6 mg, while 15 weighings of an object B gave a mean reading of 6·8 mg. Calculate the symmetrical 95% confidence interval for the amount by which the weight of A exceeds that of B.

3 The random variables X and Y are independent and have normal distributions with unknown means μ_1 and μ_2, and a common variance $\sigma^2 = 32{\cdot}84$. A symmetrical 90% confidence interval is required for the difference $\mu_1 - \mu_2$ and is to be calculated from the results of independent random samples of n observations of X and n observations of Y. Find the smallest value of n for the width of the interval to be less than 4.

6.4 Approximate confidence limits

The confidence limits derived in §6.3 are applicable only when the population distributions being sampled are normal. In this section we look at some particular cases where it is possible to calculate approximate confidence limits for a parameter θ of a non-normal distribution.

Essentially, our method will assume that we can find an unbiased estimator U of θ whose sampling distribution is approximately normal and then make use of the results of §6.3 to derive approximate confidence limits for θ.

6.4.1 Large-sample approximate confidence limits for a population mean

Let $\bar{X}$ denote the mean of a random sample of n observations from a population having mean μ and variance σ^2. Provided n is large, it follows from the Central Limit Theorem (§5.4.2) that the sampling distribution of $\bar{X}$ will be approximately normal with mean $E[\bar{X}] = \mu$ and standard error $SE[\bar{X}] = \sigma/\sqrt{n}$. Using this approximation, it follows from (4) of §6.3.1 that if $\bar{x}$ is the observed value of $\bar{X}$ then the interval having limits

$$\bar{x} \pm z_\alpha SE[\bar{X}] \tag{1}$$

is an approximate $100(1-2\alpha)\%$ confidence interval for μ. Provided σ is known, the limits (1) can be evaluated given $\bar{x}$. However, if σ is not known, we will need to approximate further by replacing $SE[\bar{X}]$ by some estimate of it. Denoting the sample values by $x_1, x_2, \ldots, x_n$, the sample unbiased estimate of σ^2 is given by (see §6.2.3)

$$s^2 = \frac{1}{n-1}\Sigma(x_i - \bar{x})^2 \equiv \frac{1}{n-1}\{\Sigma x_i^2 - n\bar{x}^2\}. \tag{2}$$

For this estimate of σ^2 the corresponding estimate of $SE[\bar{X}] = \sigma/\sqrt{n}$ is given by

$$ESE[\bar{X}] = \sqrt{(s^2/n)}. \tag{3}$$

For large n it is reasonable to assume that s^2 will not differ very much from σ^2, and consequently that $ESE[\bar{X}]$ will not differ very much from $SE[\bar{X}]$. Hence, for large n, when the population variance σ^2 is not known, approximate $100(1-2\alpha)\%$ confidence limits for the population mean μ are

$$\bar{x} \pm z_\alpha ESE[\bar{X}] \tag{4}$$

where $ESE[\bar{X}]$ is defined by (3) and $\bar{x}$ is the observed sample mean.

The larger the value of n, the closer will be the actual confidence level of the interval having limits (4) to $100(1-2\alpha)\%$. The approximation should be reasonably good for a sample size n of 40 or more, but can be quite good for smaller sample sizes when the population has a distribution which is fairly symmetrical about its mean.

EXAMPLE 1 *A random sample of 100 observations of a random variable X has values whose sum is 185·6 and whose sum of squares is 385·89. Calculate approximate 90% confidence limits for the mean of X.*

Denoting the sample observations by $x_1, x_2, \ldots, x_{100}$ we are given that

$$\Sigma x_i = 185{\cdot}6 \quad \text{and} \quad \Sigma x_i^2 = 385{\cdot}89.$$

Hence the unbiased estimates of the population mean and variance are

$$\bar{x} = 185{\cdot}6/100 = 1{\cdot}856,$$

and

$$s^2 = \frac{1}{99}\{385{\cdot}89 - 100(1{\cdot}856)^2\} \simeq 0{\cdot}4183.$$

It follows from (3) that the estimated standard error of $\bar{X}$ is

$$\text{ESE}[\bar{X}] = \sqrt{(s^2/100)} \simeq \sqrt{0{\cdot}004183}.$$

For the symmetrical 90% confidence limits we need $1-2\alpha = 0{\cdot}9$, that is, $\alpha = 0{\cdot}05$. From Table 6.1 we find that $z_{0{\cdot}05} = 1{\cdot}64$. Substituting in (4), the approximate 90% confidence limits for the mean of X are

$$\begin{aligned} 1{\cdot}856 \pm 1{\cdot}64\sqrt{0{\cdot}004183} &= 1{\cdot}856 \pm 0{\cdot}106 \\ &= 1{\cdot}750 \text{ and } 1{\cdot}962. \end{aligned}$$

EXERCISE 6.4A

1 The breaking strengths, in kg, of a random sample of 60 lengths of string were $x_1, x_2, \ldots, x_{60}$. Given that $\Sigma x_i = 435{\cdot}6$ and $\Sigma x_i^2 = 3204{\cdot}87$, calculate approximate 95% confidence limits for the mean breaking strength of such lengths of string.

2 A random sample of 100 observations from a population gave unbiased estimates of the population mean and variance equal to 15·8 and 5·6842, respectively. Deduce an approximate 99% confidence interval for the population mean.

3 The heights of a random sample of 80 male students were measured in metres and it was found that the sum of the 80 heights was 140·8 and the sum of their squares was 248·64. Calculate an approximate 90% confidence interval for the mean height of male students.

6.4.2 Large-sample approximate confidence limits for the difference between the means of two populations

Let $\bar{X}_1$ denote the mean of a random sample of n_1 observations from a population having mean μ_1 and variance σ_1^2, and let $\bar{X}_2$ denote the mean of an independent random sample of n_2 observations from a population having mean μ_2 and variance σ_2^2. Then, from §5.4 and §4.5, the sampling distribution of $\bar{X}_1 - \bar{X}_2$ has mean

$$\text{E}[\bar{X}_1 - \bar{X}_2] = \mu_1 - \mu_2, \tag{1}$$

and standard error

$$\mathrm{SE}[\bar{X}_1-\bar{X}_2]=\sqrt{\left(\frac{\sigma_1^2}{n_1}+\frac{\sigma_2^2}{n_2}\right)}. \tag{2}$$

Furthermore, provided n_1 and n_2 are large, the sampling distribution of $\bar{X}_1-\bar{X}_2$ will be approximately normal. Hence, from (4) of §6.3.3, if $\bar{x}_1$ and $\bar{x}_2$ are the observed values of $\bar{X}_1$ and $\bar{X}_2$, respectively, and n_1 and n_2 are large, approximate $100(1-2\alpha)\%$ cofidence limits for $\mu_1-\mu_2$ are

$$(\bar{x}_1-\bar{x}_2)\pm z_\alpha\,\mathrm{SE}[\bar{X}_1-\bar{X}_2], \tag{3}$$

which can be evaluated given $\bar{x}_1$, $\bar{x}_2$, σ_1^2 and σ_2^2. If σ_1^2 and σ_2^2 are unknown, then we may replace $\mathrm{SE}[\bar{X}_1-\bar{X}_2]$ by an estimate of its value. An appropriate estimate is

$$\mathrm{ESE}[\bar{X}_1-\bar{X}_2]=\sqrt{\left(\frac{s_1^2}{n_1}+\frac{s_2^2}{n_2}\right)}, \tag{4}$$

where s_1^2 and s_2^2 are the unbiased estimates of σ_1^2 and σ_2^2 derived from the samples. Since n_1 and n_2 have been assumed large in deriving (3) it is reasonable to suppose that (4) will not differ much from (2). Combining the two approximations from invoking the Central Limit Theorem and introducing the estimate (4) of (2), it follows that for large n_1 and n_2, the approximate $100(1-2\alpha)\%$ confidence limits for $\mu_1-\mu_2$ are

$$(\bar{x}_1-\bar{x}_2)\pm z_\alpha\,\mathrm{ESE}[\bar{X}_1-\bar{X}_2], \tag{5}$$

where $\mathrm{ESE}[\bar{X}_1-\bar{X}_2]$ is defined by (4). The approximation should be reasonably good provided each of n_1 and n_2 is at least 40.

EXAMPLE 2 *The lifetimes in hours of a random sample of* 80 *electric bulbs of brand A gave unbiased estimates of the population mean and variance equal to* 1070 *and* 472, *respectively. The lifetimes in hours of a random sample of* 60 *electric light bulbs of brand B gave unbiased estimates of the population mean and variance equal to* 1042 *and* 366, *respectively. Calculate an approximate* 90% *confidence interval for the difference between the mean lifetimes of the two brands of bulbs.*

From the given information and using subscript A for brand A bulbs and subscript B for brand B bulbs, we have

$$n_A=80,\quad \bar{x}_A=1070,\quad s_A^2=472,$$
$$n_B=60,\quad \bar{x}_B=1042,\quad s_B^2=366.$$

Hence, from (4), the estimate of $\mathrm{SE}[\bar{X}_A-\bar{X}_B]$ is

$$\mathrm{ESE}[\bar{X}_A-\bar{X}_B]=\sqrt{\left(\frac{s_A^2}{n_A}+\frac{s_B^2}{n_B}\right)}$$
$$=\sqrt{\left(\frac{472}{80}+\frac{366}{60}\right)}=\sqrt{12}.$$

From Table 6.1 with $\alpha = 0{\cdot}05$ we find $z_{0{\cdot}05} = 1{\cdot}64$. Substituting in (5), the approximate 90% confidence limits for $\mu_A - \mu_B$ are

$$(\bar{x}_A - \bar{x}_B) \pm 1{\cdot}64\,\text{ESE}[\bar{X}_A - \bar{X}_B]$$
$$= 28 \pm 1.64\sqrt{12} = 28 \pm 5{\cdot}68.$$

The required interval is therefore (22·32, 33·68).

EXERCISE 6.4B

1 In an investigation to determine the amounts spent on sweets per week by boys and girls in a certain age group, a survey was conducted involving random samples of 80 boys and 70 girls. The results of the survey gave unbiased estimates of the mean and the variance of the amounts in pence spent per week by boys equal to 46 and 9·8, respectively, and the corresponding estimates for girls were 39 and 12·4, respectively. Calculate approximate 99% confidence limits for the difference between the average amounts spent on sweets per week by boys and girls.

2 The following table summarises the results obtained in an experiment designed to compare the heights of stalks of wheat grown under two fertiliser treatments A and B.

	Fertiliser A	Fertiliser B
Number of stalks	50	60
Sum of heights	780	846
Sum of squares of heights	12358	12195

Find an approximate 90% confidence interval for the difference between the mean heights of stalks of wheat grown under two fertiliser treatments.

6.4.3 Approximate confidence limits for a probability

Let θ denote the unknown probability of a success in a Bernoulli experiment. Let X denote the number of successes in n independent trials of the experiment. Then from §2.6, we know that the sampling distribution of X is $\text{B}(n, \theta)$. Furthermore, provided n is large and θ is not close to 0 or 1, this distribution may be approximated by a normal distribution having mean $\text{E}[X] = n\theta$ and variance $\text{V}[X] = n\theta(1-\theta)$. Let $P = X/n$ denote the proportion of successes in the n trials. Then, under the same conditions on n and θ, the sampling distribution of P is approximately normal with mean

$$\text{E}[P] = \text{E}[X/n] = \theta, \tag{1}$$

and standard error

$$\text{SE}[P] = \text{SE}[X/n] = \sqrt{\{\theta(1-\theta)/n\}}. \tag{2}$$

Alternatively, the normal approximation follows directly from the Central Limit Theorem (§5.4.2), since, in the notation of §4.6, $P = (\Sigma X_i)/n$, where the X_i are independent random variables each having mean θ and variance $\theta(1-\theta)$.

It follows that, for large n and θ not close to 0 or 1,

$$Z = (P-\theta)/\text{SE}[P] \tag{3}$$

is approximately distributed as $N(0, 1)$. Hence, proceeding as in the preceeding sections, if p is the observed proportion of successes in the n trials, then the approximate $100(1-2\alpha)\%$ confidence limits for θ are

$$p \pm z_\alpha \text{SE}[P]. \tag{4}$$

Since θ is unknown, it is clear from (2) that SE[P] cannot be evaluated. As in §6.2.2, we now have the choice of replacing SE[P] in (4) by $\sqrt{1/(4n)}$ to provide conservative limits, or by an estimate of it. From (5) of §6.2.2 an appropriate estimate of SE[P] is

$$\text{ESE}[P] = \sqrt{\{p(1-p)/n\}}. \tag{5}$$

Thus, for large n and p not close to 0 or 1, approximate $100(1-2\alpha)\%$ confidence limits for θ are

$$p \pm z_\alpha \sqrt{\{p(1-p)/n\}}, \tag{6}$$

where p is the sample proportion of successes.

EXAMPLE 3 *In a random sample of* 400 *male voters from a very large electoral region it was found that* 140 *of them stated that they intended to vote for candidate A in a forthcoming election. Calculate approximate* 95% *confidence limits for the proportion of all male voters in the electorate who intend to vote for candidate A.*

Here, $n = 400$ and $p = 140/400 = 0{\cdot}35$, which satisfy the conditions for (6) above to apply. Also, from (5)

$$\text{ESE}[P] = \sqrt{\{0{\cdot}35(1-0{\cdot}35)/400\}} = \sqrt{0{\cdot}00056875}.$$

Substituting in (6) with $z_\alpha = z_{0{\cdot}025} = 1{\cdot}96$ (from Table 6.1), approximate 95% confidence limits for the proportion of all male voters intending to vote for candidate A are

$$0{\cdot}35 \pm 1{\cdot}96\sqrt{(0{\cdot}00056875)}$$
$$= 0{\cdot}35 \pm 0{\cdot}047 = 0{\cdot}303 \text{ and } 0{\cdot}397.$$

Thus, with approximately 95% confidence, we can say that between 30% and 40% of all male voters intend to vote for candidate A.

The confidence limits for θ given by (6) were determined using two successive approximations, the first being that of approximating the sampling distribution of P by a normal distribution, and the second that of replacing $\text{SE}[P] = \sqrt{\{\theta(1-\theta)/n\}}$ by $\text{ESE}[P] = \sqrt{\{p(1-p)/n\}}$, where p is the observed value of P. This second approximation could have been avoided as follows.

From (3), $Z = (P-\theta)/\text{SE}[P]$ is approximately distributed as $N(0, 1)$. Since, for any $Z \sim N(0, 1)$,

$$P(-z_\alpha \leqslant Z \leqslant z_\alpha) = 1-2\alpha,$$

it follows, in particular, that

$$P\left[-z_\alpha \leqslant \frac{(P-\theta)\sqrt{n}}{\sqrt{\{\theta(1-\theta)\}}} \leqslant z_\alpha\right] \simeq 1-2\alpha,$$

or, equivalently, that

$$P\left\{\frac{n(P-\theta)^2}{\theta(1-\theta)} \leqslant z_\alpha^2\right\} \simeq 1-2\alpha. \tag{7}$$

We now determine the range of values of θ satisfying the inequality in the curly brackets on the left-hand side of (7). This inequality may be expressed as a quadratic in θ in the form

$$(n+z_\alpha^2)\theta^2 - 2\left(nP + \frac{1}{2}z_\alpha^2\right)\theta + nP^2 \leqslant 0.$$

Solving this quadratic for θ and substituting in (7) we get

$$P\left[\frac{(nP+\frac{1}{2}z_\alpha^2) - \sqrt{\{nP(1-P)z_\alpha^2 + \frac{1}{4}z_\alpha^4\}}}{n+z_\alpha^2} \leqslant \theta \leqslant \frac{(nP+\frac{1}{2}z_\alpha^2) + \sqrt{\{nP(1-P)z_\alpha^2 + \frac{1}{4}z_\alpha^4\}}}{n+z_\alpha^2}\right] \simeq 1-2\alpha.$$

Hence, better approximate $100(1-2\alpha)\%$ confidence limits for θ given p are

$$\frac{(np+\frac{1}{2}z_\alpha^2) \pm z_\alpha\sqrt{\{np(1-p)+\frac{1}{4}z_\alpha^2\}}}{n+z_\alpha^2}. \tag{8}$$

In Example 3 above, we have $n = 400$, $p = 0{\cdot}35$, and $z_\alpha = z_{0\cdot025} = 1{\cdot}96$. Hence, using (8), the approximate 95% confidence limits for θ are given by

$$\frac{140 + \frac{1}{2}(1{\cdot}96)^2 \pm 1{\cdot}96\sqrt{\{140 \times 0{\cdot}65 + \frac{1}{4}(1{\cdot}96)^2\}}}{400 + (1{\cdot}96)^2} = 0{\cdot}305 \text{ and } 0{\cdot}398,$$

correct to three decimal places, as compared with the values 0·303 and 0·397 obtained using (6).

EXERCISE 6.4C

In each of the following use (6) above to determine the approximate confidence limits.

1 In a random sample of 1000 houses in a certain large city it was found that 358 had colour television sets. Calculate approximate 90% confidence limits for the proportion of all houses in the city that have colour television sets.

2 In a random sample of 500 births registered during a certain month it was found that 261 were boys. Calculate approximate 95% confidence limits for the proportion of all registered births that are boys.

3 Sweets of assorted colours are sold in tubes, each tube containing 20 sweets. Of the sweets in a random sample of 40 such tubes it was found that 268 were black. Calculate approximate 95% confidence limits for the proportion of all sweets produced that are black.

6.4.4 Approximate confidence limits for the difference between two probabilities

Let θ_1 and θ_2 denote the probabilities of a success in two independent Bernoulli experiments. Suppose that in n_1 independent trials of the first of these experiments the number of successes is X_1, and that in n_2 independent trials of the second experiment the number of successes is X_2. Then, as in §6.4.3, if n_1 and n_2 are both large and neither of θ_1, θ_2 is close to 0 or 1, the sampling distributions of $P_1 = X_1/n_1$ and $P_2 = X_2/n_2$ are approximately normal with means $E[P_i] = \theta_i$, and standard errors

$$\mathrm{SE}[P_i] = \sqrt{\{\theta_i(1-\theta_i)/n_i\}}, \qquad \text{for } i = 1, 2.$$

Since P_1 and P_2 are independent, it follows from §4.8 that the sampling distribution of $P_1 - P_2$ is approximately normal with mean

$$E[P_1 - P_2] = \theta_1 - \theta_2, \tag{1}$$

and standard error

$$\mathrm{SE}[P_1 - P_2] = \sqrt{\left\{\frac{\theta_1(1-\theta_1)}{n_1} + \frac{\theta_2(1-\theta_2)}{n_2}\right\}}. \tag{2}$$

Thus, if p_1 and p_2 are the observed sample proportions of successes, the approximate $100(1-2\alpha)\%$ confidence limits for $\theta_1 - \theta_2$ are

$$(p_1 - p_2) \pm z_\alpha \, \mathrm{SE}[P_1 - P_2]. \tag{3}$$

From (2), $\mathrm{SE}[P_1 - P_2]$ cannot be evaluated because it depends upon the unknown quantities θ_1 and θ_2. We therefore introduce a further approximation by replacing $\mathrm{SE}[P_1 - P_2]$ in (3) by its estimate

$$\mathrm{ESE}[P_1 - P_2] = \sqrt{\left\{\frac{p_1(1-p_1)}{n_1} + \frac{p_2(1-p_2)}{n_2}\right\}}, \tag{4}$$

the corresponding approximate $100(1-2\alpha)\%$ confidence limits for $\theta_1 - \theta_2$ then being

$$(p_1 - p_2) \pm z_\alpha \, \mathrm{ESE}[P_1 - P_2]. \tag{5}$$

EXAMPLE 4 *In a random sample of* 300 *female voters from the same electorate as in Example* 3, *it was found that* 156 *of them intended to vote for candidate A.*

Calculate approximate 90% confidence limits for the difference between the proportions of male and female voters in the electorate who intend to vote for candidate A.

From Example 3, for the male voters we have $n_1 = 400$ and $p_1 = 0{\cdot}35$. From the given information about the sampled females we have $n_2 = 300$ and $p_2 = 156/300 = 0{\cdot}52$.

From (4) above, we find

$$\text{ESE}[P_1 - P_2] = \sqrt{\left\{\frac{0{\cdot}35 \times 0{\cdot}65}{400} + \frac{0{\cdot}52 \times 0{\cdot}48}{300}\right\}} \simeq 0{\cdot}0374.$$

Since n_1 and n_2 are large and neither of p_1, p_2 is close to 0 or 1, the approximate 90% confidence limits for $\theta_M - \theta_F$, where θ_M and θ_F are the proportions of male and female voters who intend to vote for candidate A, are from (5)

$$\begin{aligned}&(p_1 - p_2) \pm z_{0{\cdot}05}\,\text{ESE}[P_1 - P_2]\\ &= (0{\cdot}35 - 0{\cdot}52) \pm 1{\cdot}64 \times 0{\cdot}0374 \simeq -0{\cdot}17 \pm 0{\cdot}06 = -0{\cdot}23 \text{ and } -0{\cdot}11.\end{aligned}$$

Thus, with approximately 90% confidence we can conclude that the percentage of female voters intending to vote for candidate A exceeds that of male voters by between 11% and 23%.

EXERCISE 6.4D

1 In a random sample of 200 employees at a certain factory A it was found that 92 of them had missed at least one day's work during the past year without just cause. In a random sample of 250 employees at another factory B it was found that 84 of them had missed at least one day's work during the past year without just cause. Calculate an approximate 90% confidence interval for the difference between the proportions of employees at the two factories who had missed at least one day's work during the past year without just cause.

2 In a horticultural experiment 150 seeds of variety A and 100 seeds of variety B were sown and kept under identical conditions. After three weeks it was found that 114 seeds of variety A and 85 of variety B had germinated. Calculate approximate 95% confidence limits for the difference between the germination rates after three weeks.

3 A random sample of 270 houses in a certain area showed that 99 of them were owner-occupied, while a random sample of 320 houses in another area showed that 120 of them were owner-occupied. Calculate 98% confidence limits for the difference between the proportions of the houses in the two areas that are owner-occupied.

6.4.5 Approximate confidence limits for the mean of a Poisson distribution and for the difference between the means of two Poisson distributions

Let $\bar{X}$ denote the mean of a random sample n observations from a Poisson distribution having unknown mean λ. Since the variance of the Poisson distribution is also λ (§2.7) it follows from the Central Limit Theorem that, provided n is large, the sampling distribution of $\bar{X}$ will be approximately normal with mean $\mathrm{E}[\bar{X}] = \lambda$ and standard error

$$\mathrm{SE}[\bar{X}] = \sqrt{(\lambda/n)}. \tag{1}$$

Furthermore, from (1) of §6.4.1, approximate $100(1-2\alpha)\%$ confidence limits for λ are

$$\bar{x} \pm z_\alpha \,\mathrm{SE}[\bar{X}], \tag{2}$$

where $\bar{x}$ is the observed value of $\bar{X}$. Since λ is unknown we cannot evaluate $\mathrm{SE}[\bar{X}]$ as given by (1). As in the preceding sections, we now introduce an additional approximation by replacing $\mathrm{SE}[\bar{X}]$ by an estimate. Here, since $\bar{x}$ is an unbiased estimate of λ, an appropriate estimate of $\mathrm{SE}[\bar{X}]$ is

$$\mathrm{ESE}[\bar{X}] = \sqrt{(\bar{x}/n)}, \tag{3}$$

the corresponding approximate $100(1-2\alpha)\%$ confidence limits for λ then being

$$\bar{x} \pm z_\alpha \,\mathrm{ESE}[\bar{X}]. \tag{4}$$

More accurate $100(1-2\alpha)\%$ confidence limits for λ can be derived using a procedure similar to that given at the end of §6.4.3. Since here, $\bar{X}$ is approximately normally distributed with mean λ and standard error $\sqrt{(\lambda/n)}$, it follows that

$$Z \equiv \frac{\bar{X}-\lambda}{\sqrt{(\lambda/n)}}$$

is approximately distributed as $N(0, 1)$. Hence

$$P\left\{-z_\alpha \leqslant \frac{\bar{X}-\lambda}{\sqrt{(\lambda/n)}} \leqslant z_\alpha\right\} \simeq 1-2\alpha,$$

or,

$$P\left\{\frac{(\bar{X}-\lambda)^2}{(\lambda/n)} \leqslant z_\alpha^2\right\} \simeq 1-2\alpha. \tag{5}$$

The inequality in the curly brackets on the left-hand side of (5) may be rearranged as a quadratic in λ, namely

$$\lambda^2 - 2\left(\bar{X} + \frac{z^2}{2n}\right)\lambda + \bar{X}^2 \leqslant 0,$$

or, equivalently,

$$\left\{\lambda - \left(\bar{X} + \frac{z^2}{2n}\right)\right\}^2 \leqslant \frac{z^2(4n\bar{X} + z^2)}{4n^2},$$

where $z \equiv z_\alpha$. Solving for λ and substituting in (5) gives

$$P\left\{\bar{X}+\frac{z^2}{2n}-\frac{z}{2n}\sqrt{(4n\bar{X}+z^2)} \leqslant \lambda \leqslant \left(\bar{X}+\frac{z^2}{2n}\right)+\frac{z}{2n}\sqrt{(4n\bar{X}+z^2)}\right\} \simeq 1-2\alpha.$$

It follows that, given $\bar{x}$, approximate $100(1-2\alpha)\%$ confidence limits for λ are

$$\left(\bar{x}+\frac{z_\alpha^2}{2n}\right) \pm \frac{z_\alpha}{2n}\sqrt{(4n\bar{x}+z_\alpha^2)}, \tag{6}$$

and these should be more accurate than those given by (4).

Consider now the interval estimation of $\lambda_1 - \lambda_2$, where λ_1 and λ_2 are the means of two independent Poisson distributions. Let $\bar{X}_1, \bar{X}_2$ denote the means of independent random samples of sizes n_1, n_2 from these distributions. Then,

$$\mathrm{E}[\bar{X}_1-\bar{X}_2]=\lambda_1-\lambda_2, \qquad \mathrm{SE}[\bar{X}_1-\bar{X}_2]=\sqrt{\left(\frac{\lambda_1}{n_1}+\frac{\lambda_2}{n_2}\right)}.$$

Provided n_1 and n_2 are large, the sampling distribution of $\bar{X}_1-\bar{X}_2$ will be approximately normal, and approximate $100(1-2\alpha)\%$ confidence limits for $\lambda_1-\lambda_2$ are

$$(\bar{x}_1-\bar{x}_2) \pm z_\alpha \,\mathrm{ESE}\,[\bar{X}_1-\bar{X}_2], \tag{7}$$

where

$$\mathrm{ESE}\,[\bar{X}_1-\bar{X}_2]=\sqrt{\left\{\frac{\bar{x}_1}{n_1}+\frac{\bar{x}_2}{n_2}\right\}}, \tag{8}$$

and $\bar{x}_1$, $\bar{x}_2$ are the sample observed values of $\bar{X}_1$, $\bar{X}_2$, respectively.

EXAMPLE 5 *Along a certain stretch of motorway the number of cars that become overheated on any day may be assumed to have a Poisson distribution. In a random sample of 50 wet days the total number of cars that became overheated was found to be 163, while in a random sample of 50 dry days the total number was found to be 96. Calculate (i) an approximate 95% confidence interval for the average number of cars that become overheated on a wet day, (ii) an approximate 90% confidence interval for the difference between the average numbers of cars that become overheated on a wet day and a dry day.*

(i) Let X_1 denote the number of cars that become overheated on a wet day. Then $X_1 \sim \mathrm{Po}\,(\lambda_1)$, where λ_1 is the average number per wet day. From the given data, the observed average per day is $\bar{x}_1 = 163/50 = 3{\cdot}26$. With $z_\alpha = z_{0\cdot025} = 1{\cdot}96$, it follows from (3) and (4) that approximate 95% confidence limits for λ_1 are

$$3{\cdot}26 \pm 1{\cdot}96\sqrt{(3{\cdot}26/50)} \simeq 2{\cdot}76 \text{ and } 3{\cdot}76.$$

Hence, the required interval is (2.76, 3.76).

Alternatively, for a more accurate approximation, using (6) the approximate 95% confidence limits for λ_1 are

$$\left(3{\cdot}26+\frac{1{\cdot}96^2}{100}\right)\pm\frac{1{\cdot}96}{100}\sqrt{(652+1{\cdot}96^2)}$$

$$\simeq 2{\cdot}80 \text{ and } 3{\cdot}80.$$

(ii) Let X_2 denote the number of cars that become overheated on a dry day. Then $X_2 \sim \text{Po}(\lambda_2)$, where λ_2 is the average number per dry day. From the given data, $\bar{x}_2 = 96/50 = 1{\cdot}92$. With $z = z_{0{\cdot}05} = 1{\cdot}64$, it follows from (7) and (8) that approximate 90% confidence limits for $\lambda_1 - \lambda_2$ are

$$(3{\cdot}26-1{\cdot}92)\pm 1{\cdot}64\sqrt{\left(\frac{3{\cdot}26}{50}+\frac{1{\cdot}92}{50}\right)}\simeq 0{\cdot}81 \text{ and } 1{\cdot}87,$$

and the required interval is (0·81, 1·87).

EXERCISE 6.4E

1 Inspection of a random sample of 200 new cars of a particular model revealed a total 130 defects. Assuming that the number of defects per car has a Poisson distribution determine approximate 95% confidence limits for the average number of defects per new car.

2 A total of 252 flaws were found in a random sample of 100 rolls of cloth. Calculate approximate 90% confidence limits for the average number of flaws per roll.

3 The following table gives the observed frequency distributions of the numbers of bubbles found in a random sample of 60 glass bottles produced by manufacturer A and in a random sample of 40 glass bottles produced by manufacturer B. Assuming that the numbers of bubbles per bottle have Poisson distributions find

No. of bubbles per bottle	0	1	2	3	4	5
No. of bottles by A	28	19	8	5	0	0
No. of bottles by B	15	10	9	3	2	1

(i) approximate 95% confidence limits for the mean number of bubbles per bottle produced by (a) A, (b) B;
(ii) approximate 90% confidence limits for the difference between the mean numbers of bubbles per bottle produced by A and by B.

6.5 Estimating from a grouped frequency distribution

In the preceding sections of this chapter we have considered the estimation of some characteristic feature (e.g. the mean) of a population distribution given a random sample of observations from the population.

To obtain more detailed information on an unknown population distribution a very large sample will be necessary. A convenient way of displaying the results of a large sample from a continuous distribution is by means of a *grouped frequency distribution table*, which is constructed by subdividing the entire range of sample values into a finite number (usually from 5 to 12) of class intervals and recording the number (the frequency) of values that fall in each such interval.

As a specific example, consider the population distribution of the diameters of ball bearings produced by a certain process. Suppose that the diameters of a random sample of 200 ball bearings from this process were measured in millimetres, and that the results were summarised in the form of the grouped frequency distribution displayed in Table 6.3. Here, nine equal class intervals have been used. Adopting the notation $(a, b]$ for an interval in which the lower end-point a is excluded from the interval and the upper end-point b is included in the interval we see, for example, that three of the ball bearings in the sample had diameters in the interval $(4{\cdot}75, 4{\cdot}80]$ and 18 had diameters in the interval $(4{\cdot}80, 4{\cdot}85]$.

Table 6.3 Grouped frequency distribution of the diameters of 200 ball bearings

Diameter (mm)									
$>$	4·75	4·80	4·85	4·90	4·95	5·00	5·05	5·10	5·15
$\leqslant$	4.80	4·85	4·90	4·95	5·00	5·05	5·10	5·15	5·20
Frequency	3	18	24	31	56	41	19	6	2

To determine the sample unbiased estimates of the mean and the variance of the population distribution of the diameters of such ball bearings we would need to operate on the individual diameters of the 200 sampled ball bearings. However, approximations to these estimates are possible from the grouped frequency distribution. These approximations are obtained by replacing each class interval by its mid-interval value, in which case the grouped frequency distribution in Table 6.3 is reduced to the frequency distribution shown in Table 6.4. Such a frequency distribution will yield good approximations for the mean and the variance, provided the actual observed diameters within any class interval are fairly uniformly distributed throughout that interval. Approximate

Table 6.4 Frequency distribution of the diameters of 200 ball bearings

Mid-interval value (x mm)	4·775	4·825	4·875	4·925	4·975	5·025	5·075	5·125	5·175
Frequency (f)	3	18	24	35	52	41	19	6	2
$y = 20(x - 4{\cdot}775)$	0	1	2	3	4	5	6	7	8

values for the sample unbiased estimates of the population mean and variance are then given by the formulae

$$\bar{x} = (\Sigma f x)/n \quad \text{and} \quad s_x^2 = \{\Sigma f (x - \bar{x})^2\}/(n-1),$$

respectively, where n is the sample size equal to 200 in our example. To simplify the computation of $\bar{x}$ and s_x^2, let us introduce the new variable y defined by

$$y = 20(x - 4{\cdot}775).$$

The values of y corresponding to the values of x in Table 6.4 are given in the third row of that table and are seen to be much simpler numbers to handle than the x-values. From the definition of y we have

$$x = (y/20) + 4{\cdot}775,$$

from which it follows that

$$\bar{x} = (\bar{y}/20) + 4{\cdot}775 \quad \text{and} \quad s_x^2 = s_y^2/400.$$

Using these results we can readily deduce the values of $\bar{x}$ and s_x^2 from the values of $\bar{y}$ and s_y^2, respectively. From the entries in the last two rows of Table 6.4 we find

$$\begin{aligned} \bar{y} &= (\Sigma f y)/200 = 756/200 = 3{\cdot}78, \\ s_y^2 &= \{\Sigma f y^2 - 200\bar{y}^2\}/199 = \{3392 - 200 \times 3{\cdot}78^2\}/199 \\ &\simeq 2{\cdot}6850. \end{aligned}$$

Hence, the approximate values for the sample unbiased estimates of the population mean and variance are

$$\bar{x} = (3{\cdot}78/20) + 4.775 = 4{\cdot}964,$$

and

$$s_x^2 \simeq 2{\cdot}6850/400 \simeq 0{\cdot}0067.$$

Using the results of §6.4.1, approximate 95% confidence limits for the mean diameter of the population of ball bearings are given by

$$\bar{x} \pm 1{\cdot}96\sqrt{(s_x^2/200)} = 4{\cdot}964 \pm 0{\cdot}011 = 4{\cdot}953 \text{ and } 4{\cdot}975.$$

Estimation of population quantiles

A grouped frequency distribution for a large sample of observations from a *continuous* distribution may also be used to estimate *quantiles* of the distribution. Let X denote the diameter (in mm) of a randomly sampled ball bearing. Then X is a continuous random variable; suppose that its cumulative distribution function is F, so that $F(x) = P(X \leqslant x)$ is the proportion of all ball bearings having diameters less than or equal to x mm. We recall from §6.2.2 that the sample proportion or relative frequency $R(x)$ of ball bearings having diameters $\leqslant x$ mm is an unbiased estimate of F(x). Thus, using the grouped frequency distribution displayed in Table 6.3 we can obtain an unbiased estimate R(x) of F(x) for every x which is an upper end-point of a class interval. From Table 6.3 we find, for example, that

$$\mathrm{R}(4{\cdot}80) = 3/200 = 0{\cdot}015,$$
$$\mathrm{R}(4{\cdot}85) = (3+18)/200 = 0{\cdot}105,$$
$$\mathrm{R}(4{\cdot}90) = (3+18+24)/200 = 0{\cdot}225.$$

The relevant values of x and the corresponding values of R(x) are shown in Table 6.5. In Fig. 6.8 we have plotted the points $(x, \mathrm{R}(x))$ and drawn a

Table 6.5 Values of R(x)

$x =$	4·80	4·85	4·90	4·95	5·00	5·05	5·10	5·15	5·20
R(x) =	0·015	0·105	0·225	0·380	0·660	0·865	0·960	0·990	1·000

smooth curve through them. This curve provides an estimate of the curve F(x) and may be used to obtain estimates of the quantiles of the distribution of X. Recall from §3.6.1 that the quantile ξ_p $(0 < p < 1)$ is defined as the solution of the equation F$(\xi_p) = p$. From the curve drawn in Fig. 6.8 we can read off an estimate of ξ_p for any specified p. Thus, for example, our estimate of the population median $\xi_{0\cdot5}$ is 4·975, of the lower quartile $\xi_{0\cdot25}$ is 4·91, and of the upper quartile $\xi_{0\cdot75}$ is 5·015.

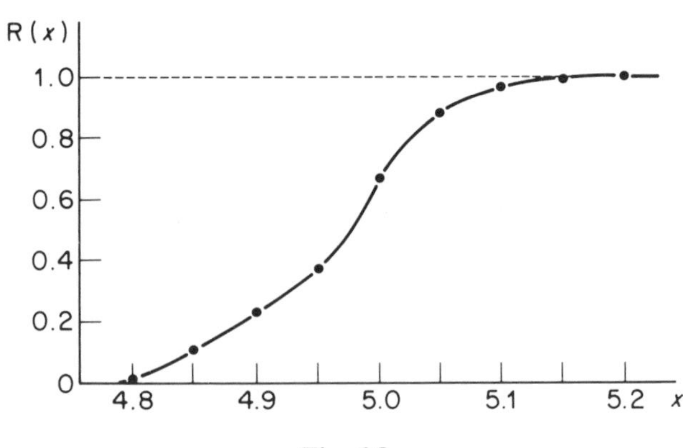

Fig. 6.8

It is important to appreciate the distinction between the above procedure and the corresponding one in descriptive statistics. In the latter the objective is to determine the quantiles of the sample data and not estimates of the population quantiles. To determine the quantiles of the sample of diameters given in Table 6.3, the plotted points in Fig. 6.8

should be joined by *straight lines* to produce a cumulative frequency polygon, which is then used to read off the sample quantiles. This procedure for determining sample quantiles is justifiable if, as assumed earlier, it is reasonable to assume that the observed sample diameters in any class interval are fairly uniformly distributed throughout that interval. As it happens, in our example, there is little discernible difference between the values of the sample quartiles and our estimates of the population quartiles.

The procedure we have described above for estimating population quantiles from a grouped frequency distribution is a crude one relying on a visual fit of a smooth curve to the plotted points. In particular, the procedure does not allow us to assess the reliability of our estimates. More formal procedures not having these deficiencies are described in more advanced texts.

EXERCISE 6.5

1 The following table is the grouped frequency distribution of the lifetimes, measured to the nearest hour, of a random sample of 400 electric light bulbs of a particular brand. Obtain estimates of the median and the semi-interquartile range of the population distribution of the lifetimes of such bulbs. (Hint: Note that since the lifetimes have been measured to the nearest hour, the true upper end-point of the first class interval, for example, is 799·5 hours.)

Lifetime (hours)	700–	800–	900–	1000–	1100–	1200–	1300–	1400–	1500–1599
Frequency	14	46	58	76	68	62	48	22	6

2 The grouped frequency distribution of the breaking strengths, measured to the nearest kg, of a random sample of 150 car seat belts produced by a certain manufacturer is shown in the following table.

Breaking strength (kg) Exceeding	Not exceeding	Number of belts
950	1000	2
1000	1050	12
1050	1100	25
1100	1150	34
1150	1200	52
1200	1250	20
1250	1300	5

(i) Obtain estimates of the mean and the standard deviation of the breaking strengths of belts produced by this manufacturer.

(ii) Estimate the probability that a randomly chosen belt produced by this manufacturer will have a breaking strength of at least 1220 kg.
(iii) Estimate the 10th and 90th percentiles of the distribution of breaking strengths of such belts.

REVIEW PROBLEMS ON CHAPTER 6

1 A random variable X can take only the values 1, 2 and 3, the respective probabilities of these values being θ, θ and $1-2\theta$, where $0<\theta<\frac{1}{2}$. Determine the mean and the variance of X in terms of θ. In a random sample of n values of X, let $\bar{X}$ denote the mean of the sample values, and let R denote the number of 3's among the sample values. Show that $p_1 = 1-(\bar{X}/3)$ and $p_2 = \frac{1}{2}\{1-(R/n)\}$ are both unbiased estimators of θ. Determine which of p_1 and p_2 has the smaller standard error. (*WJEC 1982*)

2 A random sample of n independent observations taken from a distribution having variance σ^2 yielded the values $x_1, x_2, \ldots, x_n$. The mean of these values was $\bar{x}$. Explain what is meant by the statement that s^2 is an unbiased estimate of σ^2, where

$$(n-1)s^2 = \sum_{i=1}^{n} (x_i - \bar{x})^2.$$

Show that, when $n=2$, $s^2 = \frac{1}{2}(x_1 - x_2)^2$.

Two numbers are chosen at random *with* replacement from the set $\{1, 2, 3\}$. By considering all possible choices of pairs of numbers, verify that in this case the statistic s^2 defined above is an unbiased estimate of the distribution variance. State, giving a reason for your answer, whether the same result would be true if the two numbers were chosen at random *without* replacement. (*JMB 1979*)

3 A random sample of nine observations is drawn from a population distribution having mean μ and variance σ^2. The sample mean is 6 and the sample unbiased estimate of σ^2 is 9. Given that an additional random observation from the distribution has the value 5, find unbiased estimates of μ and σ^2 based on all ten observations. (*JMB 1977*)

4 The random variable X has the Poisson distribution

$$P(X=k) = e^{-\theta}\theta^k/k!, \qquad k = 0, 1, 2, \ldots.$$

Show that (i) $E[X] = \theta$, (ii) $E[X^2 - X] = \theta^2$, (iii) $V[X] = \theta$.
A random sample of 9 observations of X had the values

8, 6, 4, 7, 5, 3, 1, 6, 5.

Calculate *two* unbiased estimates of θ and *one* unbiased estimate of θ^2 based on all 9 observations. (*WJEC 1980*)

5 The number of flaws in a one metre length of velvet follows a Poisson distribution. In a 25 m length, eight flaws were found. Obtain an estimate of the mean number, λ, of flaws per metre length of velvet, and of the standard error of this estimate. Another roll of the velvet is investigated. On the evidence above, find a length which will provide an estimate of λ with an estimated standard error of 0·08.

If the cost of production of the velvet is £3 per metre, and the cost of removing each flaw is £1, find an unbiased estimate of the expected cost of producing and making flawless a length of 10 m. (*L 1981*)

6 An experimenter wishes to determine the value of a physical constant. From experience with the apparatus used, he knows that the observations obtained will be normally distributed with mean μ equal to the true value of the constant and with variance 0·0075. He takes 27 observations using the apparatus and calculates their mean to be 3·874. Determine 95 % confidence limits for the true value of the constant. (*JMB 1979*)

7 A weighing device is undergoing tests to determine its accuracy. A certain object of known true weight 50 mg was weighed 10 times on this device and the readings in mg were

49, 51, 49, 52, 49, 50, 52, 51, 49, 48.

(i) Calculate an unbiased estimate of the variance of the errors in readings using this device.
(ii) Calculate 95 % confidence limits for the mean error in readings using this device. (Assume that the errors in the readings are independent and normally distributed.) (*WJEC 1982*)

8 In order to investigate the lengths of components produced by a machine, ten components were selected at random from a large batch. Their lengths (in metres) were 1·125, 1·127, 1·125, 1·124, 1·131, 1·132, 1·125, 1·129, 1·123 and 1·129. Use this sample to calculate symmetric 95 % confidence limits for the mean length of components in the batch, stating any assumptions that you need to make. (*C 1982*)

9 (i) A random sample of ten observations from a normal distribution had the values $x_1, x_2, \ldots, x_{10}$, and it was found that

$$\sum_{i=1}^{10} x_i = 2{\cdot}4 \quad \text{and} \quad \sum_{i=1}^{10} x_i^2 = 4{\cdot}86.$$

Calculate 95 % confidence limits for the mean of the normal distribution.
(ii) A random sample of n observations is to be drawn from a normal distribution whose mean μ is unknown and whose standard deviation is known to be 1·5. The sample values are to be used to calculate a 95 % confidence interval for μ. Find the smallest n which will give a confidence interval of width less than 0·5. (*WJEC 1979*)

10 (i) A random sample from a normal population consisted of the values 2, 4, 7, 11, 13. Calculate the mean of this sample and estimate the variance of the population. Assuming that the population variance is 25, obtain 95 % confidence limits for the population mean. (ii) A normal population has a variance of 16. Find the smallest sample to take from this population so that the 99 % confidence limits for the population mean will cover an interval of 4 units or less. (*L 1982*)

11 A random sample of n observations from a population distribution had the values $x_1, x_2, \ldots, x_n$ whose mean is $\bar{x}$. Show that for any value of c

$$\sum_{i=1}^{n} (x_i - c)^2 = \sum_{i=1}^{n} (x_i - \bar{x})^2 + n(c - \bar{x})^2.$$

Hence find the value of c for which $\sum_{i=1}^{n} (x_i - c)^2$ is a minimum.

A random sample of 12 values from a normal distribution, whose mean μ

and variance σ^2 are unknown, were such that

$$\sum_{i=1}^{12} x_i = 5472, \qquad \sum_{i=1}^{12} (x_i - 450)^2 = 1620.$$

(i) Calculate unbiased estimates of μ and σ^2.
(ii) Determine a 95% confidence interval for μ.
(iii) Given that (451, 463) was a 95% confidence interval for μ based on *another* random sample of 12 values from the same normal distribution, deduce the corresponding unbiased estimates of μ and σ^2 from this sample. *(WJEC 1981)*

12 Explain what is meant by the sampling distribution of an estimator. Given that a random sample of n observations is drawn from a normal distribution having mean μ and variance σ^2, specify the sampling distribution of the sample mean. State what can be said about the sampling distribution of the sample mean when n is large and the parent population is not normal.

In order to estimate the mean life of an electronic component, a manufacturer carried out tests on a sample of 26 of these components. From these experiments he obtained the values $\Sigma x_i = 395{\cdot}2$, $\Sigma x_i^2 = 6232$, where x_i ($i = 1$ to 26) is the life in hours of the ith component. Use these data to find (i) an unbiased estimate of the mean life of the population, (ii) an unbiased estimate of the variance of the population, (iii) a symmetric 95% confidence interval for the mean life of the population.

If, instead, the manufacturer had tested a sample of 260 components and found $\Sigma x_i = 3952$ and $\Sigma x_i^2 = 62320$, obtain revised estimates for (ii) and (iii) above. *(JMB 1980)*

13 In a distillery the alcohol content of the distillate is measured frequently. For 400 measurements at one stage of production, the alcohol contents per litre of distillate are recorded in the following table.

Alcohol content	12	13	14	15	16
Frequency	5	52	235	74	34

(i) Calculate the mean alcohol content per litre, and estimate the standard error of this mean.
(ii) Obtain 95% confidence limits for the mean alcohol content per litre.
(iii) Given that a further 400 measurements are to be made at this stage of production, find an approximate value for the probability that the mean of these measurements will not exceed 14·1. *(L 1982)*

14 The yields, x kg, of tomatoes from a random sample of 40 plants of a particular variety gave the following values: $\Sigma x_i = 240$, $\Sigma x_i^2 = 1596$. Calculate unbiased estimates of the mean μ and the variance σ^2 of the yields from plants of this variety. Assuming that your estimate of σ^2 is the true value, determine an approximate 95% confidence interval for μ. *(JMB 1980)*

15 If $\bar{X}$ is the mean of a random sample of size n_1 from a population distribution having mean μ_1 and variance σ_1^2, and n_1 is very large, what can you say about the sampling distribution of $\bar{X}$? If $\bar{Y}$ is the mean of a random sample of size n_2 from another population distribution having mean μ_2 and variance σ_2^2, and n_2 is also very large, what can you say about the sampling distribution of $\bar{Y}-\bar{X}$?

The heights, measured in metres, of 100 women drawn at random from a certain tribe had a sum of 160 and the sum of their squares was 265. Use this information to construct a 90% confidence interval for the mean height of women of this tribe.

The heights, measured in metres, of 200 men drawn at random from the same tribe, had a sum of 360 and the sum of their squares was 712. Use the information contained in the two samples to construct a 95% confidence interval for the amount by which the average height of the men in the tribe exceeds that of the women. (*WJEC 1980*)

16 From an entire entry of several thousand candidates who took an 'O' level mathematics examination, a random sample of 200 candidates was taken and the distribution of their marks is given in the following table.

Mid-interval value	4·5	14·5	24·5	34·5	44·5	54·5	64·5	74·5	84·5	94·5
Frequency	5	10	20	25	40	40	30	14	10	6

Estimate the mean and the variance of the marks of all the candidates entered for the examination. Use these estimates to calculate 95% confidence limits for the mean mark of all the candidates entered. Find the least number of candidates that should be included in a random sample if there is to be a probability of 0·95 that the sample mean mark will be within 2 marks of the mean mark for all the candidates. (*L 1981*)

17 A continuous random variable X is known to have a uniform distribution in the interval $(10, a)$, where $a > 10$, but is otherwise unknown. Write down an expression for $f(x)$, where f is the probability density function of X. Write down, in terms of a, the mean of X. Show that the variance of X is $(a-10)^2/12$.

In one observation taken at random from this distribution a value of 21 for X was obtained. Write down an unbiased estimate of a. In 50 random observations of X the following results were obtained:

$$\Sigma x_i = 1100, \qquad \Sigma x_i^2 = 35000.$$

Use the value of Σx_i to obtain an unbiased estimate of a and give an approximate 95% symmetric confidence interval for a.

Given that one of the 50 observations of X had value 60, state why a is certain to be greater than or equal to 60. Since 60 is outside the calculated confidence interval explain the apparent contradiction between this certainty and the 95% confidence interval. (*JMB 1982*)

18 (i) A bag contains ten balls of which four are red and six are white. A random sample of three balls is taken, without replacement, and $\hat{p}$ denotes the proportion of red balls in the sample. Tabulate the probability distribution of $\hat{p}$, and hence verify that $\hat{p}$ is an unbiased estimate of the population proportion (i.e. the actual proportion of red balls in the bag).

(ii) A certain city has about one million adult inhabitants of whom an unknown proportion p have never spent a holiday in a foreign country. A random sample of 1000 of the inhabitants is taken, and 784 people in the sample are found never to have spent a holiday in a foreign country. Find a 95% confidence interval for p. *(C 1981)*

19 In observations of a particular type of event, the probability of a positive result of any one observation is independent of the results of other observations and has the value θ, the same for all observations. In n observations the proportion giving positive results is p. State the mean and the standard deviation of the probability distribution of p. Say also how and in what circumstances this probability distribution can be approximated by a normal distribution. Show that, according to this approximation, the probability that p satisfies the inequality $|p-\theta| < 1{\cdot}96\sqrt{\{\theta(1-\theta)/n\}}$ is $0{\cdot}95$. In a set of 100 observations of this type, 90 gave a positive result. Obtain an inequality of the above form, and by squaring both sides of the inequality calculate from the roots of a quadratic equation an approximate 95% confidence interval for the value of θ for the type of event observed. *(JMB 1974)*

7 Hypothesis Testing

7.1 Introduction

In Chapter 6 we discussed the estimation of a parameter θ of a population distribution. A closely related problem, which arises in many practical situations, is that of testing the credibility of some hypothesised value θ_0 of θ. Frequently the hope is that the sample will provide sufficient evidence to discredit the value θ_0. For this reason, the hypothesis $\theta = \theta_0$ is generally referred to as the *null hypothesis* and labelled as H_0.

Having chosen H_0 it is then necessary to formulate an appropriate *alternative hypothesis*, H_1, about the value of θ; if the sample data lead to the rejection of H_0 then the conclusion will be that θ has a value consistent with H_1. The form that H_1 takes will depend on the nature of the problem under consideration. In some situations, it may be known or suspected that $\theta \geqslant \theta_0$, in which case the appropriate alternative hypothesis to $H_0: \theta = \theta_0$ is $H_1: \theta > \theta_0$; in other situations, it may be known or suspected that $\theta \leqslant \theta_0$, in which case the alternative hypothesis should be $H_1: \theta < \theta_0$; finally, in a situation where there is no prior information at all about the value of θ relative to θ_0, the appropriate alternative hypothesis will simply be the negation of H_0, namely $H_1: \theta \neq \theta_0$. An alternative hypothesis of the form $\theta > \theta_0$ or $\theta < \theta_0$ is referred to as a *one-sided alternative*, while the alternative hypothesis $\theta \neq \theta_0$ is referred to as a *two-sided alternative* (since it allows for both $\theta > \theta_0$ and $\theta < \theta_0$).

To illustrate how H_1 is chosen consider the type A example in §5.1, in which a new method has been proposed for teaching mathematics in primary schools. Suppose that it is known that the average attainment in a standard test by children taught by the current method is μ_0. Let μ denote the average attainment for children taught by the new method. An appropriate null hypothesis in this case would be H_0: $\mu = \mu_0$, implying that the average attainments are equal for both teaching methods. If little or nothing is known about how the new method will fare, then the appropriate alternative hypothesis will be H_1: $\mu \neq \mu_0$, allowing for the possibilities that the new method may be inferior or superior to the current method (assuming that the quality of a teaching method is adequately measured by average attainment). However, it is very likely that the proposed method has been developed over a period of time by experienced teachers and has been designed so as to improve on the current method. That being the case, a more realistic alternative hypothesis is H_1: $\mu > \mu_0$.

Returning to the more general case of testing $H_0: \theta = \theta_0$, it is clear from the considerations of Chapter 6 that it will not be possible from a sample to decide with certainty whether or not H_0 is true. Whatever decision rule is applied to sample data it may result in rejecting H_0 when in fact H_0 is true. This would be an incorrect conclusion which may have serious consequences for the investigator. It would be advantageous to have some control over such an incorrect conclusion being drawn. This can be achieved by specifying a small value α and to construct a decision rule which will have probability α only that it will lead to the rejection of H_0 when H_0 is true. That is, we require a decision rule to apply to a sample such that

$$\text{P(the rule will reject } H_0 \text{ when } H_0 \text{ is true)} = \alpha. \tag{1}$$

The specified value α is called the *significance level* of the decision rule, and the resulting test procedure is called an *α-level* or *100α%-level significance test* of $H_0\colon \theta = \theta_0$ against H_1. The values of α that are most commonly used are 0·1, 0·05, and 0·01. The more serious the consequences of wrongfully rejecting H_0, the smaller should be the chosen value for α.

7.2 Tests for the mean of a distribution

Suppose that $X \sim N(\mu, \sigma^2)$, where σ^2 is known, and that it is required to test $H_0\colon \mu = \mu_0$. Suppose further that the test is to be applied to a random sample of n observations of X and that it should have probability α of rejecting H_0 when H_0 is true (i.e. α is the significance level of the test).

We shall consider tests of H_0 based on the observed value of the mean $\bar{X}$ of the sample.

Case A: $H_0\colon \mu = \mu_0$ against $H_1\colon \mu > \mu_0$
Since $E[\bar{X}] = \mu$, a sensible decision rule for discriminating between $H_0\colon \mu = \mu_0$ and $H_1\colon \mu > \mu_0$ would be one which rejects H_0 when $\bar{X}$ is much greater than μ_0. This gives a decision rule of the form:

$$\text{Reject } H_0 \text{ if } \bar{X} > c, \tag{1}$$

for an appropriately chosen constant c. Since we require a test having significance level α, c must be chosen so that

$$P(\bar{X} > c \text{ when } H_0 \text{ is true}) = \alpha. \tag{2}$$

From §5.4.1 we know that $\bar{X}$ is normally distributed with mean μ and standard error $SE[\bar{X}] = \sigma/\sqrt{n}$. Hence, when H_0 is true,

$$Z = \frac{\bar{X} - \mu_0}{SE[\bar{X}]} \sim N(0, 1).$$

Using this result, it follows from (2) that c must satisfy the equation

$$P\left(Z > \frac{c - \mu_0}{SE[\bar{X}]}\right) = \alpha,$$

the solution to which is

$$\frac{c-\mu_0}{\mathrm{SE}[\bar{X}]} = z_\alpha,$$

where z_α is such that $P(Z > z_\alpha) = \alpha$. It follows that H_0 should be rejected only if

$$\bar{X} > c = \mu_0 + z_\alpha \,\mathrm{SE}[\bar{X}].$$

Hence, for a test of $H_0: \mu = \mu_0$ against $H_1: \mu > \mu_0$ having significance level α, the decision rule is

$$\text{Reject } H_0 \text{ if } \frac{\bar{x}-\mu_0}{\mathrm{SE}[\bar{X}]} > z_\alpha, \tag{3}$$

where $\bar{x}$ is the observed sample mean. Otherwise, H_0 is not rejected. The derivation of the decision rule (3) ensures that there is a probability of only α that it will falsely reject H_0. An $\bar{x}$ which satisfies (3) is sometimes referred to as being *significantly greater than* μ_0.

If $\bar{x}$ does not satisfy (3) then H_0 is not rejected, but this must not be interpreted as implying that H_0 is true. Such an interpretation is illogical because the same rule would lead to the non-rejection of H_0 for infinitely many choices of μ_0 (e.g. this would be so for any specified value for μ in H_0 which is greater than μ_0, since such a value will result in the left-hand side of (3) being even smaller). When H_0 is not rejected the only valid conclusion is that the sample evidence is not strong enough to reject H_0 at the chosen significance level.

For the case when σ^2 is not known, the derivation of the appropriate decision rule is similar to that above but, as in §6.3.2, Student's T is used instead of Z. This results in the decision rule:

$$\text{Reject } H_0 \text{ if } \frac{\bar{x}-\mu_0}{\mathrm{ESE}[\bar{X}]} > t_\alpha, \tag{4}$$

where t_α is the value of Student's t for $v = n-1$ (See Table 6.2) and

$$\mathrm{ESE}[\bar{X}] = \sqrt{(s^2/n)}, \tag{5}$$

where s^2 is the sample unbiased estimate of σ^2.

Case B: H_0: $\mu = \mu_0$ against H_1: $\mu < \mu_0$

For a test of $H_0: \mu = \mu_0$ against $H_1: \mu < \mu_0$, a sensible decision rule would take the form of rejecting H_0 only if $\bar{X} < c$, for some appropriate constant c. Proceeding as in Case A, the appropriate decision rule having significance level α is

$$\text{Reject } H_0 \text{ if } \frac{\bar{x}-\mu_0}{\mathrm{SE}[\bar{X}]} < -z_\alpha, \tag{6}$$

when σ^2 is known, and

$$\text{Reject } H_0 \text{ if } \frac{\bar{x}-\mu_0}{\text{ESE}[\bar{X}]} < -t_\alpha, \tag{7}$$

when σ^2 is unknown, where SE$[\bar{X}]$, ESE$[\bar{X}]$, z_α and t_α are as defined in Case A above.

Case C: H_0: $\mu = \mu_0$ against H_1: $\mu \neq \mu_0$
When the alternative hypothesis is the two-sided one $H_1: \mu \neq \mu_0$, it is clear from the discussion above that the decision rule should reject H_0 if $\bar{X}$ is small or if $\bar{X}$ is large; that is, the rule should reject H_0 if $\bar{X} < c_1$ or if $\bar{X} > c_2$, for appropriate values of c_1 and c_2. For significance level α, c_1 and c_2 must be chosen so that

$$P(\bar{X} < c_1 \text{ or } \bar{X} > c_2 \text{ when } H_0 \text{ is true}) = \alpha.$$

Since the events $(\bar{X} < c_1)$ and $(\bar{X} > c_2)$ are mutually exclusive, we have

$$P(\bar{X} < c_1 \text{ when } H_0 \text{ is true}) + P(\bar{X} > c_2 \text{ when } H_0 \text{ is true}) = \alpha.$$

This equation has a multitude of solutions (c_1, c_2). For a unique solution, the convention is to equate the two probabilities on the left-hand side of the equation in which case c_1 and c_2 are chosen so that

$$P(\bar{X} < c_1 \text{ when } H_0 \text{ is true}) = P(\bar{X} > c_2 \text{ when } H_0 \text{ is true}) = \tfrac{1}{2}\alpha.$$

From (3) and (6), the required decision rule when σ^2 is known is:

$$\text{Reject } H_0 \text{ if } \frac{\bar{x}-\mu_0}{\text{SE}[\bar{X}]} < -z_{\frac{1}{2}\alpha} \quad \text{or if} \quad \frac{\bar{x}-\mu_0}{\text{SE}[\bar{X}]} > z_{\frac{1}{2}\alpha},$$

or equivalently,

$$\text{Reject } H_0 \text{ if } \frac{|\bar{x}-\mu_0|}{\text{SE}[\bar{X}]} > z_{\frac{1}{2}\alpha}. \tag{8}$$

From §6.3.1, this decision rule will reject H_0: $\mu = \mu_0$ for any μ_0 which is outside the range specified by the 100 $(1-\alpha)$% symmetrical confidence interval for μ. An $\bar{x}$ which satisfies (8) is sometimes referred to as being *significantly different from* μ_0.

From (4) and (7), the decision rule when σ^2 is not known is:

$$\text{Reject } H_0 \text{ if } \frac{|\bar{x}-\mu_0|}{\text{ESE}[\bar{X}]} > t_{\frac{1}{2}\alpha}, \tag{9}$$

which, from §6.3.2, is equivalent to rejecting H_0: $\mu = \mu_0$ for any μ_0 outside the range specified by the 100 $(1-\alpha)$% symmetrical confidence interval for μ.

If either of the tests (8) and (9) leads to the rejection of H_0 and $\bar{x} > \mu_0$, then the sample has provided sufficient evidence (at significance level α) to reject $\mu = \mu_0$ in favour of $\mu > \mu_0$. Similarly, if H_0 is rejected and $\bar{x} < \mu_0$, then the conclusion is that $\mu < \mu_0$.

Finally, provided the sample size n is reasonably large, it follows from the Central Limit Theorem that each of the above test procedures may be applied to testing the mean of a non-normal population distribution, in which case the significance level will be approximately α.

EXAMPLE 1 *String produced by a certain manufacturer is known to be such that one-metre lengths have breaking strengths that are normally distributed with mean 7·2 kg and standard deviation 1·1 kg. Laboratory experiments suggest that a particular type of coating applied to the string will increase the mean breaking strength without affecting the standard deviation. The coating was applied to a random sample of 40 one-metre lengths and it was found that the sample mean breaking strength was 7·4 kg. Use a 5% significance level to test the hypothesis that the coating has not changed the mean breaking strength against the alternative that it has increased the mean breaking strength.*

Let μ kg denote the mean breaking strength of coated one-metre lengths of string. We wish to test, at the 5% significance level, H_0: $\mu = 7{\cdot}2$ against H_1: $\mu > 7{\cdot}2$.

Let $\bar{X}$ kg denote the mean breaking strength of a random sample of 40 coated one-metre lengths. Assuming that the standard deviation is unchanged, $\bar{X}$ will be normally distributed with mean μ kg and standard error

$$\text{SE}\,[\bar{X}] = 1{\cdot}1/\sqrt{40}.$$

Here, $\bar{x} = 7{\cdot}4$ and $\mu_0 = 7{\cdot}2$; hence

$$\frac{\bar{x} - \mu_0}{\text{SE}\,[\bar{X}]} = \frac{7{\cdot}4 - 7{\cdot}2}{1{\cdot}1/\sqrt{40}} \simeq 1{\cdot}150.$$

From Table 6.1 with $\alpha = 0{\cdot}05$ we find

$$z_\alpha = z_{0{\cdot}05} = 1{\cdot}64.$$

Since $1{\cdot}15 < 1{\cdot}64$, it follows from (3) that H_0 should not be rejected, and the conclusion is that there is insufficient evidence to support the claim that the coating will increase the mean breaking strength.

EXAMPLE 2 *Records of the heights of policemen in a certain force in 1975 showed that their average height was 185 cm. The question was posed as to whether the average height of policemen in that force in 1982 was different from that in 1975. To answer this question, the heights of a random sample of 25 policemen in the force in 1982 were measured in centimetres. The results obtained gave unbiased estimates of the population mean and variance equal to 181·6 and 22·64, respectively. Use a 1% significance level to answer the question posed.*

Let μ cm denote the average height of policemen in the force in 1982. We require to test H_0: $\mu = 185$ (no change) against H_1: $\mu \neq 185$. If $\bar{X}$ denotes the mean height of a random sample of 25 policemen, then assuming that the heights are normally distributed, the sampling distribution of $\bar{X}$ will be normal with mean μ and standard error $\text{SE}[\bar{X}] = \sigma/5$, where σ is the population standard deviation. Since σ is not known, the decision rule given by (9) is the appropriate one and H_0 should be rejected if

$$\frac{\bar{x}-\mu_0}{\text{ESE}[\bar{X}]} > t_{\frac{1}{2}\alpha}.$$

Here, $\alpha = 0{\cdot}01$ and $\nu = n-1 = 24$; from Table 6.2 with $\nu = 24$,

$$t_{\frac{1}{2}\alpha} = t_{0\cdot005} = 2{\cdot}80.$$

From the sample data we have $\bar{x} = 181{\cdot}6$, $s^2 = 22{\cdot}64$, so that

$$\text{ESE}[\bar{X}] = \sqrt{(s^2/25)} = \sqrt{(22{\cdot}64/25)} \simeq 0{\cdot}9516.$$

With $\mu_0 = 185$,

$$\frac{|\bar{x}-\mu_0|}{\text{ESE}[\bar{X}]} = \frac{|181{\cdot}6-185|}{0{\cdot}9516} \simeq 3{\cdot}57.$$

Since $3{\cdot}57 > 2{\cdot}80$, the decision rule rejects H_0, and since $\bar{x} < \mu_0$, the conclusion is that the average height of policemen in the force in 1982 is less than that in 1975.

EXERCISE 7.2

1 A random sample of 25 observations is to be taken from a normal distribution whose mean μ is unknown and whose standard deviation is 2, in order to test H_0: $\mu = 10$ against H_1: $\mu > 10$. (i) Find the decision rule to apply if the significance level is to be 0·05. (ii) Find the significance level of the decision rule which rejects H_0 if the sample mean exceeds 11.

2 When a machine is operating correctly it produces steel pins whose lengths are normally distributed with mean 2·5 cm and standard deviation 0·05 cm. Any malfunction of the machine affects only the mean length. Periodic checks are made to ensure the machine is operating correctly. Each such check consists of taking a random sample of 40 pins and calculating the mean length of the pins in the sample. Determine the rule, having a significance level of 0·01, that should be applied at each check for deciding whether or not the machine is operating correctly. What conclusion would you draw from this rule if at a check the sample mean length was (i) 2·49 cm, (ii) 2·54 cm?

3 A driver's records of his car's petrol consumption indicated an average of 11·7 km per litre with a standard deviation of 5 km per litre. The driver responded to an advertisement claiming that a gadget fitted to the car would increase the number of kilometres travelled per litre of petrol. The driver fitted the gadget to his car and after travelling 1000 kilometres he found that the car had used a total of 83 litres of petrol. Assuming that the gadget did not change the standard deviation of the consumption per litre, apply a 5% significance level test to ascertain whether or not the advertiser's claim is justified.

4 A company manufacturing electric light bulbs has a research section for developing modifications to the process aimed at increasing the life times of the bulbs. Since it is virtually impossible to predict whether a modification will be effective, several modifications have been investigated. Some of these did in fact increase the mean life time, while others decreased the mean life time. The bulbs that are currently being produced have lifetimes that are normally distributed with mean 2200 hours and standard deviation 118 hours. Any further modification that might be suggested will be used to produce 100 bulbs. It may be assumed that the lifetimes of bulbs produced are always normally distributed with standard deviation 118 hours. If $\bar{x}$ is the mean life time of the 100 bulbs produced following a particular modification, construct a decision rule based on the value of $\bar{x}$ for testing, at the significance level 0·01, the null hypothesis that the modification has not changed the mean lifetime against the alternative that it has changed it. Apply the decision rule and state your conclusion if (i) $\bar{x} = 2210$, (ii) $\bar{x} = 2231$.

5 The masses in kilogrammes of the contents of a random sample of 8 packets of sugar were: 1·01, 1·02, 0·99, 1·00, 1·01, 0·98, 1·03, 1·01. It is claimed that the average mass of the contents per packet is 1 kg. Assuming that the masses of the contents of packets are normally distributed, use a 5 % significance level to test the hypothesis that the average mass is 1 kg against the alternative that the average is not 1 kg.

6 To compare the manufacturing output of a new machine with that of the machine in current use, each of seven operators worked successive shifts on the new machine and the current machine, respectively. The outputs on the new and current machines by the operators are given in the following table.

Operator	1	2	3	4	5	6	7
New machine	48	53	45	55	46	54	49
Current machine	49	52	46	52	45	51	48

Assuming that the differences in outputs are normally distributed, use a 10 % significance level to test the hypothesis that the mean output is the same for both machines against the alternative that the mean output is greater on the new machine.

7.3 Tests for the difference between the means of two distributions

Let X_1 and X_2 denote two independent random variables having means μ_1 and μ_2, respectively, and suppose that it is required to test the null hypothesis H_0: $\mu_1 - \mu_2 = \delta$ for some specified value δ. Of particular interest is the case $\delta = 0$, corresponding to testing $\mu_1 = \mu_2$. Suppose further that the test is to have significance level α, and is to be applied to the results obtained in a random sample of n_1 observations of X_1 and an independent random sample of n_2 observations of X_2. Denote the sample means by $\bar{X}_1$ and $\bar{X}_2$. Since $E[\bar{X}_1 - \bar{X}_2] = \mu_1 - \mu_2$, an appropriate decision rule is one based on the observed value of $\bar{X}_1 - \bar{X}_2$. For the present, we shall assume that X_1 and X_2 are normally distributed with known variances σ_1^2 and σ_2^2, respectively. Then, as shown in §6.3.3, the sampling distribution of $\bar{X}_1 - \bar{X}_2$ is normal with mean $\mu_1 - \mu_2$ and standard error

$$\mathrm{SE}[\bar{X}_1 - \bar{X}_2] = \left(\frac{\sigma_1^2}{n_1} + \frac{\sigma_2^2}{n_2}\right)^{\frac{1}{2}}. \qquad (1)$$

Hence,

$$Z = \frac{(\bar{X}_1 - \bar{X}_2) - (\mu_1 - \mu_2)}{\mathrm{SE}[\bar{X}_1 - \bar{X}_2]} \sim N(0, 1) \qquad (2)$$

Case A: H_0: $\mu_1 - \mu_2 = \delta$ against H_1: $\mu_1 - \mu_2 > \delta$.
For the one-sided alternative $H_1 : \mu_1 - \mu_2 > \delta$, an appropriate decision rule is one of the form:

$$\text{Reject } H_0 \text{ if } \bar{X}_1 - \bar{X}_2 > c,$$

where c is a constant. For a test at significance level α, c must be chosen so that

$$P(\bar{X}_1 - \bar{X}_2 > c \text{ when } H_0 \text{ is true}) = \alpha. \qquad (3)$$

Using (2) with $\mu_1 - \mu_2 = \delta$ (as specified in H_0), (3) becomes

$$P\left(Z > \frac{c - \delta}{\mathrm{SE}[\bar{X}_1 - \bar{X}_2]}\right) = \alpha,$$

which, on solving, gives

$$c = \delta + z_\alpha \, \mathrm{SE}[\bar{X}_1 - X_2].$$

Thus, if $\bar{x}_1$ and $\bar{x}_2$ are the observed values of $\bar{X}_1$ and $\bar{X}_2$, respectively, the decision rule is:

$$\text{Reject } H_0 \text{ if } \bar{x}_1 - \bar{x}_2 > \delta + z_\alpha \, \mathrm{SE}[\bar{X}_1 - \bar{X}_2],$$

or, equivalently,

$$\text{Reject } H_0 \text{ if } \frac{(\bar{x}_1 - \bar{x}_2) - \delta}{\mathrm{SE}[\bar{X}_1 - \bar{X}_2]} > z_\alpha. \qquad (4)$$

Case B: H_0: $\mu_1 - \mu_2 = \delta$ against H_1: $\mu_1 - \mu_2 < \delta$
In this case, the decision rule should reject H_0 only if $\bar{x}_1 - \bar{x}_2 < c$, for an appropriate c. Proceeding as in Case A, it is left as an exercise to show that the decision rule having significance level α is:

$$\text{Reject } H_0 \text{ if } \frac{(\bar{x}_1 - \bar{x}_2) - \delta}{\mathrm{SE}[\bar{X}_1 - \bar{X}_2]} < -z_\alpha \qquad (5)$$

Case C: H_0: $\mu_1 - \mu_2 = \delta$ against H_1: $\mu_1 - \mu_2 \neq \delta$.
For the two-sided alternative H_1: $\mu_1 - \mu_2 \neq \delta$, the decision rule should reject H_0 if $\bar{X}_1 - \bar{X}_2 < c_1$ or if $\bar{X}_1 - \bar{X}_2 > c_2$. For a test at significance level α, c_1 and c_2 must satisfy the equation

$$P(\bar{X}_1 - \bar{X}_2 < c_1 \text{ when } H_0 \text{ is true}) + P(\bar{X}_1 - \bar{X}_2 > c_2 \text{ when } H_0 \text{ is true}) = \alpha.$$

As in §7.2, it is conventional to choose c_1 and c_2 so that

$$\mathrm{P}(\bar{X}_1 - \bar{X}_2 < c_1 \text{ when } \mathrm{H}_0 \text{ is true}) = \mathrm{P}(\bar{X}_1 - \bar{X}_2 > c_2 \text{ when } \mathrm{H}_0 \text{ is true}) = \tfrac{1}{2}\alpha.$$

Hence, using the results derived above, the required decision rule is:

$$\text{Reject } \mathrm{H}_0 \text{ if } \frac{|(\bar{x}_1 - \bar{x}_2) - \delta|}{\mathrm{SE}[\bar{X}_1 - \bar{X}_2]} > z_{\frac{1}{2}\alpha}, \tag{6}$$

where $\bar{x}_1$ and $\bar{x}_2$ are the observed values of $\bar{X}_1$ and $\bar{X}_2$, respectively.

When X_1 and X_2 are not normally distributed, it follows from the Central Limit Theorem that, provided n_1 and n_2 are large, any one of the above tests may still be applied, its significance level then being approximately α.

Furthermore, when σ_1^2 and σ_2^2 are not known, provided again that n_1 and n_2 are large, each of the above tests may be applied on replacing $\mathrm{SE}[\bar{X}_1 - \bar{X}_2]$ by its estimate

$$\mathrm{ESE}[\bar{X}_1 - \bar{X}_2] = \left(\frac{s_1^2}{n_1} + \frac{s_2^2}{n_2}\right)^{\frac{1}{2}}, \tag{7}$$

where s_1^2 and s_2^2 are the sample unbiased estimates of σ_1^2 and σ_2^2, respectively, and the resulting test will have a significance level approximately equal to α.

EXAMPLE 1 *It was claimed that a certain menial task can be completed more quickly by women than by men. An investigator decided to test this claim by recording the times, in seconds, taken to complete the task by random samples of* 100 *women and* 100 *men. From the recorded times, the unbiased estimates of the mean and the variance of women's times were* 49·8 *and* 18·68, *while the corresponding estimates for men's times were* 51·3 *and* 14·59. *Test, at the* 5% *significance level, whether the sample results support the claim.*

Denoting the population mean times for women and men by μ_1 and μ_2, respectively, we require a 5% significance level test of H_0: $\mu_1 = \mu_2$ against H_1: $\mu_1 < \mu_2$. Since the sample sizes (100) are large, we shall assume that the sample means $\bar{X}_1$, $\bar{X}_2$, and therefore $\bar{X}_1 - \bar{X}_2$, are normally distributed. Since the population variances are unknown, we use the sample estimates and from (7) the estimated standard error of $\bar{X}_1 - \bar{X}_2$ is

$$\mathrm{ESE}[\bar{X}_1 - \bar{X}_2] = \left(\frac{18{\cdot}68}{100} + \frac{14{\cdot}59}{100}\right)^{\frac{1}{2}} \simeq 0{\cdot}5768.$$

From (5) with $\delta = 0$, the required decision rule with approximate significance level 0·05 is:

$$\text{Reject } \mathrm{H}_0 \text{ if } \frac{(\bar{x}_1 - \bar{x}_2)}{0{\cdot}5768} < -z_{0\cdot 05} = -1{\cdot}64,$$

on referring to Table 6.1. With $\bar{x}_1 = 49{\cdot}8$ and $\bar{x}_2 = 51{\cdot}3$,

$$\frac{\bar{x}_1 - \bar{x}_2}{0{\cdot}5768} = \frac{49{\cdot}8 - 51{\cdot}3}{0{\cdot}5768} \simeq -2{\cdot}60,$$

which is less than $-z_{0\cdot05} = -1{\cdot}64$. Thus, H_0 is rejected and the conclusion is that the evidence provided by the samples does support the claim that, on average, women do complete the task more quickly than men.

EXAMPLE 2 *A manufacturer of electrical equipment purchases components in bulk. There are two possible suppliers, A and B, of a particular type of component required by the manufacturer. Since components from A are the more expensive to purchase, the manufacturer calculated that he would purchase from A only if the average lifetime of A's components exceeded that of B's components by more than* 200 *hours. The lifetimes, in hours, of a random sample of* 80 *components produced by A gave unbiased estimates of the mean and the variance of the lifetimes equal to* 1258 *and* 8836, *respectively. The lifetimes, in hours, of a random sample of* 60 *components produced by B gave unbiased estimates of the mean and the variance of the lifetimes equal to* 1029 *and* 4624, *respectively. Using a* 1% *significance level, advise the manufacturer as to which supplier he should choose.*

Let μ_A and μ_B denote the mean lifetimes, in hours, of components produced by A and B, respectively. We require a 1% significance level test of H_0: $\mu_A - \mu_B = 200$ against H_1: $\mu_A - \mu_B > 200$. If H_0 is rejected, then the manufacturer should purchase from supplier A. Since

$$n_A = 80, \quad \bar{x}_A = 1258, \quad s_A^2 = 8836,$$

and

$$n_B = 60, \quad \bar{x}_B = 1029, \quad s_B^2 = 4624,$$

it follows from (7) that

$$\text{ESE}[\bar{X}_A - \bar{X}_B] = \left(\frac{8836}{80} + \frac{4624}{60}\right)^{\frac{1}{2}} \simeq 13{\cdot}6937.$$

With $\delta = 200$ and $\alpha = 0{\cdot}01$ in (4), the required decision rule is:

$$\text{Reject } H_0 \text{ if } \quad \frac{(\bar{x}_A - \bar{x}_B) - 200}{13{\cdot}6937} > z_{0\cdot01} = 2{\cdot}33,$$

on referring to Table 6.1. Substituting the values for $\bar{x}_A$ and $\bar{x}_B$,

$$\frac{(\bar{x}_A - \bar{x}_B) - 200}{13{\cdot}6937} \simeq 2{\cdot}12.$$

Since this is less than $z_{0\cdot01} = 2{\cdot}33$, H_0 cannot be rejected at the 1% significance level, and the advice to the manufacturer is to purchase the components from B.

EXERCISE 7.3

1 A test, at significance level 0·05, is required of H_0: $\mu_1 = \mu_2$ against H_1: $\mu_1 \neq \mu_2$, where μ_1, μ_2 are the means of independent normal distributions whose variances are $\sigma_1^2 = 24{\cdot}86$ and $\sigma_2^2 = 12{\cdot}42$. A random sample of 25 observations from the first distribution had mean $\bar{x}_1 = 80{\cdot}9$, while an independent random

sample of 36 observations from the second distribution had mean $\bar{x}_2 = 78{\cdot}4$. Perform the required test and state your conclusion.

2 It has been claimed that the average mark obtained by girls in a statistics examination is higher than that obtained by boys. From random samples of 60 girls and 80 boys who took the examination, the girls' marks (x) and the boys' marks (y) were such that

$$\Sigma x = 3054, \quad \Sigma x^2 = 157572; \quad \Sigma y = 3844, \quad \Sigma y^2 = 189760.$$

Use a 1% significance level to determine whether the claim is justified.

3 To compare the speeds of two different methods, A and B, of performing a specific task, 120 men were chosen to perform the task using method A and 146 using method B. It was found that the sample means and sums of squares of the deviations from the sample means were, respectively,

$$\text{A: } 17{\cdot}1 \text{ min}, 320 \text{ min}^2; \quad \text{B: } 17{\cdot}4 \text{ min}, 178 \text{ min}^2.$$

Calculate the estimated standard error of the difference between the two sample means. Use a 5% significance level to determine if either method may be claimed to be quicker than the other, on average.

4 A union spokesman complained to company A that labourers employed there were paid lower wages on average than those employed by company B. In a randomly chosen sample of 50 labourers employed by A their weekly wages had a mean of £63.20 and a standard deviation of £1.20, while in a random sample of 50 labourers employed by B the mean and standard deviation of their wages were £63.80 and £2.20, respectively. Use a 5% significance level to determine if the union spokesman's claim is justified.

5 A claim was made that the average salary paid to teachers in independent schools exceeded that paid to teachers in state schools by more than £800 per year. The salaries of a random sample of 50 teachers in independent schools gave unbiased estimates of the population mean and variance of the salaries, in thousands of pounds, equal to 9·8 and 1·52, respectively, while the salaries of a random sample of 100 teachers in state schools gave corresponding estimates of 8·7 and 2·68, respectively. Test, using a 10% significance level, the hypothesis that the mean salary paid to teachers in independent schools is £800 more than that paid to teachers in state schools against the alternative that the difference is more than £800.

7.4 Tests for a probability

Let θ denote the unknown probability of a success in each trial of a Bernoulli experiment. Suppose that it is required to test, at significance level α, the null hypothesis H_0: $\theta = \theta_0$ on the basis of the number X of successes that will be obtained in n independent trials of the experiment. We know that $X \sim \text{B}(n, \theta)$. Since $\text{E}[X] = n\theta$, an appropriate decision rule is one based on the observed value of X.

Case A: H_0: $\theta = \theta_0$ against H_1: $\theta > \theta_0$.

For the alternative hypothesis $\text{H}_1 : \theta > \theta_0$, a sensible decision rule is one which will reject H_0 if X is large, say if $X \geqslant k$. For a test at significance level

α, the integer k must be chosen such that

$$\text{P}(X \geqslant k \text{ when } \text{H}_0 \text{ is true}) \equiv \sum_{x=k}^{n} \binom{n}{x} \theta_0^x (1-\theta_0)^{n-x} = \alpha. \qquad (1)$$

Such an equation can only be solved numerically. Furthermore, since X is a discrete random variable, it is most unlikely that an integer k can be found to satisfy (1) exactly. The following example illustrates a procedure that may be adopted in this case.

EXAMPLE 1 *The manufacturer of a new type of seeding compost claims that seeds sown in the new compost will have a higher germination rate than if they were sown in ordinary compost. For a particular variety of seed sown in ordinary compost it is known that the germination rate is 0·7. To test the manufacturer's claim an experiment was conducted in which 20 of the seeds were sown in the new compost and it was found that 18 of them germinated. Assuming a 5% significance level, determine whether the experimental evidence is strong enough to support the claim.*

Let θ denote the germination rate for seeds sown in the new compost; that is, θ is the probability that a seed sown in the new compost will germinate. A 5% significance level test is required for testing H_0: $\theta = 0{\cdot}7$ against H_1: $\theta > 0{\cdot}7$.

Let X denote the number of seeds that will germinate when 20 seeds are sown in the new compost. Then, we know that $X \sim \text{B}(n = 20, \theta)$. Consider the decision rule that rejects H_0 if $X \geqslant k$ for some positive integer k. For a significance level of 5%, k must satisfy the equation

$$\text{P}(X \geqslant k \text{ when } \text{H}_0 \text{ is true}) \equiv \sum_{r=k}^{20} \binom{20}{r} (0{\cdot}7)^r (0{\cdot}3)^{20-r} = 0{\cdot}05. \qquad (2)$$

It is now a question of finding k numerically. Referring to a table of cumulative binomial probabilities or using a calculator to evaluate the individual probabilities and to sum them, we find that

$$\begin{aligned} \text{P}(X \geqslant 20) &= \text{P}(X = 20) = (0{\cdot}7)^{20} \simeq 0{\cdot}0008, \\ \text{P}(X \geqslant 19) &\simeq 0{\cdot}0076, \\ \text{P}(X \geqslant 18) &\simeq 0{\cdot}0355, \\ \text{P}(X \geqslant 17) &\simeq 0{\cdot}1071. \end{aligned}$$

It is clear from these calculations that there is no integer k satisfying (2) exactly. In such circumstances, we aim at operating with a significance level as close as possible to and preferably less than α (less than, in order to have more protection against the wrongful rejection of H_0). Thus, in the present example, we would take our decision rule to be

$$\text{Reject } \text{H}_0 \text{ if } X \geqslant 18,$$

which has a significance level of 0·0355. Since, in our example, the observed value x of X is 18, the decision is to reject H_0 and to support the manufacturer's claim.

An alternative method of proceeding in a problem of the above type which has some advantages is to evaluate

$$p_0 = \text{P}(X \geqslant x \text{ when } \text{H}_0 \text{ is true}), \qquad (3)$$

where x is the observed value of X, and to reject H_0 if $p_0 < \alpha$. This method has the advantage of reducing the amount of computation and, when a table of cumulative binomial probabilities is available, the value of p_0 can be obtained directly from the table. In our example, $p_0 = 0{\cdot}0355$ is less than $\alpha = 0{\cdot}05$ and we are led to the same conclusion as previously.

Case B: H_0: $\theta = \theta_0$ against H_1: $\theta < \theta_0$
For the alternative hypothesis $H_1 : \theta < \theta_0$, the decision rule should take the form of rejecting H_0 if $X \leqslant k$ for an appropriate integer k. Adopting the alternative procedure described above, we need to compute

$$p_0 = P(X \leqslant x \text{ when } H_0 \text{ is true}), \tag{4}$$

where x is the observed value of X and to reject H_0 only if $p_0 < \alpha$, the specified significance level.

Case C: H_0:$\theta = \theta_0$ against H_1:$\theta \neq \theta_0$
For the two-sided alternative hypothesis H_1:$\theta \neq \theta_0$, the decision rule should lead to the rejection of H_0 if X is small or if X is large, and will take the form

$$\text{Reject } H_0 \text{ if } X \leqslant k_1 \text{ or if } X \geqslant k_2,$$

for appropriately chosen integers k_1 and k_2. For a test at significance level α, the values k_1 and k_2 must satisfy the equation

$$P(X \leqslant k_1 \text{ when } H_0 \text{ is true}) + P(X \geqslant k_2 \text{ when } H_0 \text{ is true}) = \alpha.$$

As in Case C of §7.2, we shall equate the two probabilities on the left-hand side of this equation, and choose k_1 and k_2 such that

$$P(X \leqslant k_1 \text{ when } H_0 \text{ is true}) = P(X \geqslant k_2 \text{ when } H_0 \text{ is true}) = \tfrac{1}{2}\alpha.$$

As indicated earlier, it is most unlikely that there exist integers k_1 and k_2 satisfying these equations exactly. Instead of determining appropriate values for k_1 and k_2, we can adopt the procedure described at the end of Example 1 by calculating p_0 as given by (3) or (4) and rejecting H_0 if its value is less than $\frac{1}{2}\alpha$. Now, if H_0 is true, then $E[X] = n\theta_0$; comparing the observed value x of X with $n\theta_0$ enables us to determine which of (3) or (4) is appropriate. Thus, in this case, the procedure is as follows:

(i) If $x < n\theta_0$, calculate

$$p_0 = P(X \leqslant x \text{ when } H_0 \text{ is true}); \tag{5a}$$

if this p_0 is less than $\frac{1}{2}\alpha$, reject $\theta = \theta_0$ in favour of $\theta < \theta_0$.
(ii) If $x > n\theta_0$, calculate

$$p_0 = P(X \geqslant x \text{ when } H_0 \text{ is true}); \tag{5b}$$

if this p_0 is less than $\frac{1}{2}\alpha$, reject $\theta = \theta_0$ in favour of $\theta > \theta_0$.

EXAMPLE 2 *It is suspected that a cheap imported die is biased. In 15 throws of the die a 6 occurred once only. Use a 5% significance level to determine whether this information provides sufficient evidence to uphold the claim.*

Let θ denote the probability of a 6 in each throw of the die. If the die were unbiased, then θ would be 1/6. Since there is no prior information on the direction of any bias that the die may have, we require a test of $H_0:\theta = 1/6$ against $H_1: \theta \neq 1/6$, having a significance level of 5%. Denoting by X the number of 6's that will occur in 15 throws of the die, then if H_0 is true, $E[X] = 15 \times \frac{1}{6} = 2{\cdot}5$. Since the observed value x of X is equal to 1 and is less than 2·5, the evidence points towards θ being less than 1/6. With $x = 1$ in (5*a*) we have

$$\begin{aligned} p_0 &= P(X \leqslant 1 \text{ when } H_0 \text{ is true}) \\ &= P(X = 0 \text{ when } H_0 \text{ is true}) + P(X = 1 \text{ when } H_0 \text{ is true}) \\ &= \left(\frac{5}{6}\right)^{15} + 15\left(\frac{5}{6}\right)^{14}\left(\frac{1}{6}\right) \simeq 0{\cdot}2596. \end{aligned}$$

Since H_1 is two-sided and the significance level is 0·05, the value of p_0 would need to be less than 0·025 for the rejection of H_0. Hence, on the evidence provided, there are insufficient grounds for supporting the suspicion that the die is biased in so far as obtaining a 6 is concerned.

Using a normal approximation

The evaluation of p_0 as defined above can be simplified when the conditions for approximating a binomial distribution by a normal distribution are satisfied. Recall from §3.9.1, that if $X \sim B(n, \theta_0)$, then good approximations to the values of $P(X \leqslant x)$ and $P(X \geqslant x)$ can be obtained using a normal distribution provided n is large and θ_0 is not close to 0 or 1. Introducing the continuity correction (see §3.9) for improved approximations, we have

$$P(X \leqslant x) \equiv P(X < x + 0{\cdot}5) \simeq P(Y < x + 0{\cdot}5), \qquad (6a)$$

$$P(X \geqslant x) \equiv P(X > x - 0{\cdot}5) \simeq P(Y > x - 0{\cdot}5), \qquad (6b)$$

where Y is normally distributed with mean $n\theta_0$ and variance $n\theta_0(1 - \theta_0)$.

EXAMPLE 3 *With reference to Example* 1, *suppose that* 120 *seeds were sown in the new compost and that* 94 *of them germinated. Using a* 5% *significance level test the hypothesis that the germination rate in the new compost is no different from that* (0·7) *in ordinary compost against the alternative that it is greater than* 0·7.

As in Example 1, denoting by θ the germination rate for the new compost, we need a 5% significance level test of $H_0:\theta = 0{\cdot}7$ against $H_1:\theta > 0{\cdot}7$. Let X denote the number of seeds that will germinate when 120 seeds are sown in the new compost. Then, we know that $X \sim B(n = 120, \theta)$. From (3) above with $x = 94$, we need to find

$$p_0 = P(X \geqslant 94 \text{ when } H_0 \text{ is true}).$$

Now, when H_0 is true, $X \sim B(n = 120, \theta = 0{\cdot}7)$ and

$$E[X] = n\theta = 84, \quad V[X] = n\theta(1-\theta) = 84 \times 0{\cdot}3 = 25{\cdot}2.$$

Using (6*b*) we have

$$p_0 \equiv P(X \geqslant 94 \text{ when } H_0 \text{ is true}) \simeq P(Y > 93{\cdot}5),$$

where Y is normally distributed with mean 84 and variance 25·2. Hence,

$$p_0 \equiv P\left(Z > \frac{93{\cdot}5 - 84}{\sqrt{25{\cdot}2}}\right) = 1 - \Phi(1{\cdot}89) \simeq 0{\cdot}029.$$

Since $p_0 < \alpha = 0{\cdot}05$, H_0 is rejected and the conclusion is that the germination rate for the new compost is greater than that for ordinary compost.

EXERCISE 7.4

1 The makers of the washing-up liquid 'Sparkle' claim that 35% of all housewives use their product, whereas this figure is disputed by a competitor as being an overestimate. In a random sample of 12 housewives it was found that 2 of them used 'Sparkle'. Use a 10% significance level to test the claim made by the makers of 'Sparkle' against the claim made by the competitor.

2 A person claims that he has an efficient way of identifying the suit of a playing card by touch alone. To test his claim, he was blindfolded and asked to identify the suits of 10 playing cards. Given that he correctly identified the suits of 5 of the cards, use a 10% significance level to test the hypothesis that he was merely guessing against the alternative hypothesis that his method is more efficient than guessing.

3 A coin is so damaged that it is not possible to judge whether the probability of a head is equal to, less than, or greater than $\frac{1}{2}$. In 10 tosses of the coin a head was obtained 8 times. Test the unbiasedness of the coin, using a 5% significance level.

4 Repeat Exercise 1 above given that in a random sample of 120 housewives 34 of them use 'Sparkle'.

5 Repeat question 3 given that 61 heads were obtained in 100 tosses of the coin.

6 In a random sample of 200 adults residing in a certain region, it was found that 120 of them were in favour of the fluoridation of the domestic water supply. Using a 5% significance level, test the hypothesis that 55% of the adults in the region are in favour of fluoridation against the alternative that the proportion in favour is more than 55%.

7.5 Testing the equality of two probabilities

Consider testing $H_0: \theta_1 = \theta_2$, where θ_1 and θ_2 are the respective probabilities of a success in two independent Bernoulli experiments. Suppose that the test is to be based on the numbers X_1 and X_2 of successes in n_1 and n_2 independent trials of the two experiments and is to have significance level α.

From §6.2.2, $P_1 = X_1/n_1$ and $P_2 = X_2/n_2$ are unbiased estimators of θ_1 and θ_2. Thus, a sensible decision rule for testing $H_0:\theta_1 = \theta_2$ is one based on the magnitude of $P_1 - P_2$. We shall assume that both n_1 and n_2 are large and that when H_0 is true, $\theta_1 = \theta_2 = \theta$, where θ is not close to 0 or 1. Then, as shown in §6.4.4, the sampling distribution of $P_1 - P_2$ when H_0 is true may be approximated by a normal distribution having mean zero and standard error

$$\mathrm{SE}[P_1 - P_2] = \left\{\theta(1-\theta)\left(\frac{1}{n_1}+\frac{1}{n_2}\right)\right\}^{\frac{1}{2}}. \qquad (1)$$

Since (1) involves the unknown quantity θ, we shall introduce a further approximation by replacing (1) by

$$\mathrm{ESE}[P_1 - P_2] = \left\{p(1-p)\left(\frac{1}{n_1}+\frac{1}{n_2}\right)\right\}^{\frac{1}{2}}, \qquad (2)$$

where p is an estimate of θ. Now, if H_0 is true, the two sets of trials may be combined into one set of (n_1+n_2) trials of a Bernoulli experiment in which the probability of a success is θ. Thus, the combined unbiased estimate of θ is

$$p = \frac{x_1 + x_2}{n_1 + n_2}, \qquad (3)$$

where x_1, x_2 are the observed values of X_1, X_2, respectively; we shall use this value of p in (2). It follows that

$$Z \equiv \frac{P_1 - P_2}{\mathrm{ESE}[P_1 - P_2]}$$

is approximately distributed as $N(0, 1)$.

Case A: H_0: $\theta_1 = \theta_2$ against $H_1:\theta_1 > \theta_2$
Since $E[P_1 - P_2] = \theta_1 - \theta_2$, a sensible decision rule for testing H_0: $\theta_1 = \theta_2$ against H_1: $\theta_1 > \theta_2$ is to reject H_0 if $P_1 - P_2 > c$ for some appropriately chosen c. Given that the observed values of P_1 and P_2 are p_1 and p_2, respectively, we should therefore calculate

$$p_0 = \mathrm{P}(P_1 - P_2 > p_1 - p_2 \text{ when } H_0 \text{ is true})$$

and reject H_0 in favour of H_1 if the calculated p_0 is less than α, the specified significance level. Using the above normal approximation, we have

$$p_0 \simeq \mathrm{P}\left(Z > \frac{p_1 - p_2}{\mathrm{ESE}[P_1 - P_2]}\right) = 1 - \Phi\left(\frac{p_1 - p_2}{\mathrm{ESE}[P_1 - P_2]}\right). \qquad (4)$$

Case B: H_0: $\theta_1 = \theta_2$ against H_1: $\theta_1 < \theta_2$
Arguing as in Case A, when the alternative hypothesis is H_1: $\theta_1 < \theta_2$, we

should calculate

$$p_0 = \mathrm{P}(P_1 - P_2 < p_1 - p_2 \text{ when } \mathrm{H}_0 \text{ is true})$$
$$\simeq \Phi\left(\frac{p_1 - p_2}{\mathrm{ESE}[P_1 - P_2]}\right), \tag{5}$$

and reject H_0 in favour of H_1 if the calculated p_0 is less than α.

Case C: H_0: $\theta_1 = \theta_2$ against H_1: $\theta_1 \neq \theta_2$
For the two-sided alternative hypothesis $\mathrm{H}_1 : \theta_1 \neq \theta_2$, a sensible decision rule is one that rejects H_0 if $|P_1 - P_2|$ is large (i.e. if P_1 is much greater or much smaller than P_2). Thus, the procedure is as follows:

(i) if $p_1 > p_2$, calculate p_0 as given by (4) above, or
(ii) if $p_1 < p_2$, calculate p_0 as given by (5) above,

and reject H_0 if the calculated p_0 is less than $\frac{1}{2}\alpha$, where α is the specified significance level.

EXAMPLE 1 *An intensive advertising campaign against drinking and driving was held over a period of several weeks prior to Christmas* 1982. *The police in a particular region breathalysed* 540 *drivers during a period of* 10 *days spanning Christmas day and* 122 *of these gave positive responses (i.e. exceeded the permitted alcohol limit). During the same period in* 1981, *the same police force had breathalysed* 430 *drivers and* 121 *of these had given positive responses. Using a* 5% *significance level, test whether the campaign in* 1982 *had been effective in reducing the proportion of drivers who drank in excess of the permitted limit.*

Let θ_1 and θ_2 denote the proportions of drivers exceeding the alcohol limit during the stipulated periods in 1981 and 1982, respectively. A decision rule with a significance level of 5% is required to test $\mathrm{H}_0 : \theta_1 = \theta_2$ against $\mathrm{H}_1 : \theta_1 > \theta_2$. From the 1981 data we have

$$n_1 = 430, \quad x_1 = 121, \quad p_1 = 121/430 \simeq 0{\cdot}2814,$$

and from the 1982 data we have

$$n_2 = 540, \quad x_2 = 122, \quad p_2 = 122/540 \simeq 0{\cdot}2259.$$

Assuming that $\theta_1 = \theta_2 = \theta$, the combined estimate of θ is

$$p = (x_1 + x_2)/(n_1 + n_2) = 243/970 \simeq 0{\cdot}2505.$$

Hence, using (2), the estimated standard error of $P_1 - P_2$ when H_0 is true is

$$\mathrm{ESE}[P_1 - P_2] = \left\{(0{\cdot}2505)(0{\cdot}7495)\left(\frac{1}{430} + \frac{1}{540}\right)\right\}^{\frac{1}{2}}$$
$$\simeq 0{\cdot}0280.$$

From (4),

$$p_0 = \mathrm{P}(P_1 - P_2 > p_1 - p_2 \text{ when } \mathrm{H}_0 \text{ is true})$$
$$\simeq 1 - \Phi\left(\frac{0{\cdot}2814 - 0{\cdot}2259}{0{\cdot}0280}\right) \simeq 1 - \Phi(1{\cdot}98) \simeq 0{\cdot}024.$$

Since $p_0 < \alpha = 0{\cdot}05$, we reject H_0 and conclude that the advertising campaign in 1982 had been effective.

EXAMPLE 2 *Laboratory experiments were conducted on animals to compare the efficacies of two drugs, A and B, in curing a particular type of ailment. Drug A was applied to 80 animals and drug B to 100 animals suffering from the ailment. It was found that 69 of the animals treated with A and 82 of those treated with B were cured. Use a 5% significance level to determine which drug (if any) has the higher cure rate*

Let θ_A and θ_B denote the cure rates of A and B, respectively. We require a 5% significance level test of $H_0: \theta_A = \theta_B$ against $H_1: \theta_A \neq \theta_B$. From the given sample information

$$n_A = 80, \quad x_A = 69, \quad p_A = x_A/n_A = 0{\cdot}8625;$$
$$n_B = 100, \quad x_B = 82, \quad p_B = x_B/n_B = 0{\cdot}82.$$

Assuming that H_0 is true with $\theta_A = \theta_B = \theta$, the combined estimate of θ is

$$p = (x_A + x_B)/(n_A + n_B) = 151/180 \simeq 0{\cdot}8389.$$

Hence, from (2), the estimated standard error of $P_A - P_B$ is

$$\text{ESE}[P_A - P_B] = \left\{(0{\cdot}8389)(0{\cdot}1611)\left(\frac{1}{80} + \frac{1}{100}\right)\right\}^{\frac{1}{2}}$$
$$\simeq 0{\cdot}0551.$$

Since $p_A > p_B$, we calculate

$$p_0 = \text{P}(P_A - P_B > p_A - p_B \text{ when } H_0 \text{ is true}),$$

which on using (4) becomes

$$p_0 \simeq 1 - \Phi\left(\frac{0{\cdot}8625 - 0{\cdot}82}{0{\cdot}0551}\right) \simeq 1 - \Phi(0{\cdot}77) \simeq 0{\cdot}221.$$

Since H_1 is two-sided and the significance level is 0·05, p_0 would need to be less than 0·025 for H_0 to be rejected. This not being the case, the conclusion is that the experimental evidence available is not sufficient to discriminate between the two drugs.

EXERCISE 7.5

1 A proposal has been made that mixed bathing in a city's swimming pool should be discontinued, and an opinion was expressed that the proposal would be opposed by a higher proportion of the men than of the women. A sample survey was conducted and it was found that 59 of the 80 men in the sample and 39 of the 60 women in the sample opposed the proposal. Use a 1% significance level to test the hypothesis that the proportions of men and women that oppose the proposal are equal against the alternative hypothesis that a higher proportion of men than of women oppose the proposal.

2 A market researcher for a company specialising in dietary products was asked to determine whether there was any difference between the proportions of men and of women in a particular age-group who dieted. The researcher took

samples of 200 men and 250 women in the stated age-group and found that 36 of the men and 65 of the women dieted. Using a 5% significance level, determine whether or not the sample results provide sufficient evidence to conclude that there is a difference between the two proportions; if so, state which is the higher proportion.

In a random sample of 1200 houses in city A it was found that 384 were owner-occupied, while in a random sample of 1500 houses in city B there were 438 that were owner-occupied. Using a 10% significance level test the hypothesis that the proportions of owner-occupied houses in the two cities are equal.

Market research in a certain region showed that of 1000 men questioned, 400 possessed an electric shaver. The region was then subjected to an advertising campaign on television on the merits of an electric shaver, and in a subsequent survey of 1000 men it was found that 452 possessed an electric shaver. Using a 1% significance level, determine whether the results of the two surveys provide sufficient evidence to conclude that the advertising campaign had succeeded in increasing the proportion of men possessing an electric shaver.

7.6 Tests for the mean of a Poisson distribution

Suppose that a random sample of n observations taken from a Poisson distribution having unknown mean λ is to be used to test the hypothesis $\mathrm{H}_0: \lambda = \lambda_0$. Denoting the observations by $X_1, X_2, \ldots, X_n$, it follows from §4.7 that

$$Y \equiv \sum_{i=1}^{n} X_i \sim \mathrm{Po}(n\lambda). \qquad (1)$$

Since $\mathrm{E}[Y] = n\lambda$, an appropriate decision rule for testing $\mathrm{H}_0: \lambda = \lambda_0$ is one based on the observed value of Y/n, or equivalently (since n is known), on the observed value of Y.

Case A: H_0: $\lambda = \lambda_0$ against H_1: $\lambda > \lambda_0$

When the alternative hypothesis is H_1: $\lambda > \lambda_0$, the decision rule should reject H_0 if the observed value of Y is large compared with the value of $n\lambda_0$. This suggests a decision rule of the form:

$$\text{Reject } \mathrm{H}_0 \text{ if } Y \geqslant k,$$

for some appropriately chosen integer k. For a test at significance level α, k must be chosen so that

$$\mathrm{P}(Y \geqslant k \text{ when } \mathrm{H}_0 \text{ is true}) = \alpha. \qquad (2)$$

As was the case in §7.4 for the binomial distribution, it is most unlikely that an integer k can be found satisfying (2) exactly. Proceeding as in §7.4, instead of attempting to find k, we shall calculate

$$p_0 = \mathrm{P}(Y \geqslant y \text{ when } \mathrm{H}_0 \text{ is true}),$$

where y is the observed value of Y, and H_0 will be rejected at significance level α only if $p_0 < \alpha$. Having access to a table of cumulative Poisson probabilities is the easiest way for determining the value of p_0. Without such a table, individual Poisson probabilities have to be computed and summed.

EXAMPLE 1 *The number of parking tickets issued by the traffic wardens in a certain town has averaged 1·4 per weekday. During the five weekdays following the employment of an additional traffic warden, a total of 12 parking tickets were issued. Assuming that the number of parking tickets issued per weekday has a Poisson distribution, use a 5% significance level to test whether the additional warden has led to an increase in the average number of parking tickets issued per weekday.*

Let λ denote the new average number of parking tickets issued per weekday. We require a test, at significance level 0·05, of $H_0: \lambda = 1{\cdot}4$ against $H_1: \lambda > 1{\cdot}4$.

Let $Y = X_1 + X_2 + X_3 + X_4 + X_5$, where X_i is the number of parking tickets issued on the ith weekday following the employment of the additional traffic warden. Assuming that the X_i are independent and that each has the distribution $\text{Po}(\lambda)$, it follows that $Y \sim \text{Po}(5\lambda)$. The observed value of Y is $y = 12$, and from (3) we therefore need to calculate

$$p_0 = \text{P}(Y \geqslant 12 \text{ when } H_0 \text{ is true}).$$

Now, when H_0 is true, $Y \sim \text{Po}(7)$, and therefore,

$$p_0 = \sum_{r=12}^{\infty} \text{P}(Y = r) = 1 - \sum_{r=0}^{11} \text{P}(Y = r)$$

where

$$\text{P}(Y = r) = \text{e}^{-7}\, 7^r/r!.$$

Referring to a table of cumulative Poisson probabilities or by calculating and summing the individual probabilities we find that $p_0 = 0{\cdot}053$. Since $p_0 > 0{\cdot}05$, the evidence is insufficient (at the 5% significance level) to reject H_0 in favour of H_1. However, the calculated p_0 is close to 0·05, which suggests that it may be advisable to repeat the analysis after more observations become available (this is done in Example 3).

Case B: $H_0: \lambda = \lambda_0$ against $H_1: \lambda < \lambda_0$
For the alternative $H_1: \lambda < \lambda_0$, it is left as an exercise to show that we should now calculate

$$p_0 = \text{P}(Y \leqslant y \text{ when } H_0 \text{ is true}) = \sum_{r=0}^{y} \text{e}^{-\lambda_0} \lambda_0^r/r!, \tag{4}$$

where y is the observed value of Y, and to reject H_0 only if $p_0 < \alpha$.

Case C: $H_0: \lambda = \lambda_0$ against $H_1: \lambda \neq \lambda_0$
For the two-sided alternative $H_1: \lambda \neq \lambda_0$, the decision rule should reject H_0 if Y is small or if Y is large as compared with the value of $n\lambda_0$. Denoting the observed value of Y by y, it follows from the results given in Case A and

Case B above that we should proceed as follows:

(i) If $y < n\lambda_0$, calculate $p_0 = \mathrm{P}(Y \leqslant y \text{ when } \mathrm{H}_0 \text{ is true})$, or (5*a*)
(ii) If $y > n\lambda_0$, calculate $p_0 = \mathrm{P}(Y \geqslant y \text{ when } \mathrm{H}_0 \text{ is true})$, (5*b*)

and reject H_0 only if the calculated p_0 is less than $\frac{1}{2}\alpha$, where α is the specified significance level.

EXAMPLE 2 *Over a long period of time the number of occasions that a piece of equipment has had to be repaired by a technician has averaged* 1·8 *times per week. A new technician was employed to be solely responsible for the maintenance of this equipment and, during his first four weeks, he was required to repair the equipment a total of four times. Use a* 5% *significance level to test the hypothesis that the average number of repairs per week has not changed. Assume that the number of times per week that the new technician is required to repair the equipment has a Poisson distribution.*

Denoting the average number of repairs per week by the new technician by λ, we need a 5% significance level test of $\mathrm{H}_0\colon \lambda = 1{\cdot}8$ against $\mathrm{H}_1\colon \lambda \neq 1{\cdot}8$.

Let Y denote the number of times that the new technician will be required to repair the equipment during a period of four weeks. Then, $Y \sim \mathrm{Po}(4\lambda)$ and, if H_0 is true, $\mathrm{E}[Y] = 7{\cdot}2$. Since the observed value $y = 4$ is less than 7·2 we use (5*a*) to compute

$$p_0 = \mathrm{P}(Y \leqslant 4 \text{ when } \mathrm{H}_0 \text{ is true}) = \sum_{r=0}^{4} \mathrm{e}^{-r}4^r/r! \simeq 0{\cdot}16.$$

Since the alternative hypothesis is two-sided and the significance level is 0·05, the calculated value p_0 would need to be less than 0·025 for H_0 to be rejected. As this is not so, the conclusion is that there is insufficient evidence to discriminate between the average numbers of repairs per week by the former and the new technicians.

Use of a normal approximation

The calculation of the expression for p_0 given above can be quite formidable when $n\lambda_0$ is large. From §3.9.2, when $n\lambda_0$ is large, the distribution $\mathrm{Po}(n\lambda_0)$ may be approximated by a normal distribution having mean $n\lambda_0$ and variance $n\lambda_0$. Thus, when H_0 is true,

$$Z \equiv \frac{Y - n\lambda_0}{\sqrt{(n\lambda_0)}},$$

is approximately distributed as $N(0, 1)$. Hence, on using the continuity correction (§3.9), when H_0 is true and $n\lambda_0$ is large,

$$\mathrm{P}(Y \leqslant y) = \mathrm{P}(Y < y + 0{\cdot}5) \simeq \Phi\left\{\frac{y + 0{\cdot}5 - n\lambda_0}{\sqrt{(n\lambda_0)}}\right\},$$

$$\mathrm{P}(Y \geqslant y) = \mathrm{P}(Y > y - 0{\cdot}5) \simeq \Phi\left\{\frac{y - 0{\cdot}5 - n\lambda_0}{\sqrt{(n\lambda_0)}}\right\}.$$

EXAMPLE 3 *In Example 1 above, suppose that during the 30 weekdays following the employment of the additional traffic warden, a total of 57 parking tickets were issued. Use a 5% significance level to test whether the additional traffic warden has led to an increase in the average number of parking tickets issued per weekday.*

As in Example 1, if λ is the new average number of parking tickets issued per weekday, then we require a 5% significance level test of H_0: $\lambda = 1{\cdot}4$ against H_1: $\lambda > 1{\cdot}4$.

Denoting by Y the total number of parking tickets issued over 30 weekdays, the distribution of Y is Po(30λ). In particular, if H_0 is true, $Y \sim$ Po(42). The observed value of Y is now $y = 57$, which is greater than 42, and therefore we compute

$$p_0 = \mathrm{P}(Y \geqslant 57 \text{ when } H_0 \text{ is true}) = \mathrm{P}(Y > 56{\cdot}5 \text{ when } H_0 \text{ is true})$$

$$\simeq 1 - \Phi\left(\frac{56{\cdot}5 - 42}{\sqrt{42}}\right) = 1 - \Phi(2{\cdot}24) \simeq 0{\cdot}013.$$

Since $p_0 < 0{\cdot}05$, we reject H_0 and conclude that the average number of parking tickets issued per weekday has increased.

EXERCISE 7.6

1 An employer is seeking a typist who can be relied upon not to mistype more than 1 character per page on average. An applicant for the position is given four pages to type, and, on inspection, it was found that she had mistyped a total of seven characters. Use a 5% significance level to test the hypothesis that her average number of mistyped characters per page is 1 against the alternative hypothesis that it is greater than 1. Assume that the number of mistyped characters per page has a Poisson distribution.

2 Records of absenteeism from a factory showed that the number of absentees per day had a Poisson distribution with mean 1·2. During one week of five working days, the numbers absent were 2, 1, 3, 0, 2, respectively. Use a 5% significance level to determine whether the evidence of that week suggests that the average number of absentees per day has increased.

3 The nature of a radioactive substance can be identified by the average rate of its emissions. The average rate of emissions from a type-A substance is known to be 2·4 per minute. Given that there were a total of five emissions from an unidentified source over a period of four minutes, use a 10% significance level to determine whether the observed number of emissions is consistent with the substance being of type-A. Assume that the number of emissions per minute has a Poisson distribution.

4 Manufactured cloth is regarded as being acceptable provided the average number of flaws per metre length is less than 0·4. Inspection of 100 metres revealed a total of 24 flaws. Assuming that the number of flaws per metre length has a Poisson distribution, use a 1% significance level to test whether the cloth is acceptable.

5 Carry out the test asked for in Example 2 given that during his first 20 weeks the new technician was required to repair the equipment a total of 23 times.

7.7 Testing the equality of two Poisson means

Suppose that X_1 and X_2 are independent random variables having Poisson distributions with means λ_1 and λ_2, respectively, and that it is required to test H_0: $\lambda_1 = \lambda_2$. Let $\bar{X}_1$ and $\bar{X}_2$ denote the means of independent random samples of sizes n_1 and n_2. Since $E[\bar{X}_1 - \bar{X}_2] = \lambda_1 - \lambda_2$, an appropriate test of H_0 is one based on the magnitude of $\bar{X}_1 - \bar{X}_2$.

Assuming that n_1 and n_2 are large, it follows from §7.3 that when H_0 is true the sampling distribution of $\bar{X}_1 - \bar{X}_2$ is approximately normal with mean zero and standard error

$$\mathrm{SE}[\bar{X}_1 - \bar{X}_2] = \left\{\lambda\left(\frac{1}{n_1} + \frac{1}{n_2}\right)\right\}^{\frac{1}{2}}, \tag{1}$$

where $\lambda = \lambda_1 = \lambda_2$. Now, when H_0 is true, the two samples may be regarded as one sample of size $(n_1 + n_2)$ from a Poisson distribution having mean λ. Hence, if $\bar{x}_1$ and $\bar{x}_2$ are the observed sample means, the combined unbiased estimate of λ is

$$\bar{x} = \frac{n_1\bar{x}_1 + n_2\bar{x}_2}{n_1 + n_2}. \tag{2}$$

Since λ is unknown, an appropriate estimate of $\mathrm{SE}[\bar{X}_1 - \bar{X}_2]$ is

$$\mathrm{ESE}[\bar{X}_1 - \bar{X}_2] = \left\{\bar{x}\left(\frac{1}{n_1} + \frac{1}{n_2}\right)\right\}^{\frac{1}{2}}. \tag{3}$$

We shall approximate the distribution of $\bar{X}_1 - \bar{X}_2$ when H_0 is true by the normal distribution having mean zero and standard deviation equal to $\mathrm{ESE}[\bar{X}_1 - \bar{X}_2]$ as given by (3). That is, when H_0 is true, we shall assume that

$$Z \equiv \frac{\bar{X}_1 - \bar{X}_2}{\mathrm{ESE}[\bar{X}_1 - \bar{X}_2]} \tag{4}$$

is approximately distributed as $N(0, 1)$.

Case A: H_0: $\lambda_1 = \lambda_2$ against H_1: $\lambda_1 > \lambda_2$
In this case we calculate

$$\begin{aligned} p_0 &= P(\bar{X}_1 - \bar{X}_2 > \bar{x}_1 - \bar{x}_2 \text{ when } H_0 \text{ is true}) \\ &\simeq 1 - \Phi\left\{\frac{\bar{x}_1 - \bar{x}_2}{\mathrm{ESE}[\bar{X}_1 - \bar{X}_2]}\right\} \end{aligned} \tag{5}$$

and reject H_0 only if $p_0 < \alpha$, the specified significance level.

Case B: H_0: $\lambda_1 = \lambda_2$ against H_1: $\lambda_1 < \lambda_2$
Here, we calculate

$$p_0 = P(\bar{X}_1 - \bar{X}_2 < \bar{x}_1 - \bar{x}_2 \text{ when } H_0 \text{ is true})$$
$$\simeq \Phi\left\{\frac{\bar{x}_1 - \bar{x}_2}{\text{ESE}[\bar{X}_1 - \bar{X}_2]}\right\} \tag{6}$$

and reject H_0 only if $p_0 < \alpha$.

Case C: H_0: $\lambda_1 = \lambda_2$ against H_1: $\lambda_1 \neq \lambda_2$
Allowing for both the possibilities $\lambda_1 < \lambda_2$ and $\lambda_1 > \lambda_2$, we proceed as follows:

(i) if $\bar{x}_1 - \bar{x}_2 < 0$, calculate p_0 given by (6) above, or
(ii) if $\bar{x}_1 - \bar{x}_2 > 0$, calculate p_0 given by (5) above,

and reject H_0 if the calculated p_0 is less than $\frac{1}{2}\alpha$.

EXAMPLE 1 *The number of errors per page by a typist may be assumed to have a Poisson distribution. In 100 pages typed by each of two typists, A and B, the distributions of the numbers of errors per page were as shown in the following table.*

Numbers of errors per page	0	1	2	3	4	5
Number of pages by A	72	18	6	2	1	1
Number of pages by B	59	26	11	3	1	0

Use a 10% significance level to determine whether these data provide sufficient evidence to conclude that one of the typists has a lower average number of errors per page than the other typist.

Let λ_A and λ_B denote the average numbers of errors per page by A and B, respectively. We require a 10% significance level test of H_0: $\lambda_A = \lambda_B$ against H_1: $\lambda_A \neq \lambda_B$. (Acceptance of H_1 will imply that one typist's average number of errors per page is lower than the other's).

From the given data, the observed average numbers of errors per page are

$$\bar{x}_A = (18+12+6+4+5)/100 = 0{\cdot}45,$$
$$\bar{x}_B = (26+22+9+4)/100 = 0{\cdot}61.$$

If $\lambda_A = \lambda_B = \lambda$, then the combined unbiased estimate of λ is

$$\bar{x} = (45+61)/200 = 0{\cdot}53.$$

Hence, from (3),

$$\text{ESE}[\bar{X}_A - \bar{X}_B] = \left\{0{\cdot}53\left(\frac{1}{100}+\frac{1}{100}\right)\right\}^{\frac{1}{2}} \simeq 0{\cdot}1030.$$

Since $\bar{x}_A < \bar{x}_B$, we calculate

$$p_0 = P(\bar{X}_A - \bar{X}_B < \bar{x}_A - \bar{x}_B \text{ when } H_0 \text{ is true}).$$

When H_0 is true, the distribution of $\bar{X}_A - \bar{X}_B$ may be approximated by a normal distribution having mean zero and standard deviation $\text{ESE}[\bar{X}_A - \bar{X}_B] = 0{\cdot}1030$. Hence,

$$p_0 \simeq \Phi\left(\frac{0{\cdot}45 - 0{\cdot}61}{0{\cdot}1030}\right) \simeq \Phi(-1{\cdot}55) \simeq 0{\cdot}061.$$

Since the alternative hypothesis in this example is two-sided and the significance level is 0·10, the calculated p_0 would need to be less than 0·05 to justify rejecting H_0. Since this is not so, we conclude that there is insufficient evidence to discriminate between the error rates of the two typists.

EXERCISE 7.7

1 In a horticultural experiment, some rose bushes were sprayed with insecticide A and others with insecticide B. Random samples of 50 stems having unopened buds were taken from bushes sprayed with A and from bushes sprayed with B. It was found that there were 95 live aphids on the 50 buds from bushes sprayed with A and 121 live aphids on the 50 buds from bushes sprayed with B. Use a 5% significance level to determine whether there is sufficient evidence provided by this experiment to conclude that one insecticide is more effective than the other in reducing the average number of live aphids per bud. You may assume that for each insecticide the number of live aphids per bud has a Poisson distribution.

2 During a period of 50 weeks prior to the construction of a roundabout at certain crossroads there had been a total of 25 accidents, while during a period of 80 weeks after the roundabout came into operation the total number of accidents was 18. Assuming that the number of accidents per week has a Poisson distribution, use a 1% significance level to determine whether the roundabout has reduced the average number of accidents per week.

7.8 Type-1 and type-2 errors

When any one of the procedures described in the preceding sections for testing H_0: $\theta = \theta_0$ against H_1 (which may be one-sided or two-sided) is applied to a sample (or samples), one of two conclusions may be drawn, namely (a) reject H_0 or (b) there is insufficient evidence to reject H_0 at the specified significance level. The conclusion drawn will be incorrect if either

(i) H_0 is rejected when, in fact, it is true, or
(ii) H_0 is not rejected when, in fact, it is false.

The erroneous conclusion in (i) is referred to as a *type*-1 *error*, while that in (ii) is referred to as a *type*-2 *error*.

For a decision rule designed to have significance level α, the probability that a type-1 error will occur is equal to α. By choosing α to be small, the decision rule has control over the risk probability of a type-1 error being committed.

The decision rules that have been described in this chapter give reasonably good protection against a type-2 error occurring. In particular, for values of θ specified in H_1, each rule has the property that the larger the value of $|\theta - \theta_0|$ the smaller is the probability of a type-2 error. Thus, if the true value of θ is far from θ_0 (in a direction consistent with H_1), then the probability of committing a type-2 error will be small. The following examples illustrate the procedure for calculating type-2 error probabilities.

EXAMPLE 1 In Example 1, §7.2, the breaking strengths of coated lengths of string were assumed to be normally distributed with mean μ kg and standard deviation 1·1 kg. A random sample of 40 lengths of coated string was used to test $H_0{:}\mu = 7{\cdot}2$ against $H_1{:}\mu > 7{\cdot}2$. If $\bar{X}$ is the sample mean breaking strength, then the decision rule with significance level 0·05 is

$$\text{Reject } H_0 \text{ if } \bar{X} > 7{\cdot}2 + 1{\cdot}64\,\text{SE}[\bar{X}]. \tag{1}$$

Since $\text{SE}[\bar{X}] = 1{\cdot}1/\sqrt{40} = 0{\cdot}1739$, the decision rule is to reject H_0 if $\bar{X} > 7{\cdot}485$. The probability that this rule will lead to a type-1 error is equal to 0·05. Let us now calculate type-2 error probabilities of this rule. Let μ_1 denote an arbitrary value of μ which is greater than 7·2 (so that μ_1 is consistent with H_1). Then, the probability that the above decision rule will lead to a type-2 error is

$$\beta = \text{P}(\bar{X} < 7{\cdot}485 \text{ when } \mu = \mu_1) = \Phi\left(\frac{7{\cdot}485 - \mu_1}{1{\cdot}1/\sqrt{40}}\right). \tag{2}$$

Regarded as a function of μ_1, the type-2 error probability β is often referred to as the *operating characteristic function* of the decision rule. Table 7.1 shows the values of β, to two decimal places, for selected values of $\mu_1 > 7{\cdot}2$. It is evident from the tabulated values that β decreases as the value of μ_1 increases; that is, the type-2 error probability decreases as the true value of μ increases from 7·2.

Table 7.1 Values of β given by (2)

$\mu_1 =$	7·3	7·4	7·5	7·6	7·7	7·8	7·9
$\beta\ =$	0·86	0·69	0·47	0·25	0·11	0·24	0·01

Suppose now that the manufacturer states that if the mean strength is 7·7 kg or more, then the coating is really worth adopting, and that a probability of 0·11 of failing to do so when $\mu = 7{\cdot}7$ is much too high, his feeling being that this probability should be about 0·02. This additional constraint can be met if we are given freedom of choice of the sample size. Suppose a random sample of n coated lengths of string is to be taken. Denoting the sample mean breaking strength by $\bar{X}$, our decision rule will take the form of rejecting H_0 if $\bar{X} > c$, and must be such that
(i) its probability of rejecting H_0 when $\mu = 7{\cdot}2$ is equal to 0·05,
(ii) its probability of not rejecting H_0 when $\mu = 7{\cdot}7$ is equal to 0·02.

Since $\bar{X}$ is normally distributed with mean μ and standard error $\text{SE}[\bar{X}] = 1{\cdot}1/\sqrt{n}$, c and n must be chosen so that

$$\text{P}(\bar{X} > c \text{ when } \mu = 7{\cdot}2) \equiv 1 - \Phi\left(\frac{c - 7{\cdot}2}{1{\cdot}1/\sqrt{n}}\right) = 0{\cdot}05, \tag{3}$$

and

$$\mathrm{P}(\bar{X} < c \text{ when } \mu = 7{\cdot}7) \equiv \Phi\left(\frac{c - 7{\cdot}7}{1{\cdot}1/\sqrt{n}}\right) = 0{\cdot}02. \tag{4}$$

Using Table 6.1, it follows that c and n must be chosen so that

$$\frac{c - 7{\cdot}2}{1{\cdot}1/\sqrt{n}} = z_{0{\cdot}05} = 1{\cdot}64, \tag{5}$$

and

$$\frac{c - 7{\cdot}7}{1{\cdot}1/\sqrt{n}} = -z_{0{\cdot}02} = -2{\cdot}05. \tag{6}$$

Eliminating c from these equations we have

$$7{\cdot}2 + 1{\cdot}64(1{\cdot}1/\sqrt{n}) = 7{\cdot}7 - 2{\cdot}05(1{\cdot}1/\sqrt{n}),$$

and therefore

$$n = \left(\frac{3{\cdot}69 \times 1{\cdot}1}{0{\cdot}5}\right)^2 = 65{\cdot}9.$$

Since the sample size must be an integer, we round up to the next integer value and take $n = 66$. Substituting $n = 66$ in (5) and solving for c gives

$$c = 7{\cdot}2 + 1{\cdot}64(1{\cdot}1/\sqrt{66}) \simeq 7{\cdot}42.$$

This choice of c when $n = 66$ ensures that the type-1 error probability is equal to 0·05 as specified, but the type-2 error probability may be slightly less than the specified value of 0·02. Evaluating (6) for the above values of n and c, the probability of a type-2 error when $\mu = 7{\cdot}7$ is

$$\Phi\left(\frac{7{\cdot}42 - 7{\cdot}7}{1{\cdot}1/\sqrt{66}}\right) \simeq \Phi(-2{\cdot}07) \simeq 0{\cdot}019.$$

EXAMPLE 2 *Two methods have been proposed for testing whether a coin is unbiased. The first method consists of tossing the coin four times and concluding it is biased if all four tosses fall alike. The second method consists of tossing the coin seven times and concluding that it is biased if six or more of the tosses fall alike. Determine which, if any, of the two methods has the smaller probability of committing (i) a type-1 error, (ii) a type-2 error when the probability of a head is actually* $\frac{2}{3}$.

If θ is the probability of a head when the coin is tossed, each method is testing $\mathrm{H}_0{:}\theta = \frac{1}{2}$ against $\mathrm{H}_1{:}\theta \neq \frac{1}{2}$.

First method Let X denote the number of heads that will be obtained in four tosses of the coin. The stated decision rule is to reject H_0 if $X = 0$ or if $X = 4$. Since $X \sim \mathrm{B}(n = 4, \theta)$, the probability of a type-1 error is

$$\begin{aligned}\alpha_1 &= \mathrm{P}(X = 0 \text{ or } X = 1 \text{ when } \mathrm{H}_0 \text{ is true}) \\ &= \mathrm{P}(X = 0 \text{ when } \theta = \tfrac{1}{2}) + \mathrm{P}(X = 4 \text{ when } \theta = \tfrac{1}{2}) \\ &= 1/16 + 1/16 = 1/8\end{aligned}$$

Since H_0 is not rejected if $X = 1, 2$ or 3, the probability of a type-2 error when $\theta = \frac{2}{3}$ is

$$\beta_1 = P(X = 1 \text{ or } X = 2 \text{ or } = 3 \text{ when } \theta = \tfrac{2}{3})$$
$$= \binom{4}{1}\left(\frac{2}{3}\right)\left(\frac{1}{3}\right)^3 + \binom{4}{2}\left(\frac{2}{3}\right)^2\left(\frac{1}{3}\right)^2 + \binom{4}{3}\left(\frac{2}{3}\right)^3\left(\frac{1}{3}\right)$$
$$= 64/81 \simeq 0{\cdot}7901.$$

Second method Let Y denote the number of heads that will be obtained in seven tosses of the coin. The stated decision rule is to reject H_0 if $Y \geqslant 6$ or if $Y \leqslant 1$. Since $Y \sim B(n = 7, \theta)$, the probability of a type-1 error is

$$\alpha_2 = P(Y \geqslant 6 \text{ when } \theta = \tfrac{1}{2}) + P(Y \leqslant 1 \text{ when } \theta = \tfrac{1}{2})$$
$$= \left\{\binom{7}{6}\left(\frac{1}{2}\right)^7 + \left(\frac{1}{2}\right)^7\right\} + \left\{\left(\frac{1}{2}\right)^7 + \binom{7}{1}\left(\frac{1}{2}\right)^7\right\} = 16/2^7 = 1/8,$$

and the probability of a type-2 error when $\theta = \frac{2}{3}$ is

$$\beta_2 = P(2 \leqslant Y \leqslant 5 \text{ when } \theta = \tfrac{2}{3})$$
$$= \binom{7}{2}\left(\frac{2}{3}\right)^2\left(\frac{1}{3}\right)^5 + \binom{7}{3}\left(\frac{2}{3}\right)^3\left(\frac{1}{3}\right)^4 + \binom{7}{4}\left(\frac{2}{3}\right)^4\left(\frac{1}{3}\right)^3 + \binom{7}{5}\left(\frac{2}{3}\right)^5\left(\frac{1}{3}\right)^2$$
$$= 1596/3^7 \simeq 0{\cdot}7298.$$

Since $\alpha_1 = \alpha_2 = 1/8$, the two decision rules have the same probability of committing a type-1 error, and since $\beta_2 < \beta_1$, the second method has the smaller probability of committing a type-2 error when $\theta = \frac{2}{3}$.

EXERCISE 7.8

1 The percentage yield in a chemical process may be assumed to be normally distributed with mean 62 and standard deviation 3·3. Any modification to the process which will increase the mean percentage yield to 65 or more is considered worthwhile adopting. It may be assumed that the only possible effect of a modification is to change the mean percentage yield. To determine whether or not a modification is worthwhile adopting it was decided to carry out 9 test runs using the modification and to adopt it if the mean percentage yield in the 9 runs exceeds 65. Show that this decision rule has probability 0·5 of leading to the adoption of a modification for which the mean yield is 65.

Determine the number of test runs that should be made using a modification and the associated decision rule if it is required that (i) there is a probability of only 0·025 of adopting a modification for which the mean yield is 62, (ii) there is a probability of only 0·05 of not adopting a modification for which the mean yield is 65.

2 To test the hypothesis $H_0: \lambda = 0{\cdot}2$ against the alternative $H_1: \lambda > 0{\cdot}2$, where λ is the mean of a Poisson distribution, it is decided to take a random sample of 10 observations from the distribution and to reject H_0 if the sample mean is 0.4 or greater. (i) Find the significance level of this test. (ii) Find the probability that this test will lead to a type-2 error being made when $\lambda = 0{\cdot}4$.

3 To test the unbiasedness of a coin it is decided to toss the coin 100 times and to

conclude that it is unbiased if the number of heads obtained is between 40 and 60, inclusive. Use a normal approximation to find the probabilities of concluding that (i) the coin is biased when, in fact, it is unbiased, (ii) the coin is unbiased when, in fact, the probability of a head is 0·7.

4 Let $\bar{X}_1$ denote the mean of a random sample of 25 observations from a normal distribution having mean μ_1 and unit standard deviation, and let $\bar{X}_2$ denote the mean of an independent random sample of 100 observations from a normal distribution having mean μ_2 and unit standard deviation. Write down the symmetrical 95% confidence intervals for μ_1 and μ_2 in terms of $\bar{X}_1$ and $\bar{X}_2$, respectively.

It is proposed to reject the hypothesis $H_0 : \mu_1 = \mu_2$ if the two confidence intervals do not overlap. Show that this is equivalent to rejecting H_0 if $|\bar{X}_1 - \bar{X}_2| > a$, where a is a constant to be determined. Find the significance level of this test and the probability that it will lead to a type-2 error when $\mu_1 - \mu_2 = 0{\cdot}05$.

REVIEW PROBLEMS ON CHAPTER 7

1 Explain, referring to your projects if you wish, the role of a null hypothesis in significance testing.

The national average sick leave for schoolteachers during the last 12 months was 8·4 days with a standard deviation of 2·1 days. A local authority finds that in a random sample of 100 teachers the average sick leave during the last 12 months was 8·9 days. Test whether this is significantly greater than the national average, stating clearly your null hypothesis and your significance level. (You may assume that the duration of sick leave is normally distributed). *(L 1982)*

2 When testing a hypothesis, explain the conditions under which you would use (a) a one-tailed test and (b) a two-tailed test.

The breaking strengths of a particular brand of thread are known to have a normal distribution with mean μ and standard deviation 1·4 units. A random sample of 36 newly produced pieces of thread are found to have a mean breaking strength of 9·3 units. Test, at the 5% significance level, the null hypothesis that $\mu = 9{\cdot}7$ units against the alternative hypothesis that $\mu < 9{\cdot}7$ units.

We are given that x is a typical breaking strength for the above random sample and that $\Sigma x^2 = 3240$. Assuming that neither the mean nor the standard deviation of the population of breaking strengths had in fact been known, find estimates of the population mean and variance. *(L 1981)*

3 After taking the random sample given in the table below, a seed grower wishes to know whether his *improved seed* has a larger grain than his *standard seed*, which has a mean grain length of 7·5 mm. Carry out a test of hypothesis to determine what advice you could offer the seed grower and list any questions you might wish to ask concerning the way in which the sample was obtained.

Grain length mm	5	6	7	8	9	10	11
Number of seeds	9	12	28	30	20	10	6

(L 1978)

4 A manufacturer of matches claims that there are, on average, 50 matches in each of the boxes that he makes. A customer buys eight of these boxes and counts the number, x, of matches in each box. He finds that $\Sigma x = 384$ and $\Sigma x^2 = 18{,}460$. Assuming that these boxes are a random sample from the manufacturer's production, carry out a t-test, at the 2·5% level, to determine whether the mean is significantly less than 50. State any assumptions that you need to make. (*C 1982*)

5 (i) A certain type of battery for calculators is said to last for 2000 hours. A sample of 200 of these batteries was tested; the mean life was 1995 hours and the standard deviation of the lives was 25·5 hours. Use these data to test the hypothesis that the mean life is 2000 hours against the alternative hypothesis that it is less than 2000 hours. State what level of significance you are using in your test.

(ii) Two types of battery were compared for the length of time they lasted. The data obtained are summarised in the table.

Battery type	No. tested	Sample mean	Sample SD
A	200	1995	25.5
B	150	2005	32.8

Test the hypothesis that the populations from which the samples were drawn have equal means against the alternative hypothesis of unequal means. State the level of significance you are using in your test. (*C 1982*)

6 Explain what is meant by the sampling distribution of a sample mean.

Let $\bar{X}$ denote the mean of a random sample of m observations from a distribution having mean μ_1 and variance σ_1^2, and let $\bar{Y}$ denote the mean of an independent random sample of n observations from a distribution having mean μ_2 and variance σ_2^2. Given that both m and n are large, state the approximate distribution of $\bar{X} - \bar{Y}$. Explain how σ_1^2 and σ_2^2 may be estimated from the samples when their actual values are not known.

The sum of the lengths of 100 articles manufactured in one section of a factory is 305 cm and the sum of their squares is 1225 cm^2. The sum of the lengths and the sum of squares of the lengths of 50 such articles manufactured in a different section are 180 cm and 746 cm^2. Derive an approximate 95% symmetrical confidence interval for the difference between the two distribution means.

Test, at the 5% significance level, the hypotheses that

(i) the mean length of articles manufactured in the first section of the factory is 3 cm;

(ii) the difference between the means of the lengths of articles manufactured in the two sections of the factory is zero. (*JMB 1982*)

7 Random samples of size n_1 and n_2 are taken, one from each of two normal distributions with means μ_1, μ_2 and variances σ_1^2, σ_2^2, respectively. The sample means are $\bar{x}_1$ and $\bar{x}_2$, respectively. Write down expressions for the mean and variance of $\bar{x}_1 - \bar{x}_2$.

Given that $\sigma_1^2 = 0{\cdot}04$, $\sigma_2^2 = 0{\cdot}05$ and $n_1 = n_2 = 100$, write down a symmetrical 99% confidence interval for $\mu_1 - \mu_2$ in terms of $\bar{x}_1 - \bar{x}_2$.

If, in fact, $\mu_1 = 3{\cdot}06$ and $\mu_2 = 3{\cdot}00$, determine the probability that the hypothesis $\mu_1 = \mu_2$ would not be rejected using a two-tailed test with significance level 1%. State how this probability would be affected if the population means were $\mu_1 = 3{\cdot}00$, $\mu_2 = 3{\cdot}06$. Determine whether or not the hypothesis $\mu_1 = \mu_2$ should be rejected at the 1% level of significance in each of the cases when (i) $\bar{x}_1 = 3{\cdot}07$, $\bar{x}_2 = 2{\cdot}99$; (ii) $\bar{x}_1 = 3{\cdot}07$, $\bar{x}_2 = 3{\cdot}12$. (*JMB 1980*)

8 In n independent trials with constant probability p of success in each trial, show that the ratio of the probability of $r+1$ successes to the probability of r successes is $[(n-r)p]/[(r+1)(1-p)]$ for $0 \leqslant r \leqslant n-1$.

A cubical die is thrown 10 times and it is found that it falls with a 6 uppermost on five occasions. Calculate, to four decimal places, the probabilities of a 6 occurring 0, 1, 2, 3, and 4 times in 10 throws of an unbiased die. Hence determine whether or not the occurrence of five 6's in ten throws is significant at the 5% level.

To test the die further, it is thrown 720 times. Using a normal approximation, determine the number of 6's which would be regarded as significantly high at the 5% level. (*JMB 1980*)

9 A seed manufacturer claims that a certain variety of seed has a 90% germination rate. When a random sample of 8 of these seeds were planted under the conditions specified by the manufacturer only 6 of them germinated. Use this evidence and a 10% significance level to test the manufacturer's claim against the alternative possibility that the germination rate is less than 90%. (*JMB 1982*)

10 The probability that an oyster larva will develop in unpolluted water is 0·9, while in polluted water this probability is less than 0·9. Given that 20 oyster larvae are placed in unpolluted water, find the probabilities, each to two decimal places, that the number that will develop is (i) at least 17, (ii) exactly 17.

An oyster breeder put 20 larvae in a sample of water and observed that only 16 of them developed. Use a 10% significance level to determine whether the breeder would be justified in concluding that the water is polluted. (*JMB 1981*)

11 Let p denote the probability of obtaining a head when a certain coin is tossed. (i) If $p = 0{\cdot}4$, find the probability of obtaining at least 3 heads in 10 tosses. (ii) If $p = 0{\cdot}6$, find the probability of obtaining exactly 12 heads in 20 tosses. (iii) Write down an appropriate null hypothesis and an appropriate alternative hypothesis for testing whether the coin is unbiased. To carry out this test 20 tosses of the coin are made and the number of heads that occurs is observed. Given that 15 heads occurred, carry out the test, assuming a 5% significance level. Write down a statement of the conclusion you draw about the value of p for this coin. (*JMB 1979*)

12 Mr Smith claims that the probability, p, that any egg incubated by his hens will hatch is 0·7. A friend believes that p is less than 0·7, and ten eggs are used to test Mr Smith's claim. Only three of the ten eggs hatch. Test whether this provides sufficient evidence that $p < 0{\cdot}7$.

If 100 eggs are incubated, use the normal approximation to find the largest number r such that, if r or fewer hatch, the rejection of Mr Smith's claim in favour of his friends's claim is justifiable at the 5% significance level. (*JMB 1982*)

13 Two medical investigators independently conducted experiments to determine whether a new drug would give longer relief from pain than the standard drug. The first investigator administered the two drugs at different times to each of 100 patients and found that the new drug gave longer relief from pain for 58 of the patients. Let p denote the probability that a patient will get longer relief from pain with the new drug than with the standard drug. Use a 5% significance level and an appropriate normal approximation to test the hypothesis that $p = 0{\cdot}5$ against the alternative hypothesis that $p > 0{\cdot}5$. State, in words, the conclusion you draw about the relative effectiveness of the new drug as compared with the standard drug.

The second investigator also administered the two drugs at different times to each of 100 patients. For each patient this investigator recorded the value of $w = x - y$, where x hours was the duration of relief from pain with the new drug and y hours that with the standard drug. From the 100 values obtained, the investigator calculated $\Sigma w = 180$, $\Sigma w^2 = 10324$. Using a 5% significance level and stating clearly any assumptions that you make, determine whether the results obtained by the second investigator justify the conclusion that, on average, the new drug does give longer relief from pain than the standard drug. (*JMB 1981*)

14 At an election held last year, 60% of a large population voted for Party A and 40% for Party B. In a poll of public opinion conducted today, 150 women and 100 men were asked how they would vote if there was an election now. The results of the poll were

	For Party A	For Party B
Women	88	62
Men	47	53
Total	135	115

Stating in each case your alternative hypothesis and whether you are using a one-tail or a two-tail test, investigate at the 5% significance level whether (i) the proportion of the population in favour of Party A has decreased significantly since last year, (ii) the proportions of men and women currently in favour of Party A differ significantly. (*C 1981*)

15 In a sample of 1000 persons interviewed in Manchester, 643 were in favour of British Summer Time. In Liverpool, a sample of 600 showed that 398 persons were in favour of British Summer Time. Is there sufficient evidence here to suggest that the views of the populations of Manchester and Liverpool are significantly different? (*L 1978*)

16 The number of vehicles breaking down on a particular stretch of motorway during a period of t days has a Poisson distribution with mean $0.5t$. Find, correct to three decimal places in each case, the probability that (i) there will be no breakdown during a period of two days, (ii) during a period of three consecutive days the first breakdown will occur on the third day, (iii) during a period of three consecutive days there will be no breakdown on one day and exactly one breakdown on each of the other two days.

The above mean number (0·5) of vehicles breaking down per day was based on daily records over a long period of time. It was suggested that on wet days the mean number would be greater. Observation over 10 wet days showed that a total of 10 vehicles broke down. Assuming that the Poisson distribution still applies, use a 5% significance level to test whether the suggestion is justified. *(JMB 1981)*

17 The numbers of accidents occurring in a period of t months at *blackspot* and *non-blackspot* areas in a certain town may be assumed to be independent Poisson variables with means $4t$ and t, respectively. Find the mean and the variance of the total number of accidents per month in this town. Given that the total number of accidents in a one-month period is also a Poisson variable, calculate the probability that the total number of accidents which will occur in any one-month period will be between 4 and 6 inclusive.

Write down the mean number of accidents per year in this town. Given that, in a particular year, a total of 80 accidents occurred, use a normal approximation to test, at the 1% level of significance, the claim that the mean number of accidents has increased. *(L 1980)*

18 The number of flaws in a given length of cloth may be assumed to have a Poisson distribution. The manufacturer of the cloth claims that the mean number of flaws per metre length of cloth is 0·2. To test this claim against the alternative that the mean number is greater than 0·2, it is decided to take a length of 10 metres of the cloth and to reject the claim only if this length contains 6 or more flaws. (i) Find the probability, correct to three decimal places, that this test rule will reject the claim when, in fact, the true mean number of flaws per metre is 0·2. (ii) Find the probability, correct to three decimal places, that this test rule will not reject the claim when, in fact, the true mean number of flaws per metre is 0·8. (iii) Find the number which should replace the 6 in the above test rule so that the new test rule will be such that the probabilities in (i) and (ii) will be approximately 0·05 and 0·1, respectively. *(JMB 1982)*

19 Electrical resistors produced by a certain machine when properly adjusted have resistances which are distributed normally with mean 200 Ω and standard deviation 20 Ω. A sample of 20 resistors is drawn from the current production. Find the range of values within which the sample mean must lie so that it may be accepted with 95% confidence that the machine is properly adjusted. State the probability that the hypothesis that the machine is properly adjusted will be rejected when in fact it is true. Assuming that the standard deviation is unchanged but the mean is in fact 205 Ω, find the probability that the hypothesis that the machine is properly adjusted will be accepted when the adjustment is wrong in this particular way. *(C 1980)*

20 The current medical treatment for a particular ailment has a cure rate of 80% (i.e. a patient with this ailment has a probability of 0·8 of being cured by the treatment). (i) Write down the mean and the variance of the number of patients that will be cured per 100 patients treated. (ii) Calculate the probability that, of four patients treated, at least three will be cured. (iii) A pharmaceutical company claims that it has developed a new treatment for the ailment which has a higher cure rate than the current treatment. To test this claim the new treatment is given to 20 patients. It is decided to accept the new treatment as being better than the current treatment only if at least 19 of the 20 patients are cured. Write down an appropriate null hypothesis and an appropriate alternative hypothesis for this test. Also calculate the probability that the new treatment will not be accepted as being better than the current treatment when the new treatment has a cure rate of 90%. (*JMB 1980*)

21 A manufacturer of dice makes fair dice and also slightly biased dice which are to be used in the teaching of probability and statistics. The probability distributions of the scores for the two types of die are shown in the following table.

Score	1	2	3	4	5	6
Probability for fair dice	1/6	1/6	1/6	1/6	1/6	1/6
Probability for biased dice	1/10	1/10	1/5	1/5	1/5	1/5

Calculate the expectation and the variance of the score for each type of die.

Unfortunately, some dice have been made without distinguishing marks to show whether they are fair or biased. The manufacturer decides to test such dice as follows: each die is thrown 100 times and the mean score $\bar{x}$ is calculated; if $\bar{x} > 3{\cdot}7$, the die is classified as biased, but, if $\bar{x} \leqslant 3{\cdot}7$, it is classified as fair. Find the probability that a fair die is wrongly classified as biased as a result of this procedure. To improve the test procedure the manufacturer increases the number of throws from 100 to N, where N is chosen to make as close as possible to 0·001 the probability of wrongly classifying a biased die as fair. Find the value of N. (*C 1981*)

8 Linear Relationships

8.1 Introduction

Scientific theories often establish or hypothesise that two variables are functionally related in a particular form. For example, when certain conditions are satisfied:

(i) the period T of oscillations of a simple pendulum of length L is given by $T = 2\pi\sqrt{(L/g)}$, where g is the acceleration due to gravity;
(ii) the pressure p and the volume v of a gas are related by the formula $pv^{\gamma} = c$, where γ is the specific heat of the gas and c is a constant;
(iii) in economics and biology, a frequently occurring relationship between two variables u and v takes the form $v = ab^{u}$, where a and b are constants.

In this text we restrict consideration to a linear relationship connecting two variables x and y, and we shall assume that

$$y = \alpha + \beta x,$$

where α and β are unknown constants. The graph of the above relationship will be a straight line with α being the intercept of the line with the y-axis and $\beta = \tan\,\theta$ the slope of the line; see Fig. 8.1.

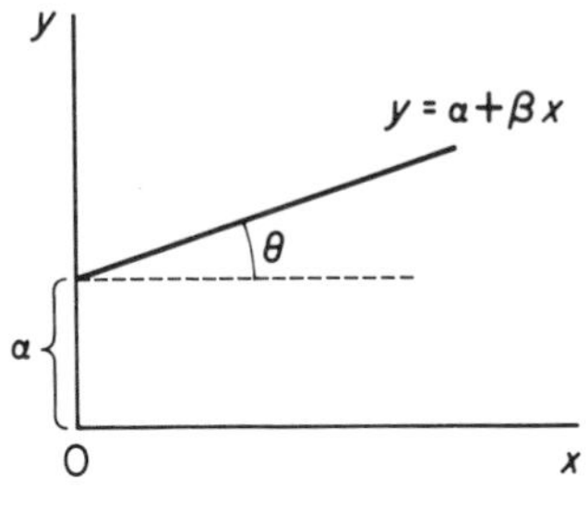

Fig. 8.1

Our restriction to linear relationships is not as severe as it may at first appear, since any functional relationship between two variables can be transformed into a linear relationship. For the relationship between T and L in (i) above, setting $T = y$, $\sqrt{L} = x$, and $2\pi/\sqrt{g} = \beta$, the corresponding relationship connecting y and x is $y = \beta x$. Taking logarithms of both sides of the formula in (ii) gives $\log p + \gamma \log v = \log c$; on setting $y = \log p$, $x = \log v$ and $\alpha = \log c$, the relationship between y and x is $y = \alpha - \gamma x$.

Finally, taking logarithms of both sides of the formula in (iii) gives $\log v = \log a + u \log b$; setting $y = \log v$, $x = u$, $\alpha = \log a$ and $\beta = \log b$, we have $y = \alpha + \beta x$.

If $y = \alpha + \beta x$ and (x_1, y_1), (x_2, y_2) are two possible values of (x, y), then

$$y_1 = \alpha + \beta x_1 \quad \text{and} \quad y_2 = \alpha + \beta x_2.$$

Solving these two equations simultaneously gives the values of α and β as

$$\alpha = \frac{x_1 y_2 - x_2 y_1}{x_1 - x_2}, \qquad \beta = \frac{y_1 - y_2}{x_1 - x_2}.$$

However, for the type of situation to be considered here (as exemplified by (i), (ii), and (iii) above), corresponding values of x and y have to be determined experimentally and these may not be absolutely correct, in which case the values of α and β given above will also be incorrect.

Let (x_i, y_i), $i = 1, 2, \ldots, n$ denote n experimentally determined values of (x, y). If these values are correct then, when plotted on a graph the points (x_i, y_i) would lie on a straight line (namely the line $y = \alpha + \beta x$). But if the values (x_i, y_i) are incorrect, then the plotted points will not lie on a straight line, as illustrated in Fig. 8.2. The problem then is to use the observed values (x_i, y_i), $i = 1, 2, \ldots, n$, to obtain a good estimate of the relationship $y = \alpha + \beta x$ connecting x and y. One method of achieving this is to 'fit' a straight line by eye to the plotted points. Such a method has many disadvantages, notably that it is subjective (so that different individuals may fit different lines) and it will not enable us to make a quantitative assessment of how close the fitted line is to the true line. A more formal method for fitting a straight line to a set of plotted points is that using the *principle of least squares*, which we describe in the next section. In §8.3 we show that this method leads to an estimate of the true linear relationship that has good statistical properties.

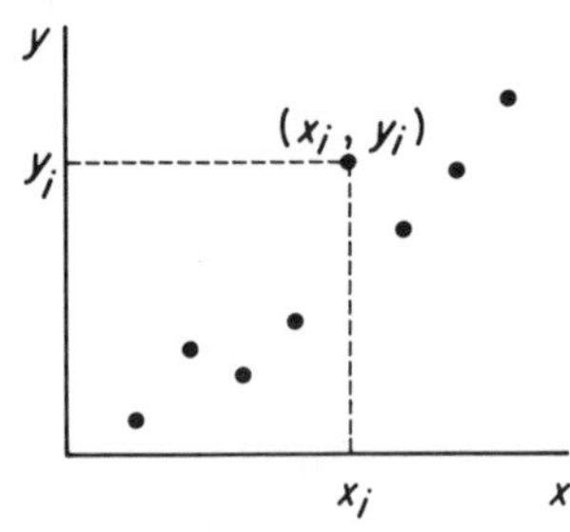

Fig. 8.2

8.2 The method of least squares

Let (x_i, y_i), $i = 1, 2, \ldots, n$, denote n experimentally observed values of (x, y), where x and y are known to be related in the linear form

$$y = \alpha + \beta x, \tag{1}$$

α and β being unknown constants. We shall assume for the present that the observed values $x_1, x_2, \ldots, x_n$ are in fact accurate (either determined accurately or the variable x has been controlled to have these values), but that the values $y_1, y_2, \ldots, y_n$ are subject to measurement error. Under these assumptions we may write

$$y_i = \alpha + \beta x_i + e_i, \qquad i = 1, 2, \ldots, n, \tag{2}$$

where $e_i = y_i - (\alpha + \beta x_i)$ is the error in the observed y-value when $x = x_i$.

We now seek a method for determining values a and b so that the line

$$y = a + bx \tag{3}$$

will be a reasonable estimate of (1). Since the observed x-values are known to be accurate, the discrepancies between the observed points (x_i, y_i) and the corresponding values $(x_i, a + bx_i)$ on the fitted line are in the y-direction only. These discrepancies, d_i, are given by

$$d_i = y_i - a - bx_i, \qquad i = 1, 2, \ldots, n. \tag{4}$$

(See Fig. 8.3). The *principle of least squares* is to choose a and b so that the sum of the squares of the discrepancies is as small as possible. Thus, a and b need to be chosen so as to minimise

$$S = \Sigma d_i^2 = \Sigma (y_i - a - bx_i)^2, \tag{5}$$

each summation being over $i = 1, 2, \ldots, n$. Throughout this chapter we shall use the symbol Σ to denote summation over $i = 1, 2, \ldots, n$. For any fixed b, the value of a which minimises (5) can be obtained by solving the equation $\mathrm{d}S/\mathrm{d}a = 0$. Differentiating (5) with respect to a we obtain

$$\frac{\mathrm{d}S}{\mathrm{d}a} = \Sigma -2(y_i - a - bx_i) = -2(\Sigma y_i - na - b\,\Sigma x_i),$$

which is zero when

$$a = (\Sigma y_i - b\Sigma x_i)/n = \bar{y} - b\bar{x}, \tag{6}$$

where $\bar{x}$ and $\bar{y}$ are the means of the observed x-values and the observed

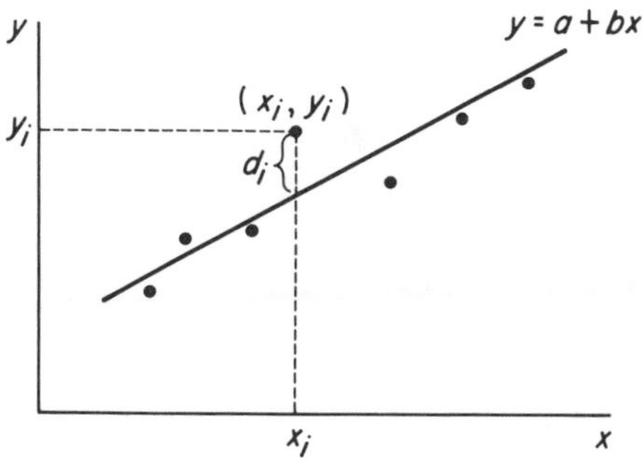

Fig. 8.3

y-values, respectively. Since $d^2S/da^2 = 2n$ is positive, the solution (6) corresponds to a minimum value of S. It follows from (6) that *the principle of least squares results in a fitted line which passes through the mean* $(\bar{x}, \bar{y})$ *of the observations.*

Substituting (6) in (5) gives

$$S = \Sigma\{(y_i - \bar{y}) - b(x_i - \bar{x})\}^2. \tag{7}$$

We now need to find the value b which minimises (7). Differentiating (7) with respect to b we obtain

$$\begin{aligned}\frac{dS}{db} &= \Sigma - 2(x_i - \bar{x})\{(y_i - \bar{y}) - b(x_i - \bar{x})\} \\ &= -2\{\Sigma(x_i - \bar{x})(y_i - \bar{y}) - b\Sigma(x_i - \bar{x})^2\},\end{aligned}$$

which is zero when

$$b = \frac{\Sigma(x_i - \bar{x})(y_i - \bar{y})}{\Sigma(x_i - \bar{x})^2}. \tag{8}$$

Since $d^2S/db^2 = 2\Sigma(x_i - \bar{x})^2$ is positive, the value of b given by (8) is one for which S is a minimum.

The values a and b given by (6) and (8) are referred to as *the least squares estimates of* α *and* β, respectively, and the corresponding line

$$y = a + bx = \bar{y} + b(x - \bar{x}) \tag{9}$$

is referred to as *the least squares estimate of the true linear relationship connecting* x *and* y. (The line defined by (9) with b given by (8) is also referred to as the *sample least squares regression line of* y *on* x, but this description is more appropriate for a variant of the above problem which will be described in §8.4.)

EXAMPLE 1 *The length y cm of a metal rod at a temperature of x°C is given by* $y = \alpha + \beta x$. *The lengths of the rod were measured at varying temperatures, the results being as shown in the following table.*

Temperature x°C	20	40	60	80	100
Length y cm	10·0	10·2	10·3	10·6	10·7

Assuming that the temperature levels are accurate and that the lengths were subject to measurement error, determine the least squares estimate of the relationship connecting y with x. Deduce the least squares estimate of (i) the length of the rod when the temperature is 70°C, (ii) the extension in the length of the rod when the temperature is increased from 70°C to 100°C.

The observed values of (x, y) are plotted in Fig. 8.4. Using (9), the least squares estimate of the relationship is given by

$$y = \bar{y} + b(x - \bar{x}), \tag{10}$$

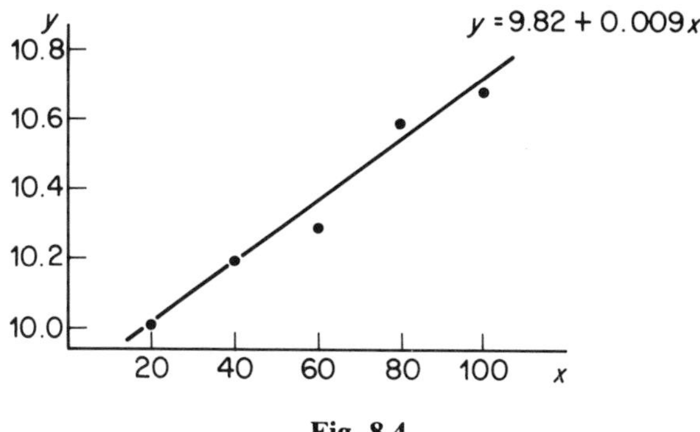

Fig. 8.4

where $\bar{x}$ and $\bar{y}$ are the means, and, from (8),

$$b = \frac{\Sigma(x_i - \bar{x})(y_i - \bar{y})}{\Sigma(x_i - \bar{x})^2}. \tag{11}$$

From the tabulated values of x and y, we find

$$\begin{aligned} \bar{x} &= (20+40+60+80+100)/5 = 60, \\ \bar{y} &= (10{\cdot}0+10{\cdot}2+10{\cdot}3+10{\cdot}6+107)/5 = 10{\cdot}36, \\ \Sigma(x_i-\bar{x})^2 &= (-40)^2+(-20)^2+0+(20)^2+(40)^2 = 4000, \\ \Sigma(x_i-\bar{x})(y_i-\bar{y}) &= -40x-0{\cdot}36-20x-0{\cdot}16+0+20x-0{\cdot}24 \\ &\quad +40x-0{\cdot}34 = 36. \end{aligned}$$

Hence, from (11),

$$b = 36/4000 = 0{\cdot}009,$$

and from (10), the least squares estimate of the linear relationship connecting x and y is

$$\begin{aligned} y &= 10{\cdot}36 + 0{\cdot}009\ (x-60) \\ &= 9{\cdot}82 + 0{\cdot}009x. \end{aligned}$$

This line has been superimposed on Fig. 8.4. (It is always advisable to plot the given data and to draw in the fitted line as a check against a gross error having been made in the computation.)

(i) The least squares estimate of the length of the rod at a temperature of 70°C is

$$y = 9{\cdot}82 + 0{\cdot}009 \times 70 = 10{\cdot}45 \text{ cm}.$$

(ii) The extension in the length of the rod when the temperature is increased from 70°C to 100°C is given by

$$(\alpha + 100\beta) - (a + 70\beta) = 30\beta,$$

the least squares estimate of which is $30b = 30 \times 0{\cdot}009 = 0{\cdot}27$ cm.

To evaluate b using (8) it is necessary to calculate the sum of the products $(x_i - \bar{x})(y_i - \bar{y})$ and the sum of the squares $(x_i - \bar{x})^2$. Alternative forms for these expressions that are often more convenient will now be derived.

On expanding $(x_i - \bar{x})(y_i - \bar{y})$ we have

$$\Sigma(x_i - \bar{x})(y_i - \bar{y}) = \Sigma(x_i y_i - \bar{x} y_i - \bar{y} x_i + \bar{x}\bar{y})$$
$$= \Sigma x_i y_i - \bar{x}\Sigma y_i - \bar{y}\Sigma x_i + n\bar{x}\bar{y}.$$

But since $\bar{x} = (\Sigma x_i)/n$ and $\bar{y} = (\Sigma y_i)/n$, it follows that

$$\Sigma(x_i - \bar{x})(y_i - \bar{y}) = \Sigma x_i y_i - \frac{(\Sigma x_i)(\Sigma y_i)}{n}.$$

Also, from (6) of §6.2.3,

$$\Sigma(x_i - \bar{x})^2 = \Sigma x_i^2 - (\Sigma x_i)^2/n.$$

Substituting these in (8), an alternative formula for b is

$$b = \frac{\Sigma x_i y_i - (\Sigma x_i)(\Sigma y_i)/n}{\Sigma x_i^2 - (\Sigma x_i)^2/n} = \frac{n\Sigma x_i y_i - (\Sigma x_i)(\Sigma y_i)}{n\Sigma x_i^2 - (\Sigma x_i)^2}. \qquad (12)$$

In this form for b, division is deferred until the final step. This is particularly advantageous if either or both of $\bar{x}$ and $\bar{y}$ consists of more figures than the individual values x_i and y_i, respectively. To illustrate, suppose that in Example 1 the length of the rod was also measured at a temperature of 10°C and the result was 9·9 cm. Including this result in our analysis we then have

$$\bar{x} = (10 + 20 + 40 + 60 + 80 + 100)/6 = 310/6 = 51{\cdot}\overline{6},$$
$$\bar{y} = (9{\cdot}9 + 10{\cdot}0 + 10{\cdot}2 + 10{\cdot}3 + 10{\cdot}6 + 10{\cdot}7)/6$$
$$= 61{\cdot}7/6 = 10{\cdot}28\overline{3}.$$

Using (8) to calculate b would now be considerably more complicated than was the case in Example 1. However, using a calculator, we easily obtain

$$\Sigma x_i = 310, \quad \Sigma x_i^2 = 22100, \quad \Sigma y_i = 61{\cdot}7, \quad \Sigma x_i y_i = 3243.$$

Thus, with $n = 6$ in (12), the least squares estimate of β is now

$$b = (6 \times 3243 - 310 \times 61{\cdot}7)/(6 \times 22100 - 310^2) = 0{\cdot}0091$$

correct to four decimal places.

Table 8.1

$u = (x - 20)/20$	0	1	2	3	4
$v = 10(y - 10)$	0	2	3	6	7

The arithmetic involved in finding the least squares estimates can also often be simplified by transforming to new variables, say $u = k_1 x - c_1$ and $v = k_2 y - c_2$, the constants k_1, k_2, c_1 and c_2 being chosen so that the values

(u_i, v_i) corresponding to (x_i, y_i) are easier to manipulate. With reference to Example 1, consider changing the variables to $u = (x-20)/20$ and $v = 10(y-10)$. The values of u_i and v_i corresponding to x_i and y_i, respectively, are shown in Table 8.1. Consider now the least squares line fitted to the values (u_i, v_i). Its equation may be written as

$$v = a' + b'u,$$

where, from (12),

$$b' = \{5\Sigma u_i v_i - (\Sigma u_i)\,(\Sigma v_i)\}/\{5\Sigma u_i^2 - (\Sigma u_i)^2\},$$

and, from (6)

$$a' = \bar{v} - b'\bar{u}.$$

From the entries in the above table, we very easily obtain

$$\Sigma u_i = 10, \qquad \Sigma u_i^2 = 30, \qquad \Sigma v_i = 18, \qquad \Sigma u_i v_i = 54.$$

Hence,

$$b' = \frac{5 \times 54 - 10 \times 18}{5 \times 30 - 10^2} = \frac{90}{50} = 1{\cdot}8,$$

and

$$a' = 3{\cdot}6 - 1{\cdot}8 \times 2 = 0.$$

It follows that the least squares estimate of the linear relationship connecting v and u is given by

$$v = 1{\cdot}8u.$$

Transforming back to x and y, the least squares estimate of the linear relationship connecting y and x is

$$10(y-10) = 1{\cdot}8\ (x-20)/20,$$

or

$$y = 9{\cdot}82 + 0{\cdot}009x,$$

exactly as obtained by our earlier method.

EXERCISE 8.2

1 The following table gives the experimentally observed values of two variables x and y which are known to be linearly related. It may be assumed that the given x-values are accurate and that the given y-values may be in error.

x	0	1	2	3	4
y	1·1	2·0	2·5	3·1	3·6

(i) By studying the entries in the table, state the sign of the slope of the linear equation connecting y with x.
(ii) Find the least squares estimate of the linear relationship.

2 Repeat question 1 for the data given in the following table.

x	5	10	15	20	25	30	35	40
y	9·4	8·8	8·1	7·4	6·9	6·1	5·3	4·8

3 The height h of a tree is related to its age, t years, by the equation $h = \lambda e^{\beta t}$. Convert this equation into one of the form $y = \alpha + \beta t$. Given that at ages 1 year, 2 years and 3 years, the measured heights of the tree were h_1, h_2 and h_3, respectively, show that the least squares estimate of β is $b = \log\{\sqrt{(h_3/h_1)}\}$.

4 When a given mass of gas is maintained at a constant pressure its volume y at temperature x is given by $y = \alpha + \beta x$. The following table shows duplicate measurements of the volume of the gas at certain temperatures. Find the least squares estimates of (i) β, (ii) α, (iii) the volume of the gas when the temperature is 55°C, (iv) the increase in the volume of the gas when the temperature is raised from 45°C to 65°C (continued in Exercise 8.3A question 5).

Temperature x°C	40	50	60	70
Volume y cm^3	1·15 1·13	1·18 1·19	1·22 1·24	1·27 1·28

5 Consider the special case where x and y are related in the form $y = \lambda x$ (i.e. the graph of y against x is known to be a straight line through the origin). Given the paired observations (x_i, y_i), $i = 1, 2, \ldots, n$, and assuming that the x_i values are accurate but the y_i values are subject to measurement error, apply the principle of least squares to show that the least squares estimate of λ is given by $m = \Sigma x_i y_i / \Sigma x_i^2$ (continued in Exercise 8.3B question 1).

8.3 Statistical considerations

As in §8.2 we shall assume that x and y are two variables linearly related in the form

$$y = \alpha + \beta x, \tag{1}$$

and that in experiments in which x has the values $x_1, x_2, \ldots, x_n$, the corresponding observed y-values, $y_1, y_2, \ldots, y_n$ are subject to measurement error. Thus, we may write

$$y_i = \alpha + \beta x_i + e_i, \qquad i = 1, 2, \ldots, n, \tag{2}$$

where e_i is the actual error in the measured value of y when $x = x_i$.

In order to derive some statistical properties of the least squares estimates obtained in §8.2, we shall further assume that *the measurement errors* $e_1, e_2, \ldots, e_n$ *are independent observations of a random error variable* ε *which is normally distributed with mean zero and variance* σ^2 (measurement errors frequently meet these assumptions). Under these assumptions, the observed y-values $y_1, y_2, \ldots, y_n$ may be regarded as independent observations of random variables $Y_1, Y_2, \ldots$, respectively, where

$$Y_i = \alpha + \beta x_i + \varepsilon, \qquad i = 1, 2, \ldots, n. \tag{3}$$

Since $\alpha + \beta x_i$ is a constant for any fixed i, and $\varepsilon \sim N(0, \sigma^2)$, it follows that $Y_i \sim N(\alpha + \beta x_i, \sigma^2)$, where $\alpha + \beta x_i$ is the true value of y when $x = x_i$.

In what follows it is most important to appreciate the distinction between the x_i and the y_i; the x_i are accurate values of a mathematical variable x, whereas the y_i are observed values of random variables Y_i $(i = 1, 2, \ldots, n)$ which are normally distributed with means $\alpha + \beta x_i$ and variance σ^2.

From §8.2, the least squares estimates of α, β, and $\eta_0 \equiv \alpha + \beta x_0$, the true value of y when $x = x_0$, are given by

$$a = \bar{y} - b\bar{x}, \tag{4}$$

$$b = \frac{\Sigma(x_i - \bar{x})(y_i - \bar{y})}{\Sigma(x_i - \bar{x})^2}, \tag{5}$$

$$y_0 = a + bx_0. \tag{6}$$

Adopting our earlier convention of using capital letters for estimators (as opposed to estimates), the least squares estimators of α, β and $\alpha + \beta x_0$ are, respectively

$$A = \bar{Y} - B\bar{x}, \tag{7}$$

$$B = \frac{\Sigma(x_i - \bar{x})(Y_i - \bar{Y})}{\Sigma(x_i - \bar{x})^2}, \tag{8}$$

$$Y_0 = A + Bx_0. \tag{9}$$

In §8.3.1 we shall show that A, B and Y_0 are unbiased estimators of α, β and $\eta_0 \equiv \alpha + \beta x_0$, respectively, and are normally distributed with respective standard errors

$$\mathrm{SE}[A] = \left\{\frac{\sigma^2 \Sigma x_i^2}{n\Sigma(x_i - \bar{x})^2}\right\}^{\frac{1}{2}}, \tag{10}$$

$$\mathrm{SE}[B] = \left\{\frac{\sigma^2}{\Sigma(x_i - \bar{x})^2}\right\}^{\frac{1}{2}}, \tag{11}$$

$$\mathrm{SE}[Y_0] = \left\{\sigma^2\left[\frac{1}{n} + \frac{(x_0 - \bar{x})^2}{\Sigma(x_i - \bar{x})^2}\right]\right\}^{\frac{1}{2}}. \tag{12}$$

Let W denote an arbitrary one of A, B and Y_0. Denoting the mean of W by μ_W,

$$Z \equiv \frac{W-\mu_W}{\text{SE}[W]} \sim N(0, 1).$$

Hence, proceeding as we did in §6.3.1, but replacing $\bar{X}$ by W, the $100(1-2\alpha)\%$ symmetrical confidence limits for μ_W are given by

$$w \pm z_\alpha \text{SE}[W], \tag{13}$$

where w is the observed value of W.

Similarly, using §7.2, again with W for $\bar{X}$, $100\alpha\%$ significance level tests for the value of μ_W are as follows.

(i) For testing H_0: $\mu_W = \mu_0$ (say) against H_1: $\mu_W < \mu_0$, H_0 should be rejected only if $(w-\mu_0)/\text{SE}[W] < -z_\alpha$.
(ii) For testing H_0: $\mu_W = \mu_0$ against H_1: $\mu_W > \mu_0$, H_0 should be rejected only if $(w-\mu_0)/\text{SE}[W] > z_\alpha$.
(iii) For testing H_0: $\mu_W = \mu_0$ against H_1: $\mu_W \neq \mu_0$, H_0 should be rejected only if $|w-\mu_0|/\text{SE}[W] > z_{\frac{1}{2}\alpha}$.

EXAMPLE 1 *Suppose that in Example* 1, §8.2 *it is known that the errors in the measured lengths of the rod are independent and normally distributed with standard deviation* 0·1.

(*i*) *Find* 95% *symmetrical confidence limits for*
(*a*) *the length of the rod when the temperature is* 70°C,
(*b*) *the extension in the length of the rod when the temperature is increased from* 70°C *to* 100°C.
(*ii*) *Using a* 5% *significance level, test* H_0: $\beta = 0{\cdot}01$ *against* H_1: $\beta < 0{\cdot}01$.

(i) In Example 1, §8.2 we showed that the least squares estimate of the length $\alpha+\beta x_0$ when $x = x_0$ is

$$y_0 = 9{\cdot}82 + 0{\cdot}009x_0,$$

so that when $x_0 = 70$,

$$y_0 = 9{\cdot}82 + 0{\cdot}63 = 10{\cdot}45.$$

From (12) with $n = 5$, $x_0 = 70$, $\bar{x} = 60$, $\sigma = 0{\cdot}1$, and $\Sigma(x_i - \bar{x})^2 = 4000$, we have

$$\text{SE}[Y_0] = \left\{0{\cdot}1^2\left[\frac{1}{5} + \frac{(70-60)^2}{4000}\right]\right\}^{\frac{1}{2}} \simeq 0{\cdot}0474.$$

From (13) the 95% symmetrical confidence limits for the true length $\alpha + 70\beta$ of the rod at temperature 70°C are given by

$$\begin{aligned} y_0 \pm z_{0{\cdot}025}\text{SE}[Y_0] &= 10{\cdot}45 \pm 1{\cdot}96 \times 0{\cdot}0474 \\ &\simeq 10{\cdot}36 \text{ and } 10{\cdot}54. \end{aligned}$$

(b) From (ii) of Example 1, §8.2, the extension in the length of the rod when its temperature is increased from 70°C to 100°C is 30β. The 95% symmetrical confidence limits for this extension are simply 30 times the corresponding limits for β. From (13), the 95% symmetrical confidence limits for β are $b \pm z_{0\cdot025}$ SE$[B]$. Here, $b = 0{\cdot}009$ and from (11) with $\sigma = 0{\cdot}1$ and $\Sigma(x_i - \bar{x})^2 = 4000$,

$$\text{SE}[B] = (0{\cdot}1^2/4000)^{\frac{1}{2}} \simeq 0{\cdot}001582$$

Thus, the 95% symmetrical confidence limit for β are

$$0{\cdot}009 \pm 1{\cdot}96 \times 0{\cdot}001581 \simeq 0{\cdot}00590 \text{ and } 0{\cdot}01210,$$

and hence, those for the extension 30β are

$$30 \times 0{\cdot}0059 \text{ and } 30 \times 0{\cdot}0121 \simeq 0{\cdot}177 \text{ and } 0{\cdot}363.$$

(ii) For a 5% significance level test of H_0: $\beta = 0{\cdot}01$ against H_1: $\beta < 0{\cdot}01$, we should reject H_0 only if

$$(b - 0{\cdot}01)/\text{SE}[B] < -z_{0\cdot05} = -1{\cdot}64.$$

As shown above, $b = 0{\cdot}009$ and SE$[B] \simeq 0{\cdot}001581$, so that

$$\begin{aligned}(b - 0{\cdot}01)/\text{SE}[b] &\simeq (0{\cdot}009 - 0{\cdot}01)/0{\cdot}001581 \\ &\simeq -0{\cdot}63,\end{aligned}$$

which is greater than $-1{\cdot}64$. Thus, the conclusion is that, on the evidence available, the null hypothesis $H_0{:}\beta = 0{\cdot}01$ cannot be rejected in favour of $H_1{:}\beta < 0{\cdot}01$.

EXERCISE 8.3A

1 A test was performed to determine the relationship between the chemical content of a particular constituent (y grammes per litre) in solution and the crystallisation temperature (x kelvin). The results were as follows.

x	0·3	0·4	1·2	2·3	3·1	4·2	5·3
y	3·2	2·4	4·3	5·4	6·6	7·8	8·8

Assuming a linear relationship $y = \alpha + \beta x$, calculate the least squares estimates of α and β, each correct to three significant figures.

Suppose that the y-determinations are subject to independent random errors each having mean zero and standard deviation 0·5 g/l. Stating clearly any further assumptions you make regarding the data, determine 95% confidence limits for β.

2 The weight percent, w, of nitrous oxide in a mixture of nitrous oxide and nitrogen dioxide at temperature t is given by the relation $w = \alpha + \beta t^{-1}$, where α and β are constants. In an experiment to estimate α and β, the temperature t was carefully controlled at four different values and three determinations of w were made at each temperature value. Letting $x = 1000t^{-1}$, the following calculations were made from the 12 observed values of (x, w).

$$\Sigma x = 43{\cdot}2, \quad \Sigma w = 13{\cdot}2, \quad \Sigma x^2 = 161{\cdot}28, \quad \Sigma xw = 44{\cdot}64.$$

(i) Determine the least squares estimate of the equation connecting w and x.
(ii) Estimate the value of w when $t = 250$.
(iii) Given that the determinations of w are subject to a normally distributed random error having mean zero and standard deviation 0·08, calculate 99% confidence limits for β. *(WJEC* 1973)

3 A liquid which is stored in ten-litre drums is subject to evaporation loss. It is believed that the quantity of liquid remaining in a drum which has been stored for five days or longer is a linear function of the duration of storage in days. A sample of five drums, each containing 10 litres of the liquid, was stored under identical conditions and on each day from the fifth ($x = 5$) to the ninth ($x = 9$) one drum was opened and the quantity of liquid in it was determined. The results obtained are given in the following table.

Duration of storage (x days)	5	6	7	8	9
Quantity of liquid (y litres)	9·6	9·3	9·1	8·9	8·6

Determinations of the quantities of liquid in drums are subject to independent errors which are normally distributed with mean zero and standard deviation 0·05 litre. Assuming that the true quantity of liquid (in litres) in a drum which has been stored for x days is equal to $\alpha + \beta x$, calculate
(i) the least squares estimates of α and β,
(ii) an estimate of the true quantity of liquid in a drum which has been stored for 10 days,
(iii) 95% confidence limits for the true quantity of liquid in a drum which has been stored for 10 days. *(WJEC 1977)*

4 The extension in the length of a steel cable may be assumed to be linearly related to the magnitude of the tension in the cable. Five identical specimens of cable gave the following results when subjected to various tensions.

Tension (x)	2·0	2·5	3·0	3·5	4·0
Extension (y)	6·0	7·6	10·8	13·8	16·8

(a) Obtain the least squares estimate of the relationship expressing y in terms of x.
(b) Given that the measured extensions are subject to normally distributed errors having mean zero and standard deviation 1·25, calculate 95% confidence limits for the extension in a cable when the tension is increased from 2 units to 4 units.

5 In Exercise 8.2 question 4, suppose that the errors in the volume measurements are independent and normally distributed with mean zero and standard deviation 0·04 cm³.
(i) Find 90% symmetrical confidence limits for (a) α, (b) β.
(ii) Use a 10% significance level to test the hypothesis $H_0: \eta = 1{\cdot}18$ against the alternative hypothesis $H_1: \eta > 1{\cdot}18$, where η is the true volume of the gas when the temperature is 55°C.

8.3.1 Derivation of the sampling distributions of A, B and Y_0

First recall from §4.8 that if $Y_1, Y_2, \ldots, Y_n$ are independent random variables with $Y_i \sim N(\mu_i, \sigma_i^2)$, then $W = \Sigma c_i Y_i$, where the c_i are constants, is also normally distributed with mean μ_W and variance σ_W^2, where

$$\mu_W = \Sigma c_i \mu_i, \qquad \sigma_W^2 = \Sigma c_i^2 \sigma_i^2.$$

We shall now proceed to express each of A, B and Y_0 as a linear combination of the Y_i as defined in §8.3, so that $\mu_i = \alpha + \beta x_i$ and $\sigma_i^2 = \sigma^2$, the x_i being constants.

We shall start with B. From (8) above,

$$B = [\Sigma(x_i - \bar{x})(Y_i - \bar{Y})]/\Sigma(x_i - \bar{x})^2.$$

Now,

$$\Sigma(x_i - \bar{x})(Y_i - \bar{Y}) \equiv \Sigma(x_i - \bar{x})Y_i - \bar{Y}\Sigma(x_i - \bar{x})$$
$$= \Sigma(x_i - \bar{x})Y_i$$

since $\Sigma(x_i - \bar{x}) = 0$. Hence

$$B = [\Sigma(x_i - \bar{x})Y_i]/\Sigma(x_i - \bar{x})^2. \qquad (14)$$

Since the x_i are constants and $\mathrm{E}[Y_i] = \alpha + \beta x_i$, it follows that

$$\mathrm{E}[B] = \frac{\Sigma(x_i - \bar{x})(\alpha + \beta x_i)}{\Sigma(x_i - \bar{x})^2}$$
$$= \frac{\alpha\Sigma(x_i - \bar{x})}{\Sigma(x_i - \bar{x})^2} + \frac{\beta\Sigma x_i(x_i - \bar{x})}{\Sigma(x_i - \bar{x})^2}.$$

Since $\Sigma(x_i - \bar{x}) = 0$ and

$$\Sigma x_i(x_i - \bar{x}) \equiv \Sigma x_i(x_i - \bar{x}) - \Sigma\bar{x}(x_i - \bar{x}) = \Sigma(x_i - \bar{x})^2,$$

we find that $\mathrm{E}[B] = \beta$, thus establishing that B is an unbiased estimator of β. Also, since $\mathrm{V}[Y_i] = \sigma^2$,

$$\mathrm{V}[B] = [\Sigma(x_i - \bar{x})^2\sigma^2]/[\Sigma(x_i - \bar{x})^2]^2 = \sigma^2/\Sigma(x_i - \bar{x})^2.$$

Furthermore, since the Y_i are independent and normally distributed,

$$B \sim N\left(\beta, \frac{\sigma^2}{\Sigma(x_i - \bar{x})^2}\right) \qquad (15)$$

Now consider A. From (7)

$$A = \bar{Y} - B\bar{x},$$

so that

$$\mathrm{E}[A] = \mathrm{E}[\bar{Y}] - \bar{x}\mathrm{E}[B].$$

But $\mathrm{E}[\bar{Y}] = n^{-1}\Sigma\mathrm{E}[Y_i] = n^{-1}\Sigma(\alpha + \beta x_i) = \alpha + \beta\bar{x}$, and $\mathrm{E}[B] = \beta$. Hence

$$\mathrm{E}[A] = \alpha + \beta\bar{x} - \bar{x}\beta = \alpha,$$

establishing the unbiasedness of A. The above form for A is not convenient for determining the variance of A because $\bar{Y}$ and B are not clearly independent (both involve the Y_i). Using (14) we have

$$A = \frac{\Sigma Y_i}{n} - \frac{\bar{x}\Sigma(x_i-\bar{x})Y_i}{\Sigma(x_i-\bar{x})^2}$$

$$= \Sigma\left\{\frac{1}{n} - \frac{\bar{x}(x_i-\bar{x})}{\Sigma(x_i-\bar{x})^2}\right\}Y_i \tag{16}$$

Since the Y_i are independent and each has variance σ^2,

$$\mathrm{V}[A] = \Sigma\left\{\frac{1}{n} - \frac{\bar{x}(x_i-\bar{x})}{\Sigma(x_i-\bar{x})^2}\right\}^2\sigma^2$$

$$= \sigma^2\left\{\frac{1}{n} + \frac{\bar{x}^2\Sigma(x_i-\bar{x})^2}{[\Sigma(x_i-\bar{x})^2]^2} - \frac{2\bar{x}\Sigma(x_i-\bar{x})}{n\Sigma(x_i-\bar{x})^2}\right\}.$$

Since $\Sigma(x_i-\bar{x}) = 0$,

$$\mathrm{V}[A] = \sigma^2\left\{\frac{1}{n} + \frac{\bar{x}^2}{\Sigma(x_i-\bar{x})^2}\right\}$$

$$= \sigma^2\{\Sigma(x_i-\bar{x})^2 + n\bar{x}^2\}/\{n\Sigma(x_i-\bar{x})^2\}$$

$$= \sigma^2\Sigma x_i^2/\{n\Sigma(x_i-\bar{x})^2\}, \tag{17}$$

on using the result $\Sigma(x_i-\bar{x})^2 = \Sigma x_i^2 - n\bar{x}^2$.

Since A, as given by (16), is a linear combination of the Y_i, it follows that the sampling distribution of A is normal with mean α and variance given by (17).

Finally, consider

$$Y_0 = A + Bx_0.$$

Substituting for A and B from (14) and (16),

$$Y_0 = \Sigma\left\{\frac{1}{n} - \frac{\bar{x}(x_i-\bar{x})}{\Sigma(x_i-\bar{x})^2} + \frac{x_0(x_i-\bar{x})}{\Sigma(x_i-\bar{x})^2}\right\}Y_i$$

$$= \Sigma\left\{\frac{1}{n} + \frac{(x_0-\bar{x})(x_i-\bar{x})}{\Sigma(x_i-\bar{x})^2}\right\}Y_i \tag{18}$$

Hence,

$$\mathrm{E}[Y_0] = \Sigma\left\{\frac{1}{n} + \frac{(x_0-\bar{x})(x_i-\bar{x})}{\Sigma(x_i-\bar{x})^2}\right\}(\alpha+\beta x_i)$$

$$= \alpha\left\{1 + \frac{(x_0-\bar{x})\Sigma(x_i-\bar{x})}{\Sigma(x_i-\bar{x})^2}\right\} + \beta\left\{\frac{\Sigma x_i}{n} + \frac{(x_0-\bar{x})\Sigma x_i(x_i-\bar{x})}{\Sigma(x_i-\bar{x})^2}\right\}$$

Using the results $\Sigma(x_i-\bar{x}) = 0$ and $\Sigma x_i(x_i-\bar{x}) = \Sigma(x_i-\bar{x})^2$, we have

$$\mathrm{E}[Y_0] = \alpha + \beta\{\bar{x} + (x_0-\bar{x})\} = \alpha + \beta x_0,$$

establishing that Y_0 is an unbiased estimator of $\alpha+\beta x_0$, the true value of y when $x = x_0$. Also,

$$V[Y_0] = \Sigma\left\{\frac{1}{n^2}+\frac{(x_0-\bar{x})^2\,(x_i-\bar{x})^2}{[\Sigma(x_i-\bar{x})^2]^2}+\frac{2(x_0-\bar{x})(x_i-\bar{x})}{n\Sigma(x_i-\bar{x})^2}\right\}\sigma^2$$

$$= \sigma^2\left\{\frac{1}{n}+\frac{(x_0-\bar{x})^2}{\Sigma(x_i-\bar{x})^2}\right\}. \qquad (19)$$

From (18), Y_0 is seen to be a linear combination of the Y_i and therefore Y_0 is normally distributed with mean $\alpha+\beta x_0$ and variance $V[Y_0]$ as given in (19).

EXERCISE 8.3B

1 Suppose x and y are two variables such that $y = \lambda x$, where λ is an unknown constant. In an experiment with x having the pre-set values $x_1, x_2, \ldots, x_n$, the corresponding values of y were measured to be $y_1, y_2, \ldots, y_n$, respectively. In Exercise 8.2 question 5 you showed that the least squares estimate of λ is $m = \Sigma x_i y_i/\Sigma x_i^2$. Assuming that the errors in the measured y-values are independent and normally distributed with mean zero and variance σ^2, show that the least squares estimator of λ is unbiased and is normally distributed with variance $\sigma^2/\Sigma x_i^2$.

The results of the experiment are shown in the following table.

$x =$	1·0	1·5	2·0	2·5
$y =$	2·6	3·7	5·3	6·0

Given that $\sigma^2 = 0{\cdot}5$, derive a 95% symmetrical confidence interval for λ.

2 Two variables x and y are known to be such that for all $0 \leqslant x \leqslant a$, $y = \alpha+\beta x$, where α and β are unknown constants. An experimental observation of the value of y corresponding to a fixed value of x is subject to a random error of mean zero and variance σ^2. In order to estimate β it is decided to carry out a total of $2n$ experiments with x fixed at values $x_1, x_2, \ldots, x_{2n}$, respectively, and to observe the corresponding values of y. By comparing standard errors, determine which of the following two sets of $2n$ values of x you would recommend as being the better for estimating β.

Set 1: $x_1 = x_2 = \ldots = x_n = 0$, $x_{n+1} = x_{n+2} = \ldots = x_{2n} = a$.

Set 2: $x_i = [(i-1)a]/(2n-1)$, $i = 1, 2, \ldots, 2n$.

3 Two variables x and y are such that $y = \alpha+\beta x$, where α and β are unknown constants. Experiments were conducted with x taking the values $1, 2, \ldots, 2n$, respectively, and the corresponding values of y were measured to be $y_1, y_2, \ldots, y_{2n}$. Assuming that the y-measurements are subject to independent random errors having mean zero and variance σ^2, show that

$$b_1 = \left[\sum_{i=n+1}^{2n} y_i - \sum_{i=1}^{n} y_i\right]\Big/ n^2$$

is an unbiased estimate of β, and that its standard error is greater than that of the least squares estimator of β.

8.4 Linear regression

Let Y_x denote a continuous random variable whose distribution depends upon the value of some other variable x. Consider first the case where the values of x can be specified, as illustrated by the following examples:

(i) Y_x = sand content of soil at a depth of x units;
(ii) Y_x = daily volume of milk from x cows;
(iii) Y_x = duration of relief from pain given a dose of x units of a pain-killing drug;
(iv) Y_x = yield of potatoes per plot resulting from the application of x units of fertiliser.

In each of these examples the value of x may be pre-specified.

The situation under discussion is illustrated in Fig. 8.5, in which we have sketched in the probability density function of Y_x for three values x_1, x_2, x_3 of the variable x and we have indicated the locations of the means $E[Y_x]$ of the three distributions.

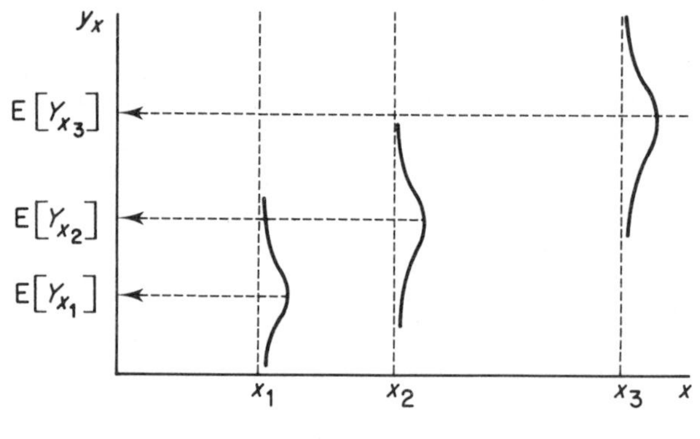

Fig. 8.5

Regarded as a function of x, the mean $E[Y_x]$ is defined to be the *regression function of* Y_x *on* x. Here, we shall restrict consideration to the case where the regression function is linear in x and we shall assume that

$$E[Y_x] = \alpha + \beta x, \tag{1}$$

for some unknown constants α and β. In many practical situations, (1) is a reasonable assumption to make for values of x within some limited range.

In order to estimate this relationship, suppose an experiment is conducted with x having the values $x_1, x_2, \ldots, x_n$, respectively. It is more convenient for what follows to adopt a change in notation by letting Y_i denote the random variable associated with $x = x_i$, for $i = 1, 2, \ldots, n$. In this notation, let the observed values of the Y_i be $y_1, y_2, \ldots, y_n$, respectively. Then

$$y_i = \alpha + \beta x_i + \varepsilon_i, \qquad i = 1, 2, \ldots, n, \tag{2}$$

where $\varepsilon_i \equiv y_i - \mathrm{E}[Y_i]$ is the deviation of the observed value of Y_i from its mean value $\mathrm{E}[Y_i] = \alpha + \beta x_i$.

Now suppose that we decide to estimate (1) by fitting the straight line

$$y = a + bx \tag{3}$$

to the data points (x_i, y_i), $i = 1, 2, \ldots, n$. If we do so using the principle of least squares as described in §8.2, then the resulting values of a and b will be precisely as given in that section, namely

$$b = [\Sigma (x_i - \bar{x})(y_i - \bar{y})]/\Sigma (x_i - \bar{x})^2 \tag{4}$$

$$a = \bar{y} - b\bar{x}. \tag{5}$$

Thus, the least squares estimate of (1) is

$$y = a + bx, \tag{6}$$

where a and b are given by (5) and (4), respectively. In the present context, the straight line (6) is referred to as the *sample least squares regression line of y on x*.

The essential difference between the estimate (6) given here and the corresponding one given in §8.2 is that the former provides an estimate of the *mean* of a random variable Y_x, whereas the latter provides an estimate of the *true* value of a mathematical variable y.

If we further assume that the random variables $Y_1, Y_2, \ldots, Y_n$, are independent and normally distributed with a *constant* variance σ^2, then the sampling distributions of the least squares estimators A, B and $A + Bx_0$ will be precisely as stated in §8.2, and the methods of §8.3 will be equally valid for inferences about α, β and $\mathrm{E}[Y_0] = \alpha + \beta x_0$.

EXAMPLE 1 *The following table gives the mass (y) of chemical that dissolved in water at each of 5 selected temperature levels (x°C).*

$x =$	10	20	30	40	50
$y =$	59	65	71	75	81

Assuming that the mean mass of chemical that dissolves in water at x°C is a linear function of x, derive the least squares estimate of the mean mass that dissolves in water at 35°C. Assuming that the masses that dissolve in water at x°C are normally distributed with variance 0·4 for all values of x, determine 90% confidence limits for the mean mass that will dissolve in water at 35°C.

Let Y denote the mean mass of chemical that will dissolve in water at x°C. We are given that $\mathrm{E}[Y] = \alpha + \beta x$. The least squares estimate of $\mathrm{E}[Y]$ when $x = 35$ is given by $y_0 = a + 35b$, where from (6) and (7),

$$b = [\Sigma (x_i - \bar{x})(y_i - \bar{y})]/\Sigma (x_i - \bar{x})^2, \qquad a = \bar{y} - b\bar{x}.$$

Using the alternative formula for b given by (12) in §8.2, we have

$$b = \frac{n\Sigma x_i y_i - (\Sigma x_i)(\Sigma y_i)}{n\Sigma x_i^2 - (\Sigma x_i)^2} = \frac{5 \times 11070 - 150 \times 351}{5 \times 5500 - 150^2} = 0{\cdot}54.$$

Also

$$a = \bar{y} - b\bar{x} = (351/5) - 0{\cdot}54 \times \frac{150}{5} = 54.$$

(It is left as an exercise to plot the data points and the fitted line on a graph.)

The least squares estimate of the mean mass of chemical that dissolves in water at 35°C is

$$y_0 = a + 35b = 54 + 35 \times 0{\cdot}54 = 72{\cdot}9.$$

From §8.3, this estimator is normally distributed with mean $E[Y_0] = \alpha + 35\beta$ and, from (12) of §8.3, its standard error is

$$\text{SE}[Y_0] = \left\{\sigma^2\left[\frac{1}{n} + \frac{(x_0 - \bar{x})^2}{\Sigma(x_i - \bar{x})^2}\right]\right\}^{\frac{1}{2}}$$

$$= \left\{0{\cdot}4\left[\frac{1}{5} + \frac{(35-30)^2}{1000}\right]\right\}^{\frac{1}{2}} = 0{\cdot}3.$$

Hence, 90% confidence limits for $E[Y_0]$ are

$$y_0 \pm 1{\cdot}64\ \text{SE}[Y_0] = 72{\cdot}9 \pm 0{\cdot}492 \simeq 72{\cdot}4 \text{ and } 73{\cdot}4.$$

EXERCISE 8.4A

1 The table shows the yields per plot of a certain crop grown under different rates of a fertiliser.

Amount of fertiliser (x)	0	1	2	3	4
Yield per plot (y)	29	35	45	54	61

(i) Calculate the equation of the sample least squares regression line of y on x, and hence obtain an estimate of the mean yield per plot when the amount of fertiliser applied is 2 units.

(ii) It may be assumed that for any given amount of fertiliser the yields per plot are normally distributed with variance 1·6, and that for the range of the amounts of fertiliser used in the experiment, the mean yield per plot is a linear function of the amount of fertiliser applied. Find a 95% confidence interval for the increase in the mean yield per plot when the amount of fertiliser applied is increased by 2.

2 The following table gives the ages in months and the weights in kilogrammes of eight babies.

Age in months	1	2	2	2	3	3	3	4
Weight in kg	4·5	6·4	5·9	6·4	6·7	6·8	7·2	7·6

(i) Calculate the equation of the samples least squares regression line of weight on age.

(ii) Suppose that the weights of babies of a given age are normally distributed with a mean which is a linear function of age and with a standard deviation of 0·4 kg. Use all the above data to calculate a 95% symmetrical confidence interval for the mean weight of 3-month old babies. Show that this interval is preferable to that deduced using only the three recorded weights of 3-month old babies.

8.4.1 The case of two random variables

In §8.4 we considered the case of a random variable Y_x associated with a specified value of the variable x. Now suppose that x is an observed value of another random variable X. Some examples are as follows.

(i) an adult female is chosen at random and her height is found to be x; let Y_x denote the weight of the chosen female;
(ii) a student taking 'A' level mathematics has to sit two papers; given that his mark on the first paper is x, let Y_x denote his mark on the second paper;
(iii) a randomly chosen tomato plant has x trusses; let Y_x denote the mass of tomatoes that will be produced by the plant;
(iv) a randomly chosen 16-year old boy is found to have a height of x; let Y_x denote the height of his father.

In each of the above examples, the value x is an observed value of another random variable X, unlike the examples in §8.4 where the value x was pre-specified.

Let X and Y denote two random variables associated with a random experiment. They will have a joint probability distribution, but here we shall restrict attention to the conditional distribution of one random variable given that the other has a specific value. Let Y_x denote the random variable whose distribution is the conditional distribution of Y when $X = x$. The mean $E[Y_x]$ of this conditional distribution, regarded as a function of x, is referred to as *the regression function of Y on x*. As in §8.4 we shall assume that

$$E[Y_x] = \alpha + \beta x, \tag{7}$$

for some unknown constants α and β.

Now suppose that in n independent trials of the random experiment concerned, the observed values of (X, Y) are (x_i, y_i), $i = 1, 2, \ldots, n$. We may then proceed exactly as in §8.4 by applying the method of least squares to obtain an estimate of (7) in the form

$$y = a + bx, \tag{8}$$

the values of a and b being precisely as in (4) and (5). The resulting equation (8) is referred to as *the sample least squares regression line of Y on x*. Furthermore, if we additionally assume that $Y_1, Y_2, \ldots, Y_n$ are independent normally distributed random variables having a common variance σ^2, and that the x_i-values have been measured accurately, then the sampling distributions of the least squares estimators A, B and $A+Bx_0$ of α, β and $\alpha+\beta x_0$, respectively, will be exactly as stated in §8.3, and the inferential methods described in that section will be equally valid for the case currently under discussion.

A new feature of the current situation is the existence of the random variable X_y, whose distribution is the conditional distribution of the random variable X given that $Y=y$. The mean $\mathrm{E}[X_y]$ of this conditional distribution is called *the regression function of X on y*. We shall again restrict consideration to the case when this function is linear by assuming that

$$\mathrm{E}[X_y] = \alpha' + \beta' y, \tag{9}$$

for some unknown constants α' and β'. Given the observations (x_i, y_i), $i = 1, 2, \ldots, n$, of (X, Y) we can again apply the method of least squares to obtain an estimate of (9) of the form

$$x = a' + b'y. \tag{10}$$

In this case the values a' and b' are chosen so as to minimise the sum of the squares of the deviations in the x-direction, these deviations being $\{x_i - (a' + b'y_i)\}$, $i = 1, 2, \ldots, n$. On observing that the roles of x and y are interchanged here as compared with our previous application of the principle of least squares, it follows from (4) and (5) that the least squares estimates of α' and β' are given by

$$b' = [\Sigma(x_i - \bar{x})(y_i - \bar{y})]/\Sigma(y_i - \bar{y})^2, \tag{11}$$

and

$$a' = \bar{x} - b'\bar{y}. \tag{12}$$

The line (10) with a' and b' given by (12) and (11) is called the *sample least squares regression line of x on y*.

From (5) and (12) we see that both sample least squares regression lines pass through the point $(\bar{x}, \bar{y})$. However, from (4) and (11), the slopes of the two sample regression lines will usually be different. The slope (defined to be the tangent of the angle that the line makes with the positive x-axis) of the regression line of y on x is, from (4), given by

$$b = [\Sigma(x_i - \bar{x})(y_i - \bar{y})]/\Sigma(x_i - \bar{x})^2,$$

whereas, from (11), the slope of the regression line of x on y is given by

$$(b')^{-1} = \Sigma(y_i - \bar{y})^2/[\Sigma(x_i - \bar{x})(y_i - \bar{y})].$$

Note that the two sample least squares regression lines serve different purposes. That of y on x, given by (8) is appropriate for estimating $\mathrm{E}[Y_x]$, the mean value of the random variable Y when the random variable X has the value x, whereas that of x on y is appropriate for estimating $\mathrm{E}[X_y]$.

Let us now amend our notation by letting X_i denote the random variable associated with the value y_i of Y, $i = 1, 2, \ldots, n$. Assuming that the X_i are independent and normally distributed with constant variance τ^2 and that the y_i-values are accurate, the sampling distributions of the least squares estimators A', B' and $A'+B'y_0$ of α', β' and $\alpha'+\beta' y_0$, respectively, can be derived following the procedure used in §8.3.1. Interchanging x and y, replacing σ^2 by τ^2, α by α' and β by β' in the results given in §8.3, we find that

(i) B′ is normally distributed with mean β' and variance

$$\mathrm{V}[B'] = \tau^2/\Sigma(y_i-\bar{y})^2,$$

(ii) A' is normally distributed with mean α' and variance

$$\mathrm{V}[A'] = \tau^2\Sigma y_i^2/[n\Sigma(y_i-\bar{y}^2],$$

(iii) $X_0 = A'+B'y_0$ is normally distributed with mean $\alpha'+\beta' y_0$ and variance

$$\mathrm{V}[X_0] = \tau^2\left\{\frac{1}{n}+\frac{(y_0-\bar{y})^2}{\Sigma(y_i-\bar{y})^2}\right\}.$$

These results enable us to determine confidence intervals and to perform significance tests relating to the values of α', β' and $\alpha'+\beta' y_0$.

EXAMPLE 2 *The following table shows the ages in years and the blood pressures of 9 women.*

Age in years (x)	36	38	42	42	47	49	55	56
Blood pressure (y)	118	115	140	125	128	145	150	147

Obtain the least squares estimate of the mean blood pressure of women aged 50.

Since we require an estimate of mean blood pressure the appropriate sample least squares regression line is that of blood pressure (y) on age (x). Its equation is

$$y = \bar{y}+b(x-\bar{x}),$$

where, from (4) above and (12) of §8.2,

$$\begin{aligned} b &= [\Sigma(x_i-\bar{x})(y_i-\bar{y})]/\Sigma(x_i-\bar{x})^2 \\ &= [n\Sigma x_i y_i-(\Sigma x_i)(\Sigma y_i)]/[n\Sigma x_i^2-(\Sigma x_i)^2]. \end{aligned}$$

From the tabulated data we have $n = 8$, $\Sigma x_i = 365$, $\Sigma x_i{}^2 = 17039$, $\Sigma y_i = 1068$, $\Sigma x_i y_i = 49351$.
Hence,

$$\begin{aligned} b &= (8\times 49351-365\times 1068)/(8\times 17039-365^2) \\ &\simeq 1{\cdot}6158. \end{aligned}$$

Since $\bar{x} = 365/8 = 45{\cdot}625$ and $\bar{y} = 1068/8 = 133{\cdot}5$, the sample least squares regression line of y on x has the equation

$$y = 133{\cdot}5+1{\cdot}6158(x-45{\cdot}625)$$

or

$$y = 59{\cdot}779+1{\cdot}6158x.$$

Thus, the least squares estimate of the mean blood pressure of women aged 50 is

$$59{\cdot}779 + 1{\cdot}6158 \times 50 \simeq 140{\cdot}6.$$

EXERCISE 8.4B

1 The following table shows the weights in kilograms of 8 turkeys at the beginning (x) and at the end (y) of a special feeding programme.

Initial weight (x kg)	2·2	2·5	2·7	3·1	3·1	3·3	3·3	3·8
Final weight (y kg)	5·8	6·0	6·1	6·3	6·4	6·5	6·6	6·7

Given that $\Sigma x = 24{\cdot}0$, $\Sigma x^2 = 73{\cdot}82$, $\Sigma y = 50{\cdot}4$, $\Sigma xy = 152{\cdot}29$, estimate the mean final weight of turkeys of intial weight 3 kg, giving your answer correct to the nearest tenth of a kilogramme.

2 The marks obtained by 10 candidates in the two 'A' level papers in mathematics in a certain year are shown in the following table.

Paper 1	74	48	36	59	80	52	55	63	18	61
Paper 2	72	22	41	43	79	33	64	38	5	68

Derive the equations of the least squares regression lines appropriate for estimating (i) the mean mark on Paper 2 by candidates having a specific mark on Paper 1, (ii) the mean mark on Paper 1 by candidates having a specific mark on Paper 2.
Plot the data points on a graph and draw in the two regression lines.

3 The following table shows the percentage nickel content (x) and the corresponding toughness (y) of each of 12 specimens of alloy steel.

% nickel (x)	2·5	3·3	2·7	3·8	2·8	3·6
Toughness (y)	46·8	59·5	53·5	65·1	53·4	64·4
% nickel (x)	3·5	2·9	3·7	3·0	3·2	3·4
Toughness (y)	63·2	53·8	63·7	55·7	56·5	59·2

The following quantities were calculated from the above data:

$$\Sigma x = 38{\cdot}4, \quad \Sigma x^2 = 124{\cdot}82, \quad \Sigma y = 694{\cdot}8, \quad \Sigma xy = 2248{\cdot}63.$$

Calculate a linear equation suitable for estimating the mean toughness of alloy steel having a specified nickel content.
Given that specimens of alloy steel having the same % nickel content have hardnesses that are independent and normally distributed with constant variance 36, obtain 95% confidence limits for the mean toughness of specimens containing 3% nickel.

REVIEW PROBLEMS ON CHAPTER 8

1 An experiment was performed to examine the effect of a nutrient concentrate on the growth of a particular strain of mould. The radius of the mould colony was measured at intervals after the day of inoculation with the concentrate. The results are shown in the table.

Day	2	4	6	8	10	12
Radius (mm)	6·2	11·0	15·5	19·0	25·1	28·2

Plot a scatter diagram, and find the equation of the regression line of radius of the colony on time. Draw this line on your scatter diagram. Assuming that the growth is linear, estimate the rate of growth. Explain why this regression line is a better line than any other straight line for predicting the radius of the colony at any given time. *(L 1982)*

2 The model $y_i = a + bx_i + \varepsilon_i$ is to be fitted to a set of n points $(x_i, y_i), i = 1$ to n, where the x_i are values of a controlled variable and the ε_i denote errors. Explain what is meant by 'the principle of least squares' for estimating the values of a and b.

In an experiment to test the effects of relative humidity on metabolic rate, nine beetles were starved for six days each in a controlled environment of a particular humidity (x_i) and the weight loss (y_i micrograms) noted. The results are shown in the table.

% relative humidity (x_i)	0	12	30	43	53	63	75	85	93
Weight loss in μg (y_i)	360	326	267	243	236	233	187	168	149

(i) Plot the data on a graph.
(ii) Calculate the least squares regression line of y on x and plot this line on the graph.
(iii) For beetles kept in the same way at percentage relative humidities of 50 and 100, estimate the weight loss in each case. *(JMB 1981)*

3 Corresponding to a given value, x_i, of a variable x there is a random variable Y_i whose mean is proportional to x_i, that is $E[Y_i] = \beta x_i$, for some constant β. If $y_1, y_2, \ldots, y_n$ are observed values of $Y_1, Y_2, \ldots, Y_n$, respectively, show that the least squares estimate of β is

$$b = \left(\sum_{i=1}^{n} x_i y_i\right) \Big/ \left(\sum_{i=1}^{n} x_i^2\right).$$

Verify that b is an unbiased estimate of β. Assuming further that $y_1, y_2, \ldots, y_n$ are independent and that each Y_i has variance σ^2, show that the standard error of b is equal to $\sigma/(\Sigma x_i^2)^{1/2}$. Given that $n = 10$, $\sigma = 1$, $\Sigma x_i = 52$, $\Sigma x_i^2 = 400$, $\Sigma y_i = 82$, $\Sigma x_i y_i = 572$, and assuming that b is normally distributed, calculate a 95% symmetric confidence interval for the mean value of Y_i when $x_i = 6$. *(JMB 1980)*

4 It is known that the true response y in a certain chemical experiment is a linear function of the operating temperature x. However, the experimental determinations of y are subject to random errors, so that when an experiment is performed at temperature x_i, the observed response y_i is such that $y_i = \alpha + \beta x_i + e_i$, where $\alpha + \beta x_i$ is the true response and e_i is the error. The following table gives the observed responses in six experiments, two at each of three temperatures.

	Temperature (x)		
	30	40	50
Observed responses (y)	14 12	10 11	7 6

Use the data to obtain the least squares estimate of the linear relationship connecting y and x. (You are given that $\Sigma xy = 2270$.)
The errors, e_i, are independent and normally distributed with zero mean and unit standard deviation. Calculate 90% confidence limits for (i) the value of α, (ii) the value of β, (iii) the true value of y when $x = 50$. (*WJEC 1978*)

5 It is known that the heart rate of a patient treated with a certain drug is approximately linearly related to the dose administered, the precise form of this linear relationship being dependent on the patient. The following table shows the heart rate, y, in beats per minute, of a patient treated with x grains of the drug on six distinct occasions.

x	1	2	3	3	4	5
y	50	60	70	80	90	100

(i) Calculate the least squares estimate of the linear relationship between y and x for this patient. (ii) Assuming that the heart rate determinations are subject to errors which are normally distributed with mean zero and standard deviation 4 beats per minute find (a) a 95% confidence interval for the increase in the patient's heart rate corresponding to an increase of 1 grain in the dose of the drug, (b) a 90% confidence interval for the heart rate of the patient if he is given a dose of 3·5 grains. (*WJEC 1980*)

6 Two variables x and y of interest in an experiment are known to be linearly related, but the coefficients in this relationship are not known. A series of 15 experiments was conducted in which 3 determinations of y were made for each of 5 values of x. The x-values are accurate but the determinations of the y-values are subject to independent random errors that are normally distributed with mean zero and standard deviation 1·25. The observed values in the series of experiments are shown in the following table.

x	1	2	3	4	5
y	19 18 21	17 16 17	12 11 13	9 10 7	3 3 4

The following quantities were calculated from the above data:

$$\Sigma x = 45, \quad \Sigma y = 180, \quad \Sigma x^2 = 165, \quad \Sigma xy = 420.$$

(i) Calculate the equation of the least squares estimate of the linear relationship between x and y. (ii) Estimate the true value of y when $x = 4$.

Determine the standard error of this estimate. Explain why this estimate of y when $x = 4$ is preferable to that obtained from averaging the three observed values of y when $x = 4$. (iii) Calculate a 90% confidence interval for the true value of y when $x = 4$. *(WJEC 1981)*

7 An investigation of a possible linear relationship between two variables x and y was conducted with x having five prespecified values, the corresponding values of y being observed. The results obtained are given in the following table:

x	5	10	15	20	25
y	55	52	50	48	45

You may assume that $\Sigma x^2 = 1375$ and that $\Sigma xy = 3630$. Given that the true relationship between x and y is $y = \alpha + \beta x$, determine the least squares estimates of α and β. Suppose that the observed values of y are subject to independent random errors that are normally distributed with mean zero and standard deviation 0·5. Calculate 90% confidence limits for (i) the true value of y when $x = 20$, (ii) the difference between the true values of y when $x = 5$ and $x = 25$. *(WJEC 1982)*

9 Correlation

9.1 The product moment correlation coefficient

Let X and Y denote two random variables associated with a random experiment. Some examples were given in §8.4.1, where it was assumed that for any specified value x of X, the distribution of Y was such that its mean, $E[Y_x]$, was linearly related to x. Sample values of (X, Y) were then used to estimate the linear relationship. Now suppose that there are no grounds for making this assumption. In such a situation, a sample of values of (X, Y) may be used to investigate whether there is some sort of pattern between the corresponding values of the two variables.

Let (x_i, y_i), $i = 1, 2, \ldots, n$ denote a random sample of n values of (X, Y). Plotting the values (x_i, y_i) on a graph, called a *scatter diagram*, will provide some indication of the presence of any pattern that may exist between corresponding values of X and Y. Three different scatter diagrams are illustrated in Figs 9.1, 9.2 and 9.3. Whereas there is a discernible pattern in Figs 9.1 and 9.2, this is not the case in Fig. 9.3. The scatter diagram in Fig. 9.1 shows clearly that the larger the value of x the larger the value of y tends to be, while in Fig. 9.2 the larger the value of x the smaller the value of y tends to be.

What we would like is some numerical measure of the strength of any pattern that may exist between the x_i and the y_i. A commonly used measure of the strength of a *linear* pattern is the *product moment correlation coefficient* r defined by

$$r = \frac{\Sigma(x_i - \bar{x})(y_i - \bar{y})}{\sqrt{[\{\Sigma(x_i - \bar{x})^2\}\{\Sigma(y_i - \bar{y})^2\}]}}, \tag{1}$$

where $\bar{x}$, $\bar{y}$ are the means of the values of x and y, respectively, each summation ranges from $i = 1$ to $i = n$, and the positive square root is taken in the denominator. Comparing (1) with formula (4) in §8.4 for the slope b of the sample least squares regression line of y on x it is seen that r and b have the same sign. It follows that:

(i) r will be positive when the values of y tend to increase as the values of x increase (as in Fig. 9.1);
(ii) r will be negative when the values of y tend to decrease as the values of x increase (as in Fig. 9.2);

(iii) r will be zero, or close to zero, when the slope b of the sample least squares regression line of y on x is zero or close to zero, so that there is no general pattern apparent (as in Fig. 9.3).

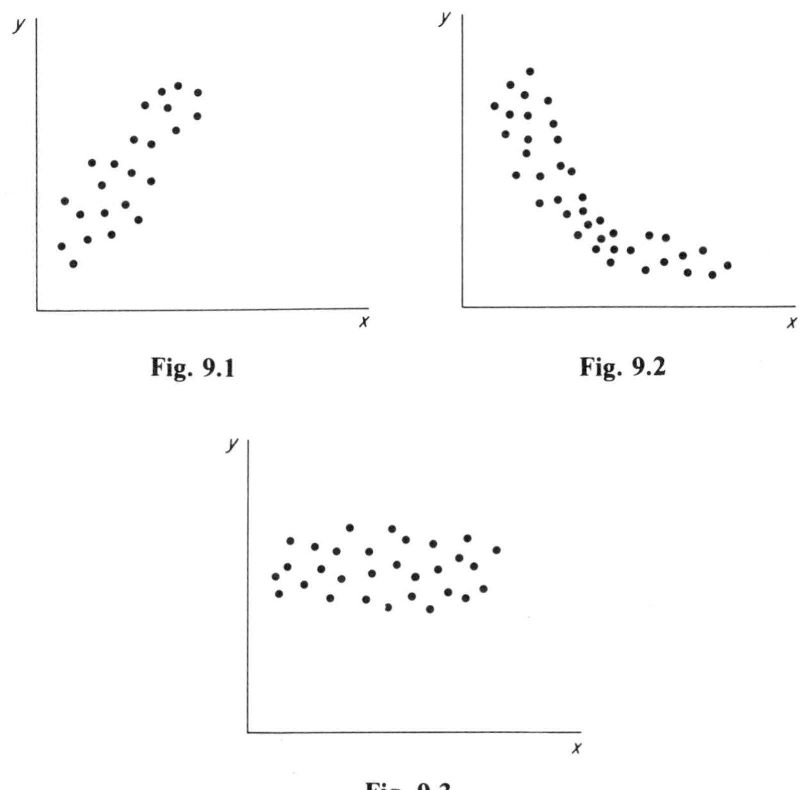

Fig. 9.1 **Fig. 9.2**

Fig. 9.3

It may be shown that r is restricted to values ranging from -1 to $+1$, and that the extreme values (± 1) are attained only when the sample values (x_i, y_i) fall exactly on a straight line, this line having positive slope when $r = +1$ and negative slope when $r = -1$. When $r = \pm 1$, the values (x_i, y_i) are said to be *perfectly correlated*, and when $r = 0$ they are said to be *uncorrelated*.

It is evident from the above properties that r is appropriate as a measure of the strength of a *linear pattern* displayed by (x_i, y_i). The closer the numerical vlaue of r is to unity, the stronger is the linearity association between the x_i and the y_i. A value of r close to zero is indicative of the lack of any linearity pattern between the x_i and y_i, but this does not necessarily mean that there is no discernible pattern there. For example, it may be verified that $r = 0$ for the data given in Table 9.1 and displayed in Fig. 9.4. For these data there is a very pronounced curvilinear relationship between the x_i and the y_i; in fact, for all six pairs of values, $y_i = -9x_i^2 + 54x_i + 7$.

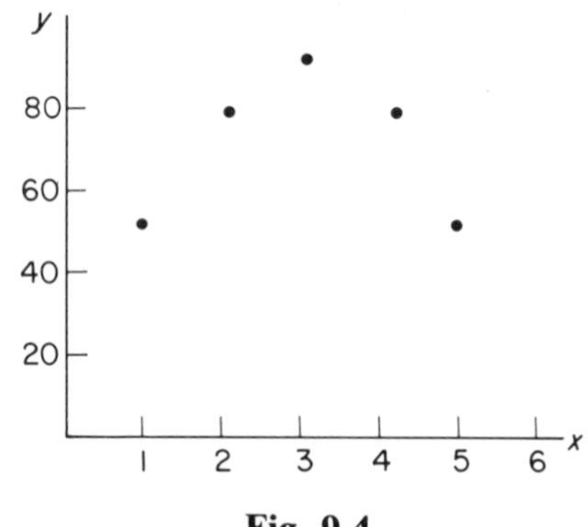

Fig. 9.4

Table 9.1

x	1	2	3	4	5
y	52	79	88	79	52

Using the expansions given in §8.2 for the various sums in (1), an alternative formula for r is

$$r = \frac{n\Sigma x_i y_i - (\Sigma x_i)(\Sigma y_i)}{\sqrt{[\{n\Sigma x_i^2 - (\Sigma x_i)^2\}\{n\Sigma y_i^2 - (\Sigma y_i)^2\}]}} \qquad (2)$$

which is often simpler than (1) for computing r, especially when using a calculator, or when the value of $\bar{x}$ or $\bar{y}$ involves more figures than the observed values.

A further arithmetical simplification for computing r may be achieved by using linear transformations as described near the end of §8.2. Transforming from x_i to $u_i = k_1 x_i - c_1$ and from y_i to $v_i = k_2 y_i - c_2$, it is readily verified from (1) that the correlation coefficient between the u_i and v_i is identically equal to that between the x_i and y_i.

We mentioned earlier the need for caution when interpreting a value of r close to zero as implying that there is no discernible pattern; and that drawing the scatter diagram should avoid any misinterpretation. Caution is also called for when interpreting a value of r which is numerically close to 1. The scatter diagram will indicate a strong linear pattern but this does not mean that there is a causal effect. For example, a scatter diagram of annual crime rates and teachers' salaries over a period of years would exhibit a strong positive correlation, but it is clear from the nature of the variables that an increase in one does not cause an increase in the other.

Inference (estimation and hypotheses testing) on the value of the population correlation coefficient (for the joint distribution of X and Y) is beyond the scope of this text.

EXERCISE 9.1

1 Verify that for the data in Table 9.1 above, the value of r is equal to zero.

2 An investigation is to be made of a possible association between the heights and the masses of boys of the same age. Would you anticipate that the value of the product moment correlation coefficient obtained from the results of such an investigation will be (i) positive, (ii) close to zero?

The following table gives the height (in cm) and the mass (in kg) of each of 10 boys of the same age.

Boys	1	2	3	4	5	6	7	8	9	10
Height (cm)	131	132	135	138	139	141	144	147	149	153
Mass (kg)	33	34	37	36	38	42	50	48	51	62

(i) Draw a scatter diagram for the data and calculate the value of the product moment correlation coefficient between height and mass. Comment on your result in the light of your answers to the question posed above.

(ii) If, in the above investigation, the heights had been recorded in inches and the masses in pounds, what would then be the value of the product moment correlation coefficient between height and mass?

3 Calculate and interpret the value of the product moment correlation coefficient for the data in the following table.

x	4	5	9	14	18	22	24
y	2·6	2·2	1·1	1·6	0·7	1·3	0·6

9.2 Comparing two sets of ranks

9.2.1 Introduction

Sometimes, observations of a variable under investigation cannot be measured reliably but they can be ranked according to some criterion. Examples of such variables are depth or richness of colour, fragrance, beauty, skill and artistic value. Although observations on such a variable cannot be measured on a realistic numerical scale it is often possible to rank them according to preference or to some other criterion.

Consider two sets of rankings (from 1 to n) that have been assigned independently to n items. The assignments may have been made by two persons or by applying two different criteria. Corresponding to the rank order $1, 2, \ldots, n$ in Set I, let the rank order in Set II be $x_1, x_2, \ldots, x_n$, as displayed in Table 9.2. Note that $x_1, x_2, \ldots, x_n$ is some ordered arrangement of the n integers $1, 2, \ldots, n$.

Table 9.2 Two sets of ranks of n items

Set I ranking	1	$2 \ldots i \ldots n$
Set II ranking	x_i	$x_2 \ldots x_i \ldots x_n$

9.2.2 Measure of agreement

Suppose the objective is to assess the extent or degree of agreement between the two sets of ranks. The discrepancies between the two sets of ranks displayed in Table 9.2 are $d_i = i - x_i$, $i = 1, 2, \ldots, n$, and one possible measure of the overall discrepancy is $t = \Sigma d_i^2$. When there is complete agreement between the two sets of ranks the value of t will be zero, while the larger the value of t the greater is the discrepancy. When there is complete disagreement, so that one set is simply the reverse of the other, then it may be shown that $t = \frac{1}{3}n(n^2-1)$, which is the maximum value that t can take.

The above properties of t indicate that the smaller its value the better is the agreement. However, a small value of t could arise when, in fact, the set II ranks have been assigned randomly. Thus, given that t has a small value, before concluding that there is consistency in the ways the sets of ranking were assigned, we would need to ascertain that it is unlikely that such a small t could have arisen from a random assignment. That is, in the terminology of Chapter 7, we need to formulate a significance test.

Consider the null hypothesis H_0 that, relative to the Set I ranks, the Set II ranks were assigned at random. Let T denote the random variable whose value $t = \Sigma d_i^2$ is to be calculated from the observed sets of ranks. For any observed t we need to calculate $p_0 = P(T \leqslant t$ when H_0 is true) and we will reject H_0 in favour of a degree of agreement between the two ways in which the items were ranked only if p_0 is less than the preassigned significance level (or probability of a type-1 error).

To evaluate p_0 we need to know the sampling distribution of T when H_0 (random assignment of ranks) is true. When H_0 is true there are $n!$ equally probable rank orderings and we will need to evaluate the value of T for each of these in order to find the sampling distribution of T. This clearly is a very time consuming exercise even for a relatively small n. Fortunately tables have been compiled for determining p_0 for varying values of n. One such table, part of which is reproduced in Table 9.3 by kind permission of the University of London Schools Examinations Board, appears in the booklet of formulae and tables used in that board's examinations. Using this table we find, for example, that when $n = 7$, $P(T \leqslant 40) = 0{\cdot}278$ and $P(T \leqslant 8) = 0{\cdot}0119$. This table may be used whenever there are no tied ranks in either set of ranks. We shall restrict our discussion to rankings in which ties are not permitted.

Table 9.3 Probability that Σd^2 exceeds, or is less than, certain values for $5 \leq n \leq 10$

$n = 5$ Max. $\Sigma d^2 = 40$			n = 6 Max. $\Sigma d^2 = 70$			$n = 7$ Max. $\Sigma d^2 = 112$			$n = 8$ Max. $\Sigma d^2 = 168$			$n = 9$ Max. $\Sigma d^2 = 240$			$n = 10$ Max. $\Sigma d^2 = 330$		
Σd^2		P	Σd^2		P	Σd^2		P	Σd^2		P	Σd^2		P	Σd^2		P
$\leqslant$	$\geqslant$		$\leqslant$	$\geqslant$		$\leqslant$	$\geqslant$		$\leqslant$	$\geqslant$		$\leqslant$	$\geqslant$		$\leqslant$	$\geqslant$	
18	22	0·475	28	42	0·357	54	58	0·482	78	90	0·441	112	128	0·440	160	170	0·473
16	24	0·392	26	44	0·329	52	60	0·453	74	94	0·397	108	132	0·405	154	176	0·433
14	26	0·342	24	46	0·282	50	62	0·420	68	100	0·332	104	136	0·371	148	182	0·393
12	28	0·258	22	48	0·249	48	64	0·391	64	104	0·291	100	140	0·339	140	190	0·341
10	30	0·225	20	50	0·210	46	66	0·356	60	108	0·250	96	144	0·307	132	198	0·292
8	32	0·175	18	52	0·178	44	68	0·331	56	112	0·214	92	148	0·276	124	206	0·246
6	34	0·117	16	54	0·149	42	70	0·297	54	114	0·195	88	152	0·247	116	214	0·204
4	36	0·0667	14	56	0·121	40	72	0·278	52	116	0·180	84	156	0·218	114	216	0·194
2	38	0·0417	12	58	0·0875	38	74	0·249	48	120	0·150	80	160	0·193	108	222	0·165
0	40	0·0083	10	60	0·0681	36	76	0·222	46	122	0·134	76	164	0·168	100	230	0·132
			8	62	0·0154	34	78	0·198	44	124	0·122	72	168	0·146	92	238	0·102
			6	64	0·0292	32	80	0·177	42	126	0·108	68	172	0·125	90	240	0·0956
			4	66	0·0167	30	82	0·151	40	128	0·0983	64	176	0·106	84	246	0·0774
			2	68	0·0083	28	84	0·133	38	130	0·0855	62	178	0·0969	78	252	0·0616
			0	70	0·0014	26	86	0·118	36	132	0·0756	56	184	0·0738	74	256	0·0524
						24	88	0·100	34	134	0·0661	50	190	0·0540	72	258	0·0481
						22	90	0·0833	32	136	0·0575	48	192	0·0484	68	262	0·0403
						20	92	0·0694	30	138	0·0481	40	200	0·0294	62	268	0·0302
						18	94	0·0548	28	140	0·0415	34	206	0·0184	56	274	0·0219
						16	96	0·0440	24	144	0·0288	28	212	0·0107	50	280	0·0153
						14	98	0·0331	20	148	0·0184	26	214	0·0086	44	286	0·0101
						12	100	0·0240	16	152	0·0109	22	218	0·0054	42	288	0·0087
						10	102	0·0171	14	154	0·0077	20	220	0·0041	36	294	0·0053
						8	104	0·0119	12	156	0·0054	16	224	0·0023	30	300	0·0029
						6	106	0·0062	10	158	0·0036	14	226	0.0015	22	308	0·0011
						4	108	0·0034	6	162	0·0011	12	228	0·0010	16	314	0·0004
						2	110	0·0014	4	164	0·0006	10	230	0·0007	10	320	0·0001

EXAMPLE 1 *A teacher ranked her 8 pupils for their ability in mathematics. Her rankings and those of the marks obtained by the 8 pupils in a mathematics examination are shown in Table 9.4. Using a 5% significance level determine whether these results provide sufficient evidence to conclude that the teacher has some proficiency in ranking her pupils' performances in an examination.*

Table 9.4 Teacher's and examination marks ranks of 8 pupils

Pupil	A	B	C	D	E	F	G	H
Teacher's ranks	3	2	1	5	8	7	6	4
Examination ranks	4	1	3	8	5	6	7	2

Let us set up the null hypothesis H_0 that the teacher allocates her ranks at random to the 8 pupils. Let T denote the sum of the squares of the discrepancies between the teacher's ranks and those based on the marks in the examination. For the given data, the observed value of T is

$$t = (-1)^2 + (1)^2 + (-2)^2 + (-3)^2 + (3)^2 + (1)^2 + (-1)^2 + (2)^2 = 30.$$

Referring to Table 9.3 with $n = 8$ we find that if H_0 is true, then

$$p_0 = P(T \leqslant 30) = 0{\cdot}0481$$

Since $p_0 < 0{\cdot}05$, we reject H_0 at the 5% significance level and conclude that the teacher does have some proficiency in ranking her pupils' performances in an examination.

EXERCISE 9.2

1 Two motoring magazines carried out independent surveys of the new car models at a motor show. Each one ranked the models according to the improvements that had been introduced into the models. The rankings of the 10 new models (A–J) are given in the table below. Calculate a measure of the degree of agreement between the two sets of ranks and use a 1% significance level to test whether this degree of agreement is better than would be reasonable under random allocation of ranks.

Model	A	B	C	D	E	F	G	H	I	J
Magazine I	2	3	6	1	5	4	9	7	10	8
Magazine II	1	2	4	3	7	6	5	8	10	9

2 Six bulls were ranked in order of merit at an agricultural show by the official judge and by three assistants who were training to be judges. The rankings given by the judges are shown in the following table. Which of the assistants would you regard as having given a rank order agreeing most closely with that of the official judge? Using a 5% significance level, determine which of the assistants (if any) may be regarded as having given ranks which are not significantly different from those given by the official judge.

Official judge	1	2	3	4	5	6
Assistant A	1	4	3	5	6	2
Assistant B	2	1	3	5	4	6
Assistant C	1	2	5	3	6	4

9.3 Spearman's rank correlation coefficient

In §9.1 we used the sample product moment correlation coefficient as a statistic for assessing a possible association between two random variables. However, we did not formalise this as a significance test because such a formalisation is beyond the scope of this text and has to make certain assumptions about the form of the joint distribution of the two random variables under investigation. We now offer an alternative method based on replacing the sample values by their rankings. The method will be equally valid for two variables which are measurable only on an ordinal scale.

Consider a random sample of pairs of observed values of X and Y. First rank the observed values of X and the corresponding values of Y. Recording the rankings of the sample values of X as $1, 2, \ldots, n$, let y_i denote the ranking of the sample value of Y corresponding to the sample value of X which has rank i, $i = 1, 2, \ldots, n$ (see Table 9.2). Let $d_i = i - y_i$, $i = 1, 2, \ldots, n$ denote the discrepancies between the two sets of rankings. It is then not difficult to show that formula (1) or (2) in §9.1 for the product moment correlation coefficient applied to the pairs of values (i, y_i) reduces to

$$r_s = 1 - \frac{6\Sigma d_i^2}{n(n^2-1)} \tag{1}$$

which is known as *Spearman's rank correlation coefficient*. From the properties of r given in §9.1, it follows that

(i) $-1 \leqslant r_s \leqslant 1$;
(ii) $r_s = +1$ implies perfect positive correlation, or equivalently, complete agreement between the two sets of ranks, so that $d_i = 0$ and $\Sigma d_i^2 = 0$;
(iii) $r_s = -1$ implies perfect negative correlation, or equivalently, complete disagreement between the two sets of ranks, one set being a complete reversal of the other; in this case, it may be shown that $\Sigma d_i^2 = \frac{1}{3}n(n^2-1)$.

Let ρ_s (where ρ is the Greek letter rho) denote the population value of Spearman's rank correlation coefficient. If there is no association between corresponding values of X and Y (or X and Y are independent random variables), then $\rho_s = 0$. If high values of X tend to pair off with high values of Y then $\rho_s > 0$, while if high values of X tend to pair off with low values of Y then $\rho_s < 0$.

In §9.2.2 we were concerned only with assessing the extent of the agreement between two sets of ranks and, consequently, we derived a significant test equivalent to testing $H_0 : \rho_s = 0$ (random allocation) against the one-sided alternative $H_1 : \rho_s > 0$ (some degree of agreement). In the situation we are now discussing, the two-sided hypothesis $H_1 : \rho_s \neq 0$ is the more appropriate alternative so as to allow consideration of a possible positive or negative correlation.

From the properties of r_s given above, a *numerically* large r_s would cast doubt on the null hypothesis $H_0 : \rho_s = 0$. Following the procedure described in Chapter 7, if R_s denotes the random variable whose observed value is r_s, then to test $H_0 : \rho_s = 0$ against $H_1 : \rho_s \neq 0$ we should proceed as follows:

(i) if $r_s > 0$, evaluate $p_0 \equiv P(R_s \geqslant r_s$ when H_0 is true);
(ii) if $r_s < 0$, evaluate $p_0 \equiv P(R_s \leqslant r_s$ when H_0 is true);
and, if the chosen significance level is α, H_0 should be rejected only if the calculated p_0 is less than $\frac{1}{2}\alpha$.

We do not need to determine the sampling distribution of R_s to evaluate p_0 since this is readily done using Table 9.3 on noting from (1) that $R_s \geqslant r_s$ is equivalent to $T \leqslant t$ and $R_s \leqslant r_s$ is equivalent to $T \geqslant t$, where T is the random variable whose observed value is $t = \Sigma d_i^2$.

EXAMPLE 1 *The following table shows the initial weights (in grams) and the gains in weight (in grams) of 7 young female rats of the same age fed on a high protein diet over a period of eight weeks.*

Rat	1	2	3	4	5	6	7
Initial weight (g)	50	64	76	65	74	60	69
Gain in weight (g)	128	159	158	119	133	112	96

Calculate Spearman's rank correlation coefficient. Use a 5% significance level to test whether there is any association between initial weight and gain in weight; state your conclusion in words.

The ranked values (from smallest to largest) of the initial weights and the corresponding ranked values of the gains are as displayed in Table 9.5.

From the entries in the last row

$$t = \Sigma d_i^2 = 9 + 16 + 1 + 1 + 1 + 0 + 16 = 44,$$

$$\text{so that } r_s = 1 - \frac{6 \times 44}{7 \times 48} = 0{\cdot}214 \text{ to 3 decimal places.}$$

Table 9.5 Ranks of initial weights and gains in weight of 7 rats.

Rat	1	2	3	4	5	6	7
Initial weight rank	1	3	7	4	6	2	5
Gain in weight rank	4	7	6	3	5	2	1
Discrepancy d_i =	−3	−4	1	1	1	0	4

We now test H_0: no association, against H_1: there is an association. Since $r_s > 0$ we need to evaluate

$$p_0 = P(R_s \geqslant 0{\cdot}214 \text{ when } H_0 \text{ is true}) = P(T \leqslant 44 \text{ when } H_0 \text{ is true})$$

From Table 9.3 with $n = 7$ we find $p_0 = P(T \leqslant 44) = 0{\cdot}331$.

Since p_0 is greater than 0·025, there is insufficient evidence to conclude that there is any association between the initial weight and the gain in weight.

Suppose, instead, that the two sets of ranks were such that $t = \Sigma d_i^2 = 12$, so that $r_s = 1 - (6 \times 12)/(7 \times 48) = 0{\cdot}786$. Then

$$p_0 = P(R_s \geqslant 0{\cdot}786) = P(T \leqslant 12) = 0{\cdot}024.$$

Here, since p_0 is less than 0·025, we would reject H_0 at the 5% significance level and conclude that there is a positive association (or correlation) between initial weight and gain in weight; that is, the heavier the rat is initially the greater its gain in weight tends to be.

EXERCISE 9.3

1 In Question 2 of Exercise 9.1 rank the values of the two variables (height and mass), and calculate Spearman's rank correlation coefficient. Assuming that the only possible alternative to there being no association between the two variables is that they are positively correlated, apply a 1% significance level test to draw a conclusion on the association between the two variables.

2 In Question 3 of Exercise 9.1 rank the values of the two variables (x and y) and calculate Spearman's rank correlation coefficient. What conclusion do you draw about the association between the two variables?

REVIEW PROBLEMS ON CHAPTER 9

1 Ten students sat two physics tests, one practical and one theoretical. Their marks out of 10 are recorded in the following table.

Practical test	8	6	10	8	5	6	8	10	7	7
Theoretical test	6	7	8	6	7	4	9	10	5	8

Draw a scatter diagram of the pairs of marks. Show that the product moment correlation coefficient for the data is equal to $(\sqrt{15})/7$. *(L 1983)*

2 A *Designer* and a *Buyer* were asked to forecast, in order of their sales potential, the ranks of ten styles of ladies' shoes for last Autumn's production. These forecasts and the ranks of the actual sales are shown in the table below. Calculate Spearman's Σd^2 to compare each forecast with the actual sales. Compare also the two forecasts with each other, commenting on the results. Using the data in the table, suggest a method of making a forecast which might be more accurate than that of the *Designer* or the *Buyer* alone.

Shoe styles	A	B	C	D	E	F	G	H	J	K
Actual ranks	5	8	1	9	4	2	7	10	6	3
Buyer's ranks	7	6	2	9	5	3	8	10	4	1
Designer's ranks	2	10	1	7	3	4	6	8	9	5

(*L 1980*)

3 The data in the following table are the lengths x cm of the wings and the lengths y cm of the tails of 10 birds of a certain species. Given that $\Sigma x^2 = 1137{\cdot}86$, $\Sigma y^2 = 574{\cdot}15$, $\Sigma xy = 808{\cdot}08$, calculate (a) the product moment correlation coefficient, (b) a rank correlation coefficient.

Using your rank correlation coefficient discuss whether the result leads you to think that wing length and tail length in the species are related.

x	10·4	10·8	10·2	10·3	10·2	10·7	10·8	11·2	10·6	11·4
y	7·4	7·6	7·2	7·4	7·1	7·4	7·8	7·7	7·8	8·3

(*L 1982*)

[For a group of equal values assign each the average of the ranks that would have been assigned had they been unequal.]

4 The positions in a league of 8 rugby clubs at the end of a season and the average attendances (in hundreds) at home matches during that season are shown in the following table. Calculate a coefficient of rank correlation between position in the league and average home attendance. Refer to the appropriate table of critical values provided in the formulae booklet to comment on the significance of your result, stating clearly the null hypothesis being tested.

Club	A	B	C	D	E	F	G	H
Position	1	2	3	4	5	6	7	8
Attendance	30	32	12	19	27	18	15	25

(*L 1984*)

Answers

Exercise 1.2 (p. 2)

1 $\{0, 1, 2, 3, 4\}$. **2** $\{0, 1, 2, 3, 4, 5\}$. **3** $\{1, 2, 3\}$.
4 $\{0, 1, 2, 3, 4, 5\}$. **5** $\{(W, W), (W, R), (R, W), (R, R)\}$.
6 {(Peter's choice, Paul's choice): (1, 1), (1, 2), (1, 3), (2, 1), (2, 2), (2, 3), (3, 1), (3, 2), (3, 3)}.

Exercise 1.3 (p. 8)

1 $S\{1, 2, 3, 4, 5, 6\}$ (i) $\{1, 3, 5\}$ (ii) $\{2\}$ (iii) $\{1, 2, 4, 5, 6\}$ (iv) $\{1, 2, 3, 4, 6\}$ (v) ϕ
(vi) $\{6\}$ (vii) $\{6\}$. **2** x = score on red die, y = score on black die
$S = \{(x, y): x = 1, 2, 3, 4, 5, 6;\ y = 1, 2, 3, 4, 5, 6\}$
(i) {(1, 3), (2, 2), (2, 6), (3, 1), (3, 5), (4, 4), (5, 3), (6, 2), (6, 6)}
(ii) {(1, 1), (2, 2), (3, 3), (4, 4), (5, 5), (6, 6)}
(iii) {(2, 2), (2, 4), (2, 6), (4, 2), (4, 4), (4, 6), (6, 2), (6, 4), (6, 6)}
(iv) {(1, 5), (1, 6), (2, 6), (5, 1), (6, 1), (6, 2)} (v) {(2, 2), (2, 6), (4, 4), (6, 2), (6, 6)}
(vi) {(1, 1), (1, 5), (1, 6), (2, 2), (2, 6), (3, 3), (4, 4), (5, 1), (5, 5), (6, 1), (6, 2), (6, 6)}
(vii) {(1, 1), (3, 3), (5, 5)} (viii) {(1, 2), (1, 4), (1, 5), (1, 6), (2, 1), (2, 3),
(2, 4), (2, 5), (3, 2), (3, 4), (3, 6), (4, 1), (4, 2), (4, 3), (4, 5), (4, 6), (5, 1), (5, 2), (5, 4),
(5, 6), (6, 1), (6, 3), (6, 4), (6, 5)}
(ix) B and D; none.
3 (i) $A \cap B$ (ii) $C \cap B'$ (iii) $B' \cap C'$ (iv) $(A \cap B') \cup (A' \cap B)$
(v) $A \cup B \cup C$ (vi) $A' \cap B' \cap C'$.
5 (i) $A \cap B \cap C$ (ii) $A \cap B' \cap C'$ (iii) $(A \cap B \cap C)'$ (iv) $A' \cap B' \cap C'$.

Exercise 1.4 (p. 12)

1 0·3. **2** (i) 0·5 (ii) 0·5 (iii) 0·3 (iv) 0·3. **3** (i) 0·12 (ii) 0·42 (iii) 0·72.
4 (i) 0·64 (ii) 0·12 (iii) 0·13 (iv) 0·51. (v) 0·88 (vi) 0·37
5 (i) 0·52 (ii) 0·3 (iii) 0·72 (iv) 0·18 (v) 0·28. **6** $h = \frac{1}{4};\ -\frac{1}{2} \leqslant \alpha \leqslant 1$.

Exercise 1.5A (p. 14)

1 (i) $\frac{1}{2}$ (ii) $\frac{1}{5}$ (iii) $\frac{1}{2}$ (iv) $\frac{1}{5}$.
2 (i) $\frac{2}{9}$ (ii) $\frac{5}{9}$ (iii) $\frac{1}{3}$.
3 (i) $\frac{7}{8}$ (ii) $\frac{1}{2}$ (iii) $\frac{3}{8}$ (iv) $\frac{1}{2}$ (v) $\frac{1}{2}$. **4** $\frac{1}{5}$.

Exercise 1.5B (p. 17)

1 $\frac{1}{54}$. **2** (i) $\frac{5}{9}$ (ii) $\frac{4}{9}$. **3** $1 - \dfrac{12 \times 11 \times 10 \times \ldots \times (13-n)}{12^n}, 2 \leqslant n \leqslant 12;$ 5.
4 (i) (a) $\frac{1}{4}$ (b) $\frac{1}{2}$ (ii) (a) $\frac{5}{19}$ (b) $\frac{10}{19}$. **5** (i) (a) $\frac{4}{25}$ (b) $\frac{4}{75}$ (c) $\frac{16}{25}$ (d) $\frac{1}{5}$
(e) $\frac{104}{225}$ (f) $\frac{52}{225}$ (ii) (a) $\frac{29}{185}$ (b) $\frac{2}{37}$ (c) $\frac{118}{185}$ (d) $\frac{1}{5}$ (e) $\frac{86}{185}$ (f) $\frac{26}{111}$.

Exercise 1.5C (p. 21)

1 (i) $\frac{1}{22}$ (ii) $\frac{3}{11}$ (iii) $\frac{3}{44}$ **2** (i) $\frac{1}{6}$ (ii) $\frac{5}{18}$ (iii) $\frac{1}{6}$.
3 (i) $\frac{1}{5525}$ (ii) $\frac{72}{5525}$ (iii) $\frac{16}{5525}$. **4** $\frac{53}{105}$. **5** (i) $\frac{7}{15}$ (ii) $\frac{1}{15}$.

Exercise 1.6 (p. 24)

1 $\frac{1}{2}$. **2** $\frac{5}{9}$. **3** (i) $\frac{1}{5}$ (ii) $\frac{1}{3}$. **4** (i) $\frac{3}{4}$ (ii) $\frac{1}{2}$ (iii) $\frac{1}{4}$ (iv) $\frac{5}{8}$. **5** $\frac{6}{35}$.
6 (i) $\frac{3}{11}$ (ii) $\frac{3}{7}$. **7** $\frac{3}{4}$; $\frac{3}{10}$.

Exercise 1.7A (p. 27)

1 0·7. **2** $1-2p+2p^2$. **3** (i) $\frac{31}{135}$ (ii) $\frac{62}{135}$. **4** 0·32.

Exercise 1.7B (p. 29)

1 $\frac{8}{23}$. **2** (i) $\frac{8}{23}$ (ii) $\frac{9}{23}$ (iii) $\frac{6}{23}$. **3** $\frac{16}{105}$. **4** 0·14. **5** $\frac{25}{71}$.

Exercise 1.8 (p. 33)

1 $\frac{11}{850}$. **2** (i) $\frac{119}{120}$ (ii) $\frac{5}{12}$. **3** 0·66.
4 (i) $\frac{17}{48}$ (ii) (a) $\frac{3}{23}$. (b) $\frac{5}{23}$. **5** $\frac{89}{144}$; $\frac{216}{499}$.

Exercise 1.9A (p. 36)

3 $\frac{1}{6}$ $\frac{1}{6}$ $\frac{1}{36}$ $\frac{1}{6}$ $\frac{1}{6}$ Yes. **4** $\frac{1}{2}, \frac{1}{3}$. **6** (i) $\frac{1}{12}$ (ii) $\frac{1}{9}$. **8** *A* and *B*; *A* and *C*.

Exercise 1.9B (p. 38)

1 No two are independent. **4** (i) every pair independent.
(ii) no three are independent.

Exercise 1.10 (p. 41)

1 (i) $\frac{1}{4}$ (ii) $\frac{3}{4}$. **2** 0·1621; $\frac{1543}{1621} = 0.9519$ to 4 d.p. **3** $(1-p)^n$.
4 (i) $\frac{31}{72}$ (ii) $\frac{6}{31}$. **5** (i) 0·504 (ii) 0·398. **6** $\frac{15}{16}$.
7 $\frac{19}{32}$. **8** $\frac{98}{125}$.

Exercise 1.11 (p. 45)

1 (i) $\frac{3}{8}$ (ii) $\frac{7}{8}$ (iii) $\frac{1}{2}$. **2** $\frac{5}{16}$. **3** 0·2632. **4** (i) $\frac{1701}{8192}$ (ii) $\frac{277}{65536}$.
5 0·01585. **6** $\frac{1}{3} < p \leqslant 1$. **7** 1. **8** $\frac{5}{16}$.

Review problems on Chapter 1 (p. 46)

1 (i) $\frac{2}{15}$ (ii) $\frac{1}{2}$. **2** (i) $\frac{1}{17}$ (ii) $\frac{247}{1700}$ (iii) $\frac{13}{51}$ (iv) $\frac{13}{51}$ (v) $\frac{46}{833}$.
3 (i) $\frac{7}{24}$ (ii) $\frac{1}{40}$ (iii) $\frac{1}{120}$.
4 $\frac{3}{13}, \frac{3}{13}, \frac{67}{286}$, not right, $\frac{3}{13}, \frac{40}{169}, \frac{540}{2197}$. **5** (i) (a) $\frac{1}{21}$
(b) $\frac{41}{42}$ (c) $\frac{1}{30}$ (ii) $\frac{1}{31}$. **6** 0·2 (i) (a) 0·0168 (b) 0·3154 (ii) 0·1937.
7 (i) (a) $\frac{2}{5}, \frac{2}{5}, \frac{2}{5}, \frac{2}{5}$ (b) $\frac{2}{5}, \frac{3}{10}, \frac{1}{5}, \frac{1}{10}$ (iii) $\frac{1}{5}$. **8** (i) $\frac{1}{3}$ (ii) $\frac{2}{3}$.
9 (i) $\frac{1}{11}$ (ii) $\frac{21}{55}$ (iii) $\frac{3}{11}$ (iv) $\frac{2}{55}$ (v) $\frac{36}{55}$ (vi) $\frac{5}{11}$.
10 $\frac{3}{7}, \frac{1}{2}, \frac{9}{35}, \frac{3}{5}$. **11** (i) $\frac{5}{9}$ (ii) $\frac{3}{4}$.
12 (i) $\frac{7}{15}$ (ii) (a) 0·68 (b) 0·88 (c) $\frac{5}{17}$. **13** 0·52, $\frac{1}{2}, \frac{9}{35}$, 0.3.
14 (i) 0·3 (ii) 0·3 (iii) 0·5. **15** (i) $\frac{1}{5}$ (ii) $\frac{51}{160}$ (iii) $\frac{17}{25}$. **16** (i) 0 (ii) $\frac{1}{2}$
(iii) $\frac{1}{9}$ (iv) $\frac{1}{18}$; independent. **17** (i) (b) $\frac{3}{4}, \frac{3}{10}$. **18** (i) $\frac{2}{5}$ (ii) $\frac{3}{10}$ (iii) $\frac{3}{10}$; $\frac{7}{25}$.
19 (i) $\frac{2}{5}$ (ii) $\frac{4}{15}$ (iii) $\frac{2}{15}$ (iv) 0·999 (iv) 0·233. **20** 0·0256, 0·984, $\frac{12}{49}$.
21 (i) $p^6(1-p)$ (ii) $p^6(1-p)^2$ (iii) $p^6(1-p)$; $p^6(1-p)(5-3p)$; $\frac{5}{6}$.
22 (i) 0·12 (ii) 0·184 (iii) 0·32 (iv) 0.25.

Exercise 2.1 (p. 51)

1 {1, 2, 3, 4, 5, 6}. **2** {0, 1, 2}. **3** {0, 1, 2, 3, 4, 5}.
4 {0, 1, 2, 3, . . . , 13}. **5** {1, 2, 3, 4, 5, 6}. **6** {0, 1, 2, 3, . . . }.
7 {1, 2, 3, . . . , 49}. **8** {1, 2, 3, . . . }.

Exercise 2.2 (p. 54)

1

x	0	1	2	3	4
$16\mathrm{P}(X = x)$	1	4	6	4	1

2

x	0	1	2	3
$220\mathrm{P}(X = x)$	84	108	27	1

3

x	1	2	3	4	5	6
$36\mathrm{P}(X = x)$	1	3	5	7	9	11

4

x	0	1	2	3	4
$\mathrm{P}(X = x)$	0·6561	0·2916	0·0486	0·0036	0·0001

5

x	0	1	2	3
(i) $15625\mathrm{P}(X = x)$	9261	5292	1008	64
(ii) $1150\mathrm{P}(X = x)$	665	420	63	2

6 $p = \frac{1}{3}$.

Exercise 2.3A (p. 57)

2 2. **3** 1·5. **4** (i) 1·8 (ii) (a) 1 (b) $\frac{11}{7}$.
5 (i) 6·6 pence (ii) 13·2 pence.

Exercise 2.3B (p. 61)

1 (i) $1-2\mathrm{E}[X]$ (ii) $\frac{3}{2}\mathrm{E}[X]-\frac{5}{2}$ (iii) $\mathrm{E}[X^3]-5$
(iv) $4\mathrm{E}[X^4]+4\mathrm{E}[X^3]+\mathrm{E}[X^2]$ (v) $1-\mathrm{E}[X]-2\mathrm{E}[X^2]$.
2 (ii) 14. **3** $p = \frac{1}{2}$.

Exercise 2.4A (p. 63)

1 2, 2. **2** 1, $\frac{3}{4}$. **3** 6, $\frac{161}{36}$. **4** 0, 0·4.
5 (i) 0, 0·48 (ii) 0, 0·48. **6** No unique mode, $\frac{23}{18}$.

Exercise 2.4B (p. 65)

1 0·894. **2** 1·2. **3** 10·9.

Exercise 2.5 (p. 67)

1 (i) 3, 3 (ii) 4, 6 (iii) 5, 9 (iv) 0, $1\frac{1}{2}$ (v) 3, 9.
2 $a = \frac{1}{4}$, $b = -2$ or $a = -\frac{1}{4}$, $b = 2$. **3** £99·20, £26·80. **4** 0·9, 0·7; 4·8, 1·4.

Exercise 2.6 (p. 71)

1 Bin$(4, \frac{1}{6})$, 0, $\frac{2}{3}$, $\frac{5}{9}$. **2** 4. **3** 6·4.
4 Bin(100, 0·2); 20, 16; £80, £8; £80. **5** $\frac{1}{4}n$.

Exercise 2.7A (p. 76)

2 (i) 0·861 (ii) 0·129. **3** (i) 0·819 (ii) 0·122 (iii) 0·0399 (iv) 0·992.
4 (i) 0·532 (ii) 0·169. **5** (i) (a) e^{-2} (b) $1-5e^{-2}$ (c) $3e^{-2}$ (ii) 5.
6 (i) 0·002 (ii) 0·997. **7** Mode at largest integer less than α; $\alpha-1$, α.

Exercise 2.7B (p. 79)

1 0·323 **2** (i) 0·607 (ii) 0·303 (iii) 0·090.
3 $\binom{500}{r}(0.01)^r(0{\cdot}99)^{500-r}$, $5^r e^{-5}/r!$ (i) 0·125 (ii) 0·491. **4** 0·647, 7·58.

Exercise 2.8 (p. 83)

1 (i) $0{\cdot}6(0{\cdot}4)^{x-1}$, $x = 1, 2, 3, \ldots$; Geo(0·6) (ii) 0·064 (iii) 15, 10.
2 (ii) (a) $\frac{15}{16}$ (b) $\frac{2}{7}$. **3** (i) Geo$(\frac{1}{4})$; 4
(ii) $P(X=1) = \frac{1}{4}$, $P(X=r) = \frac{1}{4}(\frac{2}{3})^{r-2}$, $r \geqslant 2$; $3\frac{1}{4}$. **4** Geo$(n/2^{n-1})$; 16.

Review problems on Chapter 2 (p. 84)

1 $\frac{278}{15}, \frac{5692}{15}, \frac{274}{15}, \frac{2024}{225}$.

2

x	0	1	2	3	4
$210P(X=x)$	1	24	90	80	15

; 2·4, 0·8, 1·6, 0·8.

3 $1-2A+(A/2^{M-1})$. **4** 8, 6. **5** (i) $\frac{2}{11}$ (ii) $\frac{5}{11}$; $\frac{18}{11}$, $\frac{72}{121}$; $\frac{18}{11}$, $\frac{90}{121}$.
6 $1\frac{1}{2}$, $\frac{3}{4}$; 60%. **7** (i) (a) $\frac{21}{38}$ (b) $\frac{5}{19}$ (c) $\frac{7}{38}$ (ii) $6\frac{37}{38}$. **8** 3, 2; 11, 8.
9 0·122. **10** (i) 0·185 (ii) 4 (iii) 2·68 (iv) 6.
11 0·00825, 0·491. **12** 0·481. **13** (i) (a) $e^{-(\lambda+\mu)}$ (b) $\frac{1}{2}\mu\lambda^2 e^{-(\lambda+\mu)}$
(c) $\frac{1}{6}(\lambda+\mu)^3 e^{-(\lambda+\mu)}$ (ii) (a) 0·001 (b) 0·140 (c) $\frac{135}{512}(=0{\cdot}264)$.
14 0·021, 0·600. **15** (i) (a) 0·135 (b) 0·947
(ii) (a) 0·144 (b) 0·111.
16 4, 10, 13, 11, 12; £18·75. **17** (i) (a) 0·986 (b) 0·223 (ii) 6, 6.
18 (i) 0·062 (ii) 0·195 (iii) 0·594.
19 0·046, 0·913 (0·908 using Poisson approximation).
20 $(R-1)/2^{R-1}$, $R = 4, 5, 6, \ldots$ (i) 4 (ii) $5\frac{1}{2}$.
21 (i) 79 (ii) 109 (iii) $10x-6N$ $(x < N)$, $4N(x \geqslant N)$; $N = 55$.

Exercise 3.2A (p. 94)

1 $\frac{400}{3}$, $\frac{2}{9}$. **2** (i) $3/(4a^3)$ (ii) $\frac{11}{16}$. **3** (i) $\frac{3}{32}$ (ii) 0·176.
4 (ii) $\frac{49}{256}$; $\frac{49}{128}$. **5** 2; $\frac{2}{5}$; $\frac{1}{40}$. **6** (i) (a) $\frac{1}{10}$ (b) $\frac{2}{3}$ (ii) $\frac{2}{5}$.
7 (i) $\frac{117}{125}$ (ii) $\frac{1}{125}$. **8** (i) 0·1 (ii) (a) 0 (b) 1. **9** $c = 0{\cdot}1$, $k = -0{\cdot}3$.
10 (i) $\frac{7}{8}$ (ii) $\frac{1}{4}$.

Exercise 3.2B (p. 98)

1 $\frac{1}{2}$. **2** 0·8. **3** $\frac{7}{30}$, $\frac{3}{28}$. **4** $\frac{2}{3}$. **5** $\frac{7}{8}$; $\frac{7}{8}$.

Exercise 3.3 (p. 100)

1 (i) 1250 (ii) 1248 **2** £455. **3** (i) 0 (ii) $2a$ (iii) $\frac{2}{3}a$.
5 (i) $\frac{1}{2}\pi r$ (ii) $\frac{4r}{\pi}$. **6** (i) $\frac{2}{3}\lambda$ (ii) 16, £3.

Exercise 3.4 (p. 103)

1 0, $\frac{5}{21}$. **2** 1·8, 0·24. **3** $6\frac{7}{8}$, $\frac{95}{64}$. **4** $\frac{1}{2}(b+a)$, $\frac{1}{12}(b-a)^2$.
5 94/15, 254/225. **6** 1·36, 0·1504.

Exercise 3.5 (p. 105)

1 (i) $1, \frac{4}{3}$ (ii) $\frac{1}{2}, \frac{1}{12}$. **2** (i) $-1, \frac{2}{3}$ (ii) $\frac{1}{2}, \frac{1}{24}$; $a = \pm\sqrt{6}, b = 1$.
3 $2/\{(r+1)(r+2)\}$; $\frac{1}{6}, \frac{1}{180}$. **4** $\frac{2}{3}a^2, \frac{4}{45}a^4$. **5** $1, \frac{1}{6}; \frac{5}{6}$.

Exercise 3.6A (p. 108)

1 $\frac{1}{32}x^2(6-x), 0 \leqslant x \leqslant 4$. **2** $\frac{1}{4}(2+3x-x^3), -1 \leqslant x \leqslant 1$.
3 $\dfrac{4(x-1)}{3x}, 1 \leqslant x \leqslant 4$. **4** $1-(1-x)^3, 0 \leqslant x \leqslant 1$.
5 $\frac{1}{20}(x-2)(x-4), 4 \leqslant x \leqslant 6; \frac{1}{10}(3x-14), 6 \leqslant x \leqslant 8$.
6 $\frac{1}{5}x^4, 0 \leqslant x \leqslant 1; \frac{1}{5}(4x-3), 1 \leqslant x \leqslant 2$.

Exercise 3.6B (p. 110)

1 1·6, 1·23, 2·29. **2** 0·206; 0·0914, 0·370. **3** 6·33; 5·45, 7·17.
4 1·37(5); 1·06, 1·69. **5** 0·347; 0·275.

Exercise 3.7 (p. 114)

1 (i) $2x-x^2, 0 \leqslant x \leqslant 1$ (ii) (a) $2y, 0 \leqslant y \leqslant 1$
(b) $\dfrac{2(z-1)}{z^3}, z \geqslant 1$.
2 $3-\dfrac{120}{y}$ (i) $\dfrac{120}{y^2}, 40 \leqslant y \leqslant 60$ (ii) 0·4 (iii) 48 k.p.h.
3 $\dfrac{y}{2r\sqrt{(4r^2-y^2)}}, 0 \leqslant y \leqslant 2r$. **4** $Y \sim U(0, 1)$. **5** $2e^{-2w}, w > 0$.
6 (i) $\frac{1}{4}(3+u), -3 \leqslant u \leqslant -1; \frac{1}{4}(1-u), -1 \leqslant u \leqslant 1$
(ii) $4w, 0 \leqslant w \leqslant \frac{1}{2}; 4(1-w), \frac{1}{2} \leqslant w \leqslant 1$. **7** (i) $1/(2\sqrt{y}), 0 \leqslant y \leqslant 1$
(ii) $1, 0 \leqslant z \leqslant 1$ (iii) $1/(2w^2), \frac{1}{3} \leqslant w \leqslant 1$.

Exercise 3.8A (p. 118)

1 0·988. **2** 0·147. **3** 0·486. **4** 0·985. **5** 0·371.
6 0·362. **7** 0·259. **8** 0·592. **9** 0·253. **10** −0·316.

Exercise 3.8B (p. 120)

1 (i) (a) 0·5 (b) 0·9495 (c) 0·4721 (d) 0·8186 (e) 0·3830 (f) 0·4772
(ii) (a) 3·64 (b) 0·718. **2** (i) 0·703 (ii) 0·829 (iii) 0·124 (iv) 0·414.

Exercise 3.8C (p. 122)

1 0·5328. **2** (i) 0·5, (ii) 0·0122. **3** (i) B (ii) A.
4 A: 94 or higher, B: from 78 to 93, C: from 62 to 77, D: 61 or less.
5 (i) 0·0455 (ii) 0·3174. **6** 11·88. **7** 25 p.
8 (i) 0·819 (ii) 12·13. **9** (i) B (ii) B; A.

Exercise 3.9A (p. 126)

1 0·149. **2** 0·864. **3** (i) 0·040 (ii) 0·042 (iii) 0·271 (iv) 0.
4 (i) 0·007 (ii) 0·755; $r = 41$. **5** 917

Exercise 3.9B (p. 127)

1 (i) 0·007 (ii) 0·003. **2** 0·729. **3** (i) 0·054 (ii) 0·824; 31.

Exercise 3.10 (p. 130)

1 (i) $\frac{1}{5}$ (ii) (a) 0·1352 (b) 0·6321. **2** B. **3** (i) 1·44 (ii) 1·73.
4 $Y \sim U(0, 1)$. **5** (i) e^2 (ii) $(e^2)/(y^2 e^{1/y}), 0 < y < \frac{1}{2}$.

Review problems on Chapter 3 (p. 130)

1 (i) 0·68 (ii) 0·62 (iii) 0·30 (iv) 0·64, (v) 0·04, £7·05.
2 (i) £5400 (ii) £270; £100. **3** (i) $\frac{1}{2}$ (ii) $\frac{1}{2}(1-\cos 1) \simeq 0{\cdot}2298$
(iii) $\frac{1}{4}\pi^2 - 2 \simeq 0{\cdot}4674$. **4** (i) 12 (ii) $\frac{1}{2}$ (iii) $x^4(3-2x^2), 0 < x < 1$
(iv) $6y(1-y), 0 < y < 1$. **5** (ii) $\frac{3}{4}$ (iii) $1 - \frac{1}{27}(3-x)^3, 0 \leqslant x \leqslant 3$.
6 (i) $\frac{1}{4}x^2, 0 \leqslant x \leqslant 1; 1 - \frac{1}{12}(4-x^2), 1 \leqslant x \leqslant 4$ (ii) $\frac{7}{8}$ (iii) $\dfrac{5z-1}{6z^3}, \frac{1}{5} \leqslant z \leqslant \frac{1}{2}$.
7 (i) $\frac{1}{8}$ (ii) $\frac{5}{16}$; 1·3125 (iii) $g(y) = 2, 1{\cdot}0625 \leqslant y \leqslant 1{\cdot}5625$.
8 P.d.f. of F $= 2/a, a < f < 1\frac{1}{2}a$; p.d.f. of V $= 8a/(v+2a)^2, 2a < v < 6a$.
9 $\frac{2}{3}; r\sqrt{2}; \frac{2}{\pi}\sin^{-1}(\frac{k}{2r})$. **10** (i) $1\frac{1}{2}$ (ii) $1{\cdot}5 \ln 3 \simeq 1{\cdot}6479$; $3 - 2{\cdot}25(\ln 3)^2 \simeq 0{\cdot}2844$
(iii) 0·4 (iv) 1·2; 2. **11** (i) Method 1 (ii) Method 2. **12** (i) 0·960, 0·788
(ii) 0·857 (iii) 99%. **13** (i) 1529 (ii) 0·330
(a) Bin(100, 0·33); 0·33, 0·002211; (b) 0·0834.
14 (i) P: 0·0912, Q: 0·7501, R: 0·1587 (ii) 42·32 cm (iii) £189·69 (iv) £205·79.
15 Fine; No. **16** 1, 0; 0·983, 0·785; 0·742 (Po) or 0·736 (Normal).
17 (i) 3 (2·87) (ii) 0·0287 (iii) 1·75 m. **18** £9363·30; 19·65%
(i) 20,000, 9363·30 (ii) 19800, 10299·63. **19** (i) 0·227 (ii) 55 (54·68) (iii) 78·7.
20 (i) 0·144 (ii) 0·111 (iii) 0·046. **21** 31·9%; 1·0193 kg; 1·074 kg.
22 e^{-kt_1}; $6e^{-3kt_0}(1-e^{-kt_0})^2$. **23** (i) 97·72 (ii) 82·92.

Exercise 4.1 (p. 139)

1 (i) $1\frac{1}{2}, \frac{1}{4}$ (ii) $\frac{1}{2}, \frac{3}{4}$ (iii) $\frac{1}{12}$.

2 (i)

		x = 0	1	2	3
y	0	0	0	0·15	0·05
	1	0	0·3	0·3	0
	2	0·05	0·15	0	0

(ii)

x	0	1	2	3
P(X = x)	0·05	0·45	0·45	0·05

y	0	1	2
P(Y = y)	0·2	0·6	0·2

z	0	1
P(Z = z)	$\frac{1}{2}$	$\frac{1}{2}$

3 (i)

		x = 1	2	3	4
y	1	1/64	0	0	0
	2	6/64	1/64	0	0
	3	12/64	6/64	1/64	0
	4	18/64	12/64	6/64	1/64

(ii) $\dfrac{25}{16}, 5, \dfrac{177}{32}$.

4

		x			
		0	3	6	9
y	0	8/216	12/216	6/216	1/216
	1	36/216	36/216	9/216	0
	2	54/216	27/216	0	0
	3	27/216	0	0	0

5 $1-p$; $p(1-p)$;

		x	
		0	1
y	0	p^2	$(1-p)^2$
	1	$p(1-p)$	$p(1-p)$

;$p = \frac{1}{2}$.

Exercise 4.2 (p. 141)

1 $\frac{1}{2}, \frac{3}{4}$. **2** $5, \frac{177}{32}$. **3** 5. **4** (i) $\frac{1}{4}$ (ii) $-\frac{1}{2}, 6, \frac{27}{32}$.

Exercise 4.3 (p. 144)

1 (i) $\frac{1}{5}$ (ii) Not independent

(iii)

z	0	1	2	3	4	5
$25\text{P}(Z = z)$	5	3	4	10	2	1

2 (i)

		x		
		0	1	2
y	0	1/45	4/45	1/45
	1	6/45	12/45	6/45
	2	3/45	9/45	3/45

(ii) Not independent.

3 (i) $\frac{11}{12}, \frac{35}{144}$; 1·3, 0·81

(ii)

		x		
		0	1	2
y	0	4/120	18/120	2/120
	1	8/120	36/120	4/120
	2	6/120	27/120	3/120
	3	2/120	9/120	1/120

z	-2	-1	0	1	2	3	4	5	6
$120\,P(Z=z)$	2	18	8	36	11	27	7	9	2

$\frac{101}{60}$, $\frac{12539}{3600}$.

Exercise 4.4 (p. 146)

1 $\frac{1}{4}$. **2** (i) $\frac{13}{54}$ (ii) $\frac{23}{270}$. **3** (i) $\frac{29}{32}$ (ii) $\frac{25}{32}$.

Exercise 4.5A (p. 149)

1 $7\frac{1}{2}$, $26\frac{1}{4}$, $\frac{9}{20}$. **2** 3, $4\frac{7}{9}$. **3** (i) 7 (ii) 41. **4** $\frac{3}{4}$, $\frac{27}{80}$.

Exercise 4.5B (p. 151)

1 15 cm, $5\frac{2}{3}$ cm^2. **2** (i) 10, 25 (ii) 0, 25 (iii) -5, 125.
3 (i) $3\frac{1}{2}$ (ii) $\frac{455}{12}$ (iii) 7 (iv) $\frac{35}{6}$ (v) $\frac{329}{12}$.

Exercise 4.6 (p. 153)

1 30, 0·75. **2** 100, 250. **3** 36, 140.
4 $2\pi(\sigma_R^2+\mu_R^2+\mu_R\mu_H)$. **5** 5, 15.

Exercise 4.7 (p. 155)

1 (i) 0·970 (ii) 0·021. **2** (i) 0·895 (ii) 4. **3** (i) $\frac{3}{8}$.

Exercise 4.8 (p. 157)

1 (i) 275, 1·3 (ii) 0·0105. **2** (i) 0·827 (ii) 0·548. **3** 0·3797.
4 (i) 0·0062 (ii) 0·0084. **5** (i) 0·348 (ii) 0·155 (iii) 0·651.

Review problems on Chapter 4 (p. 158)

1 (i)

		x			
		0	1	2	3
y	0	4/32	0	0	0
	1	0	2/32	5/32	9/32
	2	0	2/32	6/32	0
	3	0	4/32	0	0

(ii) $1\frac{1}{4}$, $\frac{3}{4}$.

2 (ii) 2·2.

3

		x		
		0	1	2
y	0	5/30	10/30	3/30
	1	5/30	6/30	1/30

z	0	1	2	3
$30P(Z=z)$	5	15	9	1

1·2, 0·56; Bin (4, 0·3), 1·2, 0·84. **4** (ii) 1, 2 (iii) Not independent (iv) $4\alpha+1$.
5 $\frac{1}{3}$, 1; $\frac{161}{36}$, $5\frac{1}{2}$. **6** $P(Y=r)=r^{-1}P(Y=r-1)$ (i) 0·05 (ii) 0·16 (iii) 0·61.
7 (i) (a) 0·986 (b) 0·223 (iii) 6, 6.

8 (i) 0·1015 (ii) 0·2851 (iii) $\frac{27}{64}$. **9** (i) 0·0023 (iii) 0, 60.
10 (i) $\frac{2}{5}$ (ii) $\frac{1}{2}$ (iii) 0·375 (iv) 0·701 (v) 0·70, 0·01.
11 5, 25; 0·0155. **12** (i) 0·02275 (ii) 0·186 (iii) 0·118 (iv) 0·841.
13 (i) 0·910 (ii) 0·978 (iii) 16465. **14** (i) 0·401 (ii) 0·227 (iii) 24.
15 $\frac{1}{16}$, 0·257; $\frac{1}{2}$, 0·712; 7. **16** (i) 0·31 (ii) 0·037 (iii) 0·0005.
17 1000, 172; 0·16, 0·022.
18 29·54, 0·033 (i) 0·878 (ii) 0·049. **19** 0·579.
20 (i) 0·9938 (ii) 4730·2 litres (iii) 0·1056 (iv) 244456 to 255544.

Exercise 5.2 (p. 168)

1

$\bar{x}_2$	0	$\frac{1}{2}$	1	$1\frac{1}{2}$
$10P(\bar{X}_2 = \bar{x}_2)$	1	4	3	2

$\bar{x}_4$	$\frac{1}{2}$	$\frac{3}{4}$	1
$5P(\bar{X}_4 = \bar{x}_4)$	1	2	2

2 (i) 3.2 (ii) 3

(iii)

$\bar{x}$	$2\frac{1}{3}$	$2\frac{2}{3}$	$3\frac{1}{3}$	$3\frac{2}{3}$	4
$10P(\bar{X} = \bar{x})$	2	2	1	4	1

m	2	3
$10P(M = m)$	3	7

(iv) 0·6.

3 $P(X = x) = \frac{1}{5}$, $x = 1, 2, 3, 4, 5$; $\mu = 3$, $\sigma^2 = 2$

s^2	$\frac{1}{2}$	2	$4\frac{1}{2}$	8
$10P(S^2 = s^2)$	4	3	2	1

$E[S^2] = 2\frac{1}{2}$

4

s^2	0	$\frac{1}{2}$	2	$4\frac{1}{2}$	8
$25P(S^2 = s^2)$	5	8	6	4	2

$E[S^2] = 2$.

Exercise 5.4A (p. 172)

1

$\bar{x}$	2	$2\frac{1}{3}$	$2\frac{2}{3}$	3	$3\frac{1}{3}$	$3\frac{2}{3}$	4	$4\frac{2}{3}$	5	6
$125P(\bar{X} = \bar{x})$	8	24	24	8	12	24	12	6	6	1

2

x	1	2	3
$6P(X = x)$	3	2	1

$E[X] = 1\frac{2}{3}$, $V[X] = \frac{5}{9}$

(i)

$\bar{x}_3$	1	$1\frac{1}{3}$	$1\frac{2}{3}$	2	$2\frac{1}{3}$	$2\frac{2}{3}$	3
$216P(\bar{X}_3 = \bar{x}_3)$	27	54	63	44	21	6	1

(ii) $1\frac{2}{3}$, $\frac{1}{3}$.

3 25, 375; 25, 93·75. **4** 2, 1.

Exercise 5.4B (p. 173)

1 (i) 0·9938 (ii) 12. **2** 0·2481. **3** (i) 0·9756 (ii) 43 or 44. **4** 0·0401, $c = 15{\cdot}68$ (i) $\overline{Y} \sim N(61, 80)$ (ii) $W \sim N(5, 144)$, 0·6616.

Exercise 5.4C (p. 176)

1 0·1837. **2** 0·0835. **3** $0, \dfrac{1}{12n}$; 36. **4** $3\frac{1}{2}, \frac{35}{360}$; 0·0544.

Exercise 5.5 (p. 179)

1 (i)

p_3	0	$\frac{1}{3}$	$\frac{2}{3}$	1
$27\text{P}(P_3 = p_3)$	8	12	6	1

(ii) $\frac{1}{3}, \frac{2}{45}$.

2 $\frac{1}{64}; \frac{63}{40960}$.

Review problems on Chapter 5 (p. 179)

1 (i) 4, 14·4 (ii) (a)

$\bar{x}$	$1\frac{1}{3}$	2	$3\frac{1}{3}$	$4\frac{2}{3}$	$5\frac{1}{3}$	$6\frac{2}{3}$
$\text{P}(\bar{X} = \bar{x})$	0·1	0·1	0·3	0·2	0·2	0·1

(b) $\text{E}[\bar{X}] = \mu$ (c) 2·4.

2 $2\frac{1}{2}, 1\frac{1}{4}$ (i) $2\frac{1}{2}, \frac{5}{12}$ (ii) $\text{P}(M = 1) = \frac{5}{32}$, $\text{P}(M = 2) = \frac{11}{32}$, $\text{P}(M = 3) = \frac{11}{32}$; $\frac{7}{8}$.

3 $2, \frac{2}{3}$ (i)

$\bar{x}$	1	$1\frac{1}{3}$	$1\frac{2}{3}$	2	$2\frac{1}{3}$	$2\frac{2}{3}$	3
$27\text{P}(\bar{X} = \bar{x})$	1	3	6	7	6	3	1

(ii)

m	1	2	3
$27\text{P}(M = m)$	7	13	7

; sample mean.

4 (i)

y	1	2	3
$27\text{P}(Y = y)$	1	7	19

(ii)

z	0	$\frac{1}{3}$	1	$1\frac{1}{3}$
$27\text{P}(Z = z)$	3	12	6	6

5

m	0	1	2
$\text{P}(M = m)$	$p^2(3-2p)$	$1-6p^2+4p^3$	$p^2(3-2p)$

6 0·9545. **7** 162·5, 0·25; 173·5, 0·64; 11·0, 0·89; 0·1446.
8 (i) 0·5 (ii) 0·1587. **9** 0·683; 0·00217.

10 (i)

p_1	0	$\frac{1}{3}$	$\frac{2}{3}$
$P(P_1 = p_1)$	0·1	0·6	0·3

; 0·4; 0·04

(ii) 0·4, 0·08 (iii) 200%.

Exercise 6.2A (p. 185)

2 $a+b = 1$; $(a^2+b^2)\sigma^2$; $a = b = \frac{1}{2}$. **3** 2. **4** (i) 4·98, 0·01 (ii) 0·6826.

Exercise 6.2B (p. 188)

1 0·6, 0·06928; 0·07071. **2** 0·02; 0·014, 0·05. **3** 0·6, 0·03536.

Exercise 6.2C (p. 191)

2 3·3, 3·9. **3** 2317. **4** 1·93, 1·178 (i) 3·86 (ii) 14·136.

5 $\dfrac{1}{2(n-1)}$.

Exercise 6.2D (p. 195)

1 $\theta(1-\theta)/20$, $\theta(1-2\theta)/20$; T_2.
2 (i) $a_1 = b_1 = \frac{1}{3}$ (ii) $a_2 = \frac{2}{3}$, $b_2 = -\frac{1}{3}$; $2\sigma^2/(9n)$, $5\sigma^2/(9n)$.
3 $g(y) = 4y^3/\theta^4$, $0 < y < \theta$; $\frac{4}{5}\theta$ (i) $T_1 = \frac{5}{4}Y$ (ii) $k = 1\frac{1}{2}$ (iii) T_1.
4 $c = 3$; θ^2. **5** $4\gamma/\pi$, $2(\pi^2-8)\gamma^2/\pi^2$; $\pi/4$, $(\pi^2-8)\gamma^2/(8n)$. **6** 2·46.

Exercise 6.3A (p. 201)

1 71·16, 80·44. **2** 64, 1·22. **3** 2·997, 3·075; Yes.
4 43. **5** $\bar{X} - 0{\cdot}885$, $\bar{X} + 1{\cdot}179$; 0·081.

Exercise 6.3B (p. 206)

1 0·31, 1·31. **2** 20·55, 33·05 (i) wider (ii) narrower.
3 337·1, 343·9. **4** 732·0, 757·1; Yes. **5** 0·25, 3·75.

Exercise 6.3C (p. 208)

1 2·12, 7·88. **2** 1·40, 2·20. **3** 45.

Exercise 6.4A (p. 210)

1 7·05, 7·47. **2** 15·18, 16·42. **3** 1·74, 1·78.

Exercise 6.4B (p. 212)

1 5·59p, 8·41p. **2** 0·86, 2·14.

Exercise 6.4C (p. 214)

1 0·333, 0·383. **2** 0·478, 0·566. **3** 0·302, 0·368.

Exercise 6.4D (p. 216)

1 (0·048, 0·200). **2** −0·188, 0·008. **3** −0·101, 0·085.

Exercise 6.4E (p. 219)

1 0·54, 0.76. **2** 2·26, 2·78.
3 (i) (a) 0·602, 1·064 (b) 0·904, 1·596 (ii) −0·765, −0·068.

Exercise 6.5 (p. 223)

1 1108; 146·2. **2** (i) 1142·33 kg, 64·7625 kg (ii) 0·67 (iii) 1052 kg, 1225 kg.

Review problems on Chapter 6 (p. 224)

1 $3-3\theta$, $5\theta-9\theta^2$; p_2. **2** Not true. **3** 5·9, 8·1. **4** 5, 4·5; 24.
5 0·32; 0·1131; 50 m. **6** 3·841, 3·907. **7** (i) 2 (ii) −1·012, 1·012.
8 1·1248, 1·1292. **9** (i) −0·253, 0·733 (ii) 139.
10 (i) 7·4, 21·3; 3·017, 11·783 (ii) 27. **11** $c=\bar{x}$ (i) 456, 108 (ii) 449·4, 462·6
(iii) 457, 89·2562. **12** $N(\mu, \sigma^2/n)$ (i) 15·2 (ii) 8·9984
(iii) (13·99, 16·41); 8·6857; (14·84, 15·56). **13** (i) 14·2, 0·0408 (ii) 14·12, 14·28
(iii) 0·0071. **14** 6, 4; (5·38, 6·62). **15** (1·55, 1.65); (0·102, 0·298).
16 49·35, 414·0477; (46·53, 52·17); 397.
17 $f(x) = 1/(a-10)$, $10 < x < a$; $5+\frac{1}{2}a$; 32; 34; (25·8, 42·2).

18 (i)

$\hat{p}$	0	$\frac{1}{3}$	$\frac{2}{3}$	1
$30P(\hat{P}=\hat{p})$	5	15	9	1

(ii) (0·758, 0·810).

19 θ, $\sqrt{\{\theta(1-\theta)/n\}}$; (0·826, 0·945).

Exercise 7.2 (p. 234)

1 (i) Reject H_0 only if $\bar{x} > 10{\cdot}66$ (ii) 0·006.
2 Conclude that machine is malfunctioning if $|\bar{x}-2{\cdot}5| > 0{\cdot}02$
(i) operating correctly (ii) malfunctioning with mean > 2·5.
3 Claim is justified. **4** Reject the null hypothesis if $|\bar{x}-2200| > 30{\cdot}46$
(i) No change (ii) The mean has increased.
5 Claim cannot be rejected. **6** Mean output greater on the new machine.

Exercise 7.3 (p. 238)

1 Conclude that $\mu_1 > \mu_2$. **2** Claim is justified.
3 0·1755; cannot discriminate between the two methods.
4 Claim is justified. **5** Claim is not justified.

Exercise 7.4 (p. 243)

1 Claim is justified. **2** Method is more efficient than guessing.
3 Cannot reject the unbiasedness of the coin.
4 Reject makers' claim and conclude that less than 35% use 'Sparkle'.
5 Conclude that the coin is biased in favour of a head.
6 Cannot reject the hypothesis that 55% of the adults favour fluoridation.

Exercise 7.5 (p. 246)

1 Cannot reject the hypothesis that equal proportions of men and women favour the proposal.
2 Conclude that a higher proportion of women than men do diet.
3 Cannot reject the hypothesis that the proportions in the two cities are equal.
4 Conclude that the campaign has been successful.

Exercise 7.6 (p. 250)

1 Cannot reject the null hypothesis.
2 The evidence is not strong enough to conclude that the average number has increased.

3 Is consistent with the substance being type-A.
4 The cloth is acceptable. **5** Conclude average has been reduced.

Exercise 7.7 (p. 253)

1 Insufficient evidence to discriminate between the insecticides.
2 Conclude that the roundabout has reduced the average number of accidents per week.

Exercise 7.8 (p. 256)

1 16; reject a modification if the mean percentage yield exceeds 63·62.
2 (i) 0·143 (ii) 0·433. **3** (i) 0·036 (ii) 0·019. **4** $a = 0{\cdot}588$; 0·0085; 0·0058.

Review problems on Chapter 7(p. 257)

1 Null hypothesis $\mu = 8{\cdot}4$; $\bar{x} = 8{\cdot}9$ is significantly greater than 8·4 at the 1 % significance level. **2** Reject the null hypothesis and conclude $\mu < 9{\cdot}7$; 9·3, 3·6103.
3 For any significance level > 0·014, conclude that the improved seed has a larger grain on average. **4** The sample mean is significantly less than 50.
5 (i) For any significance level > 0·005, conclude that the mean life is < 2000 hours, (ii) For any significance level > 0·002 conclude that $\mu_A < \mu_B$.
6 (− 1·068, − 0·032) (i) Cannot reject the null hypothesis (ii) reject the hypothesis of equal means and conclude that the mean length of articles manufactured in the first section is less than that of articles manufactured in the second section.
7 $(\bar{x}_1 - \bar{x}_2 - 0{\cdot}0774, \bar{x}_1 - \bar{x}_2 + 0{\cdot}0774)$; 0·72 (i) reject; (ii) do not reject.
8 0·1615, 0·3230, 0·2907, 0·1550, 0·0543; significant; 137.
9 Cannot reject the claim. **10** (i) 0·87 (ii) 0·19; not justified.
11 (i) 0·8327 (ii) 0·1797 (iii) H_0: $p = 0{\cdot}5$, H_1: $p \neq 0{\cdot}5$; reject unbiasedness and conclude that $p > 0{\cdot}5$. **12** Conclude that $p < 0{\cdot}7$; 61.
13 Cannot discriminate between the two drugs; conclusion is justified.
14 (i) H_0: $p_A = 0{\cdot}6$ v H_1: $p_A < 0{\cdot}6$; one-tail test; conclude that H_0 is true (ii) H_0: $p_M = p_F$ v H_1: $p_M \neq p_F$; two-tail test; cannot reject H_0.
15 Insufficient evidence to discriminate.
16 (i) 0·368 (ii) 0·145 (iii) 0·167; suggestion is justified.
17 5, 5; 0·497; 60; the claim is justified.
18 (i) 0·017 (ii) 0·191 (iii) 5. **19** 191·2 to 208·8; 0·05; 0·605.
20 (i) 80, 16 (ii) 0·8192 (iii) H_0: $p = 0{\cdot}8$ v H_1: $p > 0{\cdot}8$; 0·608.
21 Fair dice: $3\frac{1}{3}$, $\frac{35}{12}$; biased dice: 3·9, 2·49; 0·121; 594.

Exercise 8.2 (p. 269)

1 (i) positive (ii) $y = 1{\cdot}24 + 0{\cdot}61x$. **2** (i) negative (ii) $y = 10{\cdot}11 - 0{\cdot}134x$.
3 $y = \log h$, $\alpha = \log \lambda$. **4** 0·0045 (ii) 0·96 (iii) 1·21 (iv) 0·09.

Exercise 8.3A (p. 273)

1 2·56, 1·23; 1·02, 1·44. **2** (i) $w = 2{\cdot}9 - 0{\cdot}5x$ (ii) 0·9 (iii) − 586, − 414.
3 (i) 10·78, − 0·24 (ii) 8·38 (iii) 8·28, 8·48.
4 (i) $y = 5{\cdot}56x - 5{\cdot}68$ (ii) 8·02, 14·22.
5 (i) (a) 0·844, 1·076 (b) 0·0024, 0·0066 (ii) accept H_1.

Exercise 8.3B (p. 277)

1 (2·12, 2·88). **2** Recommend Set 1. **3** $SE[B_1] = \sigma\sqrt{(2/n)}$.

Exercise 8.4A (p. 280)

1 (i) $y = 28{\cdot}2 + 8{\cdot}3x$, 44·8 (ii) (15·03, 18·17).
2 (i) $y = 4{\cdot}083 + 0{\cdot}9417x$ (ii) (6·59, 7·23).

Exercise 8.4B (p. 284)

1 6·3 kg. **2** (i) $y = 1{\cdot}1065x - 13{\cdot}9146$ (ii) $x = 0{\cdot}6723y + 25{\cdot}4285$.
3 $y = 16{\cdot}2175 + 13{\cdot}0258x$; (51·50, 59·09).

Review problems on Chapter 8 (p. 284)

1 $M = 17{\cdot}51 - 17{\cdot}5 \log T$; 4·385.
2 Radius = $1{\cdot}92 + 2{\cdot}226x$ Days; 2·226 mm per day.
3 (ii) $y = 348{\cdot}95 - 2{\cdot}14x$ (iii) 242, 135. **4** (7·992, 9·168).
5 $y = 23 - 0{\cdot}325x$ (i) 19·64, 26·36 (ii) (−0·407, −0·243) (iii) 5·69, 7·81.
6 (i) $y = 36 + 13x$ (ii) (a) (10·52, 15·48) (b) (78·62, 84·38).
7 (i) $y = 24 - 4x$ (ii) 8, 0·3953 (iii) (7·35, 8·65).
8 57·2, −0·48 (i) 47·15, 48·05 (ii) 8·56, 10·64.

Exercise 9.1 (p. 291)

2 0·9565. **3** −0·8146.

Exercise 9.2 (p. 294)

1 $\Sigma d^2 = 36$; significant; good agreement.
2 B; B only

Exercise 9.3 (p. 297)

1 0·9758; significant; positively correlated.
2 −0·8214; negatively correlated.

Review problems on Chapter 9 (p. 297)

2 20, 34; use averages of the two ranks.
3 (a) 0·8688 (b) 0·8485.
4 0·4286; not significant; H_0: no association.

Index